Killifishes of the World
Old World Killis I

Dr. Lothar Seegers

Verlag: A.C.S. GmbH, Germany

Inhalt
Contents

Erläuterung der Symbole *Key to the symbols*	Innenseite des Umschlags *See inside of cover*
Vorwort *Foreword*	Seite 3 *page 3*
Killifische - was ist das? *What are Killifishes*	Seite 4 *page 5*
Systematische Einordnung der in den Bänden "Killifishes of the World" aufgeführten Gattungen *Systematical overview of the genera listed in the* *volumes of "Killifishes of the World"*	Seite 6 *page 6*
Die Fortpflanzung der Killifische *How Killifishes spawn and breed*	Seite 8 *page 9*
Die Gattungen *The genera*	Seite 10 *page 10*
Die Arten *The species*	Seite 15 *page 15*
Bildteil *Plates*	Seite 17 *page 17*
Freie Seiten zum Einkleben demnächst erscheinender Ergänzungen *Free pages to stick in the forthcoming supplements*	Seite 137 *page 137*
Index der Code-Nummern / *Index of code numbers*	Seite 143 / *page* 143
Alphabetischer Index / *Alphabetical index*	Seite 148 / *page* 148
Literatur / *Bibliography*	Seite 153 / *page* 153
Die wichtigsten Killifischgemeinschaften *The most important Killifish associations*	Seite 155 *page 155*

Erklärungen der Abkürzungen in den wissenschaftlichen Namen
Key to the abbreviations of the scientific names

Beispiel/ *example:*	*Aphyosemion* Gattung *Genus*	*gardneri* Art *Species*	*nigerianum* Unterart *Subspecies*	CLAUSEN, Beschreiber *Describer*	1963 Publikationsjahr *Year of the publication*

sp./spec.: = species (lat.): Art/*species*
Hinter einem Gattungsnamen meint dies: Ein Artname steht (noch) nicht zur Verfügung, die Art ist bislang nicht eindeutig bestimmt bzw. noch nicht formell beschrieben./
Following the genus name this means: A species-name is not yet available, the species has not yet been determined or formally described.

ssp.: = subspecies (lat.): Unterart/*subspecies*
Einige Arten haben ein sehr großes Verbreitungsgebiet; innerhalb dieses Gebietes gibt es Populationen, die sich äußerlich zwar deutlich von anderen Populationen unterscheiden, genetisch jedoch zur gleichen Art gehören. Solche Populationen erhalten als Unterart einen wissenschaftlichen Namen. Ist die Unterart bislang unbenannt, so steht hier nur ssp./
Some species inhabit an area of a very wide range; within this area there may be populations which differ significantly in appearance from other populations, but clearly belong to the same species. Such populations may get a third scientific name indicating a subspecies. If a subspecies name has not yet been formally given, the abbreviation ssp. is added.

cf.: = confer (lat.): vergleiche/*compare*
Einem Artnamen vorangestellt meint dies: Das vorliegende Exemplar oder die entsprechende Population weicht in gewissen Details von der typischen Form ab, jedoch nicht so gravierend, daß es oder sie einer anderen Art zugeordnet werden könnte./
Placed in front of a species name this means: The specimen shown or the respective population to which it belongs differ in some minor details from the typical form, but these differences do not justify to place it into a species of its own.

sp. aff.: = species affinis (lat.): ... ähnliche Art/*similar to ...*
Einem Artnamen vorangestellt meint dies: Die vorliegende Art ist bisher noch nicht bestimmt, sie ähnelt jedoch der genannten und bereits beschriebenen Art./
Placed in front of a species name this means: The species at hand is not yet determined but it is very similar to that one named in the following.

Hybride/*hybrid*: Kreuzungsprodukt, Mischling zweier Arten/*hybrid or cross-breed of two species*

Vorwort

Wir stellen hiermit den ersten Band über die Killifische der Alten Welt vor. Da die Formenfülle in dieser Fischgruppe so groß ist, daß sie den Rahmen eines einzigen Bandes sprengt, wird es einen weiteren Band über die Killifische der Alten Welt geben. Anschliessend werden wir uns der Neuen Welt zuwenden um mit den dort vorkommenden Vertretern die Killifische zu ergänzen und abzurunden. "Killifishes of the World" ist also auf mehrere Bände angelegt, von denen wir hier den ersten Band vorlegen möchten.

Soweit wir wissen, hat es bisher noch kein Buch gegeben, in dem alle bekannten und erreichbaren Killifische und ähnlichen Formen derart umfassend abgebildet wurden, dieser Band dürfte daher in diesem Sinne einzigartig sein.

Aber dennoch ist uns natürlich auch bewußt, daß dieser und die folgenden Bände nicht alle Killifische dieser Erde enthalten können. Nachdem in den 70er und 80er Jahren der afrikanische Kontinent mehr oder weniger gezielt nach neuen und bis dahin unbekannten Arten abgesucht wurde und eine Flut neuer Formen in die Aquaristik gelangte, hat sich dies nun auf Amerika verlagert. Jährlich werden dort zur Zeit viele neue und zum Teil wunderschöne Arten und sogar Gattungen "entdeckt". Zwar sind wir auch was solche Neueinführungen der letzten Zeit betrifft in diesem Buch recht aktuell, aber was noch nicht entdeckt ist, das können wir auch noch nicht zeigen.

Für derartige Fälle haben wir unsere Zeitung für den Aquarianer, die AQUALOG news, in der jeder Nummer neu importierte Arten in Einklebebildern beigefügt sind. Hinten in diesem Buch befindet sich der entsprechende Raum um die jeweiligen Fotos einzukleben. Wie wir aber zwischenzeitlich erfahren mußten, ist die Zahl neuimportierter Fische hin und wieder so groß, daß wir uns entschlossen haben, ganze Ergänzungsbögen anzubieten, die ebenfalls eingeklebt werden können. Sie sehen also, Ihre AQUALOG-Bände sind ausbaufähig und Sie können durch unser System stets auf dem aktuellsten Stand bleiben wenn Sie möchten.

Der hier vorliegende Band "Old World Killis I" - Killifische der Alten Welt, Teil I - zeigt Ihnen die Farbenpracht vor allem der afrikanischen Killifische. Damit diese schönen Fische aquaristisch erhalten bleiben, haben sich in der ganzen Welt Killifischgemeinschaften gegründet. Sie sind bestrebt, diese Arten und ihre Fundortpopulationen in reiner Form nachzuzüchten. Dazu ist es aber erforderlich, diese verschiedenen Fundortformen zu kennen und zu dokumentieren, denn sonst kommt es leicht zu Kreuzungen und zum Verschwinden mancher Formen oder gar Arten. Eine Tafel in diesem Buch zeigt einige solcher Artkreuzungen. Die Dokumentation verschiedener Fundortpopulationen der Arten ist ein erklärtes Ziel der AQUALOG-Bände "Killifishes of the World". Wir hoffen, auf diese Weise auch ein Referenzbuch für den Schutz der einzelnen Killifisch-Arten und ihrer Fundortformen vorgelegt zu haben, das in Aquaristik und praktischem Artenschutz vor Ort hilfreich sein mag.

Foreword

This is the first of a series of books on Killifishes; this volume deals especially with Killis from the 'Old World'. As there are so many species in this particular group of fishes we will cover the 'old world' Killis in two books. Then, all Killis from the 'New World' will be introduced in a third, completing volume. 'Killifishes of the World' is therefore a reference work that is designed to show you all Killis that are known worldwide today.

As far as we are informed nobody has attempted yet to cover the whole range of Killifishes in a book that shows all known and available Killis comprehensively on multicoloured pictures - we think, at least in this way, this reference work is unique.

Still, we are well aware that even this reference work cannot claim to be complete - there is probably no way to show all existing Killifishes of the world. In the 70s and 80s, the African continent has been thoroughly searched for new species and as a result a sheer 'flood' of previously unknown Killi species became known to the aquaristic world. Then, it was the American continent's turn and until today, merely every year new species and even genera are discovered there. We gave our best to be as up-to-date as possible, but what has not yet been discovered, we can hardly show...

This is why we invented the newspaper for aquarists, AQUALOGnews, where in each issue newly discovered species are added as peel-back stickers. In each AQUALOG book there are empty pages in the back where the relevant stickers can be attached. As sometimes the number of new imports or discoveries is too high to be covered by the stickers in AQUALOGnews, we decided to additionally publish sheets with several stickers when indicated. This way, you can keep your AQUALOG book easily up-to-date for a long time if you wish.

This first volume on Killifishes from the old world - Old World Killis I - impressively demonstrates the variety and blaze of colour of the Killis; in this book, most of them come from Africa. In order to preserve the great variety of Killifishes, all over the world Killifish Associations have been founded. They want to breed the species and and the populations in their pure forms. Therefore it is necessary to thoroughly document the population - otherwise the species can be inadvertently mixed or cross-bred which could result in the extinction of a species or even a genus. One plate in this book shows some of these species 'mixtures'. It is our aim to document some of the populations in order to help to preserve and protect the species and their habitats. We sincerely hope that these AQUALOG reference books can add to the worldwide efforts to ensure the survival of the species.

Mörfelden-Walldorf, May 1997

Publisher and author

Killifische - was ist das?

Bei den Aquarianern sind die in diesem Band vorgestellten Arten als "Killifische" bekannt. Dieser Begriff stammt ursprünglich aus dem Altniederländischen und bezeichnete eigentlich jene Fische, die die früheren niederländischen Siedler New Yorks (das einstmals Neu-Amsterdam hieß) in den dortigen Gräben und Kleingewässern vorfanden. Derartige Gewässer heißen auf Altniederländisch Kil, und so wurden die den europäischen Siedlern unbekannten Fische eben als Kilvis, Killfish, oder später Killifish bezeichnet. Im Amerikanischen findet sich heute auch die Schreibweise Killie. Mit dem Begriff "to kill" = töten hat die Herkunft des Wortes Killifisch also nichts zu tun.

Nach heutigem Verständnis waren es vor allem *Fundulus heteroclitus*, die in den USA schon im 18. Jahrhundert als "Kilvis" bezeichnet wurden, sie tragen den Namen "Killifish" (oder auch "Mudfish") in der amerikanischen Umgangssprache selbst heute noch. Im amerikanischen Raum wird der Begriff "Killifishes" aber auch im ichthyologisch-wissenschaftlichen Zusammenhang verwendet.

Die ersten lebenden Killifische kamen um die Jahrhundertwende als Einzelimporte aus der neuen Welt nach Europa, es handelte sich um *Fundulus*- und *Cyprinodon*-Arten. Schon bald bereicherten auch tropische "Fundulen" die Aquaristik. 1903 wurde *Rivulus santensis* aus Brasilien nach Europa eingeführt, der Import der ersten *Aphyosemion*- und *Epiplatys*-Arten erfolgte 1905. Diese Fische erregten einiges Aufsehen, und in der "Wochenschrift für Aquarien- und Terrarienkunde" und den "Blätter für Aquarien- und Terrarienkunde" wurde über sie berichtet. In den "Blättern" von 1908 erschien eine Aufsatzreihe von Paul ARNOLD über "Westafrikanische Fundulus-Arten", in deren erster Folge eine Tafel den Aquarianern jener Zeit erstmals afrikanische Killifische im Farbbild zeigte. Vorgestellt wurden jeweils Männchen und Weibchen von "Fundulus Arnoldi" (heute *Aphyosemion arnoldi*), "Fundulus gularis Blgr. var. A (blau)" (heute

Aphyosemion deltaense) und "Fundulus gularis Blgr. var. B (gelb)" (heute *Aphyosemion sjoestedti*). Aufgrund des steigenden Interesses brachten schon bald Seeleute der vor allem Westafrika befahrenden Schiffahrtslinien Fische mit nach Europa, wo besonders in Hamburg Händler, aber auch versierte oder gar wissenschaftlich interessierte Aquarianer wie Paul ARNOLD, Johannes THUMM, später Fritz MAYER, Hermann MEINKEN, Erhard ROLOFF oder andere, ungeduldig auf die Neuheiten warteten. Von Hamburg aus wurden die neuen "Prachtfundulen" schon bald auch in weitere Teile der Welt exportiert, vor allem in die USA. In den 20er und 30er Jahren kamen selbst Killifische, deren Identität erst vor kurzem aufgeklärt werden konnte, zu den Aquarianern. Nach dem II. Weltkrieg wurden zunächst die Restbestände wieder zu Zuchtstämmen aufgebaut, die die Kriegs- und Nachkriegswirren überstanden hatten. Bald schon aber kündeten Berichte in der DATZ ("Die Aquarien- und Terrarienzeitschrift") von neu erfolgten Killifisch-Importen.

Aquaristisch besonders populär wurden die Killifische in den 60er Jahren mit der Gründung der Killifisch-Gemeinschaften in der ganzen Welt. Die erste dieser Gemeinschaften war die 1961 gegründete American Killifish Association (A.K.A.). Die Gründung dieser Gemeinschaften geschah zudem zu einer Zeit, als einzelne Aquarianer, genannt seien hier vor allem Dr. W. FOERSCH, E. ROLOFF und J.J. SCHEEL, durch Publikationen mit hervorragenden Fotos auf die Killifische aufmerksam machten. Insbesondere sei hier das 1968 erschienene Buch von J.J. SCHEEL "Rivulins of the Old World" erwähnt, das mit seinen brillanten Farbaufnahmen bei so manchem ernsthaften Aquarianer den Anstoß gab, sich mit diesen Fischen ebenfalls zu beschäftigen. 1964 erschien das erste Heft des "The Journal of the American Killifish Association". Bereits die Gestaltung dieses ersten Heftes macht deutlich, daß die Gründer der AKA eigentlich eher wissenschaftliches Interesse an den Fischen hatten. Schon bald aber machten die Aquarianer den größeren Anteil der Mitglieder aus, und so wurden die stärker aquaristisch ausgerichteten "Killie Notes" herausgegeben.

Bereits nach kurzer Zeit etablierten sich weitere Killifischgemeinschaften: In der früheren DDR die "ZAG Eierlegende Zahnkarpfen", in Großbritannien die "British Killifish Association" (B.K.A.), im früheren Westdeutschland die "Deutsche Killifisch-Gemeinschaft" (DKG), weitere Vereinigungen folgten anschließend überall in der Welt, eine Reihe von ihnen ist im Anhang dieses Buches aufgeführt.

Killifische in der Wissenschaft

Wir kennen nun die Herkunft des Namens "Killifisch" und seine aquaristische Geschichte. Was aber sind nun Killifische?

Der oben skizzierte kurze Abriß der Geschichte des Killifischhobbys läßt bereits einige Punkte zur Einordnung der Killifische erkennen. Die Bedeutung des Begriffes hat sich allerdings im Laufe der Zeit sehr geändert, und dies hat vor allem wissenschaftliche Gründe. Während von seiner Entstehung her der Begriff eigentlich nur auf nordamerikanische *Fundulus*-Arten angewendet werden dürfte, versteht jeder Aquarianer darunter heute eine Gruppe von bunten Aquarienfischen vorwiegend tropischer Herkunft. Verfolgen wir einmal, wie sich der Begriff des Killifisches gewandelt hat.

Die erste Monographie, die nur den Killifischen und ihren nächsten Verwandten gewidmet war, wurde 1895 von dem amerikanischen Ichthyologen GARMAN veröffentlicht. Allerdings hatte er fälschlich einen Salmler aus Westafrika (*Neolebias unifasciatus* STEINDACHNER, 1894) sowie einen Karpfenfisch aus Ostasien (*Fundulichthys virescens* SCHLEGEL, 1850) als Killifische angesehen. In seinem Werk behandelte GARMAN alle zu jener Zeit bekannten eierlegenden und lebendgebärenden Zahnkarpfen. Insgesamt fiel es ihm aber schwer, die Killifische in seinem Sinne zu definieren.

Der Engländer REGAN (1911) klassifizierte die von ihm als Microcyprini bezeichneten Zahnkarpfen neu und trennte sie in lebendgebärende und eierlegende Zahnkarpfen auf. Diese Gliederung blieb lange Zeit erhalten, in der Aquaristik wurden beide Gruppen stets getrennt gesehen, für beide gibt es jeweils Spezialvereinigungen. Erst

What are Killifishes?

The species shown in this book commonly are known among aquarists as "Killifishes". This term originates from the old dutch and originally meant those fishes which were collected by the early dutch settlers in the ponds, ditches and small streams of the area of the modern New York which then was named New Amsterdam. Such small waters were called "Kil" in the old dutch language, and consequently the fishes which were unknown to the european settlers were called by them Kilvis, Killfis or Killifish. The spelling "Killie" frequently can be found as another version in some texts of mainly american origin. The term "Killifish" has nothing to do with "to kill" or to murder.

As far as we know today, in 18th century America mainly Fundulus heteroclitus were called 'Kilvis' and even today this fish has the name 'Killifish' or 'Mudfish' in colloquial speech. In the American sphere, this name is also used in its ichthyological, scientific sense.

The first living specimens were imported at the beginning of the century from the New World to Europe. The single animals that came to our regions then were from the genera Fundulus and Cyprinodon. But soon also the tropical "Funduls" became known to the aquatic world. In 1903 Rivulus was imported to Europe from Brazil, imports of Aphyosemion and Epiplatys species followed in 1905. These fishes raised quite some interest and it was reported on them in magazines and journals like the German "Wochenschrift für Aquarien- und Terrarienkunde" and "Blätter für Aquarien- und Terrarienkunde". In the latter, a series of articles on the West African Fundulus species by Paul ARNOLD was published. The first of these articles contained for the first time a plate that showed coloured pictures of the African Killifishes. The plate introduced a male and a female of the following species: "Fundulus Arnoldi" (today: Aphyosemion arnoldi), "Fundulus gularis BLGR.var.A (blue)" (today: Aphyosemion deltaense) and "Fundulus gularis BLGR.var.B (yellow)" (today: Aphyosemion sjoestedti). Due to the rising interest, sailors from the major ship companies that sailed Africa started to bring with them larger amounts of these fishes to Europe and especially Hamburg where traders but also scientifically interested aquarists like Paul ARNOLD, Johannes THUMM, and later Fritz MAYER, Hermann MEINKEN, Erhard ROLOFF and others were impatiently waiting for the newest imports from Africa. Hamburg soon was the basis for exports of the new "Prachtfundulen", especially to the United States. In the 20s and 30s, Killis that only recently have been identified got into the hands of enthusiastic aquarists. After WW II new breeding stocks were founded on the remaining species that had survived the chaos of war and its aftermath. And soon the DATZ (a German aquatic magazine) reported about new imports of Killis.

In the 60s, with the founding of Killifish Associations all over the world, the Killis became really popular among aquarists. The first association was the American Killifish Association (A.K.A.) that was founded in 1961. The founding of the associations coincided with the publication of reports with brilliant photographs by renowned aquarists like Dr.W. FOERSCH, E. ROLOFF and J.J. SCHEEL which further increased the interest in these fishes. Here I'd like to mention the 1968 publication by J.J. SCHEEL, "Rivulins of the Old World", a book whose outstanding quality certainly made many aquarists aware of the family of Killis in the first place. In 1964 the first issue of "The Journal of the American Killifish Association" was published. The layout of this journal proves that the founders of the association had primarily a scientific interest in Killifishes. But soon the hobbyists constituted the majority in the association and as a consequence the more 'aquatic' "Killie Notes" was published. Very soon other Killifish Associations were established: in the former GDR the "ZAG Eierlegende Zahnkarpfen", in Britain the "British Killifish Association" (B.K.A.), in the former FRG the "Deutsche Killifisch-Gemeinschaft" (DKG) and many many more in the rest of the world; some of them are listed in the appendix of this book.

Killifishes and science

Now you gained an insight into the history of the name and the distribution in the hobby of the Killifishes. But what are they?

The short overview above already gives some clues for the possible categorization of the Killis. Still, the meaning of the name 'Killifish' has considerably changed in the course of time, mainly for scientific reasons. According to the genesis of the name, only Fundulus species from North America should be called 'Killis'. But today aquarists mostly think of Killifishes as a group of colourful fishes from tropical regions. Let's have a look on the history of this perculiar transformation of a fish name.

The first monograph that dealt with Killifishes and their next relatives was published in 1895 by the American ichthyologist GARMAN. But he made the mistake to identify a West African characin fish (Neolebias unifasciatus STEINDACHNER, 1894) and an East Asian cyprinid fish (Fundulichthys virescens SCHLEGEL, 1850) as Killifishes. In his book, GARMAN dealt with all at the time known egg-laying and live-bearing Cyprinodontoidei. But on the whole, he had difficulties to clearly classify Killifishes in his sense.

In 1911, C. T. REGAN from England attempted a new classification of the Cyprinodonts which he called Microcyprini and divided them into egg-laying and live-bearing groups. This division was kept up for a long time; the two groups

neuerdings sehen einige Wissenschaftler die Beziehungen zwischen beiden Gruppen nicht mehr so strikt getrennt. Abschließend einander zugeordnet sind beide Gruppen wohl aber noch nicht.

In der Folge beschäftigten sich vor allem mehrere amerikanische Wissenschaftler mit der Einordnung der Killifische in das Gesamtsystem der Fische oder die Zuordnung bestimmter Gruppen von Killifischen zueinander, so etwa EIGENMANN, HUBBS, JORDAN oder SMITH. Der letztere (SMITH, 1938) deckte die Konfusion um die heutigen *Oryzias*- und *Aplocheilus*-Arten auf, die bis dahin falsch benannt worden waren.

Der Amerikaner MYERS beschäftigte sich mehrfach mit den Killifischen. Seiner letzten Einordnung (MYERS, 1955) wurde vor allem in der Aquaristik lange Zeit gefolgt, vermutlich weil sie recht einfach und auch für den Aquarianer nachvollziebar war. Er gliederte eine Familie der Cyprinodontidae in die folgenden sieben Unterfamilien:

- Cyprinodontinae
- Fundulinae
- Rivulinae
- Oryziatinae
- Procatopodinae
- Pantanodontinae
- Orestiatinae.

Eine schon 1931 von MYERS vorgeschlagene Gruppe war in der Auflistung vermutlich vergessen worden: die Lamprichthyinae.

Der Amerikaner SETHI (1960) behielt im Grunde diese Einteilung bei, doch erhob er die von MYERS als Unterfamilien eingestuften Gruppen zu selbständigen Familien. Die eurasischen *Aphanius*-Arten trennte er als Aphaniidae von den nordamerikanischen Cyprinodontidae ab. Als 1961 mit der American Killifish Association die erste Killifischgemeinschaft gegründet wurde, sahen Aquarianer wie Wissenschaftler die Killifische somit gleichermaßen als eine Einheit. Alle oben aufgeführten Unterfamilien der Familie Cyprinodontidae wurden als Killifische aufgefaßt, die Killifischwelt war noch in Ordnung.

Seither wurden viele neue Arten aufgesammelt, vielfach zogen Aquarianer nur zu diesem Zweck gezielt durch Urwald und Busch.

Systematische Einordnung der in den Bänden "Killifishes of the World" aufgeführten Gattungen und die Zahl ihrer Arten und Unterarten

Ordnung:	**Beloniiformes**	
Familie:	**Adrianichthyidae Weber, 1913**	
Gattungen:	*Adrianichthys* WEBER, 1913	(1)
	Xenopoecilus REGAN, 1911	(3)
Familie:	**Horaichthyidae Kulkarni, 1940**	
Gattung:	*Horaichthys* KULKARNI, 1940	(1)
Familie:	**Oryziidae (= Oryziatidae Sethi, 1960)**	
Gattung:	*Oryzias* JORDAN & SNYDER, 1906	(16)
Ordnung:	**Cyprinodontiformes Berg, 1940**	
Familie:	**Aplocheilichthyidae Sethi, 1960**	
Unterfamilie:	Aplocheilichthyinae MYERS, 1928	
Gattungen:	*Aplocheilichthys* BLEEKER, 1863	(44)
	Hylopanchax POLL & LAMBERT, 1965	(1)
	Hypsopanchax MYERS, 1924	(6)
	Laciris HUBER, 1981	(1)
	Lamprichthys REGAN, 1911	(1)
	Pantanodon MYERS, 1955	(2)
	Plataplochilus AHL, 1928	(6)
	Procatopus BOULENGER, 1904	(3)
Unterfamilie:	Fluviphylacinae ROBERTS, 1970	
Gattung:	*Fluviphylax* WHITLEY, 1965	(4)
Familie:	**Poeciliidae Garman, 1895**	
	(rund 165 Arten, nicht bei den Killifischen aufgeführt; about 165 species, mentionned separately from Killifishes)	
Familie:	**Anablepidae Garman, 1895**	
	(5 Arten, nicht bei den Killifischen aufgeführt; 5 species, mentionned separately from Killifishes)	
Familie:	**Cyprinodontidae Gill, 1865**	
Unterfamilie:	Cyprinodontinae GILL, 1965	
Gattungen:	*Cualac* MILLER, 1956	(1)
	Cyprinodon LACÉPÈDE, 1803	(48)
	Floridichthys HUBBS, 1926	(2)
	Jordanella GOODE & BEAN, 1879	(2)
	Megupsilon MILLER & WALTERS, 1972	(1)
Unterfamilie:	Cubanichthyinae PARENTI, 1981	
	Cubanichthys HUBBS, 1926	(2)
Familie:	**Aphaniidae Sethi, 1960**	
Gattung:	*Aphanius* NARDO, 1827	(12)
Familie:	**Fundulidae Jordan & Gilbert, 1882**	
Gattungen:	*Adinia* GIRARD, 1859	(1)
	Fundulus LACÉPÈDE, 1803	(38)
	Leptolucania MYERS, 1924	(1)
	Lucania GIRARD, 1859	(3)
Familie:	**Valenciidae Parenti, 1981**	
Gattung:	*Valencia* MYERS, 1928	(2)

Neue Formen wurden in der Folge beschrieben, von Arten, die zuvor nur von Spiritusexemplaren aus wissenschaftlichen Museumssammlungen bekannt waren, gelangten erstmals lebende Exemplare in die Hände von Aquarianern und Wissenschaftlern. Sogar ganz neue Gattungen kamen hinzu. Dadurch konnten die Untersuchungen insgesamt auf eine breitere Basis gestellt werden. Dabei zeigte sich mit zunehmender Fülle neuer Arten, daß auch die wissenschaftliche Einordnung den neuen Befunden angepaßt werden mußte. Nun ist die Ichthyologie eine lebendige (Teil-) Wissenschaft, die aufgrund neuer Forschungen ebenso zu neuen Aussagen kommt wie andere Bereiche der Biologie, etwa die Genetik, von der auch der Nicht-Biologe rasche Wissenschaftsfortschritte geradezu erwartet. So kann es nicht ausbleiben, daß es zu Konflikten zwischen dem Wissensstand der Aquarianer und den neueren Einordnungen durch die Wissenschaft kommt. Nicht immer vermögen die Aquarianer den Neuzuordnungen der Wissenschaftler einfach zu folgen, oft aber auch findet in der Ichthyologie ein Diskussionsprozeß aufgrund neuerer Arbeiten statt, wie er in anderen Wissenschaftsbereichen ebenfalls selbstverständlich ist. Die Aquarianer können aber verständlicherweise nur schwerlich die Veränderungen in der wissenschaftlichen Diskussion nachvollziehen, für sie ändert sich schon wieder ein gutbekannter Fischname. Daß dies Unverständnis auslöst, liegt auf der Hand, läßt sich aber kaum ändern.

Derartige neuere Forschungen und die Diskussion darum haben seit geraumer Zeit auch die Zuordnung der Killifische erfaßt und das altbekannte Schema von der einen Familie der Killifische mit ihren Unterfamilien als unzutreffend

Systematical overview of the genera listed in the volumes of "Killifishes of the World" and the number of their respective species and subspecies

Familie:	**Profundulidae Hoedeman & Bronner, 1951**	
Gattung:	*Profundulus* HUBBS, 1924	(5)
Familie:	**Goodeidae Jordan, 1923**	
Unterfamilie:	Goodeinae JORDAN, 1923	
	(Etwa 35 Arten, nicht bei den Killifischen aufgeführt;	
	about 35 species, mentionned separately from Killifishes)	
Unterfamilie:	Empetrichthyinae JORDAN, EVERMANN & CLARK, 1930	
Gattungen:	*Crenichthys* HUBBS, 1932	(6)
	Empetrichthys GILBERT, 1893	(4)
Familie:	**Orestiidae Jordan, 1923**	
Gattung:	*Orestias* VALENCIENNES, 1839	(5-43)
Familie:	**Aplocheilidae Bleeker, 1860**	
Gattungen:	*Adamas* HUBER, 1979	(1)
	Aphyoplatys CLAUSEN, 1976	(1)
	Aphyosemion MYERS, 1924	(114)
	Aplocheilus MCCLELLAND, 1839	(5)
	Diapteron HUBER & SEEGERS, 1977	(5)
	Epiplatys GILL, 1862	(32)
	Foerschichthys SCHEEL & ROMAND, 1981	(1)
	Fundulosoma AHL, 1924	(1)
	Nothobranchius PETERS, 1844	(31)
	Pachypanchax MYERS, 1933	(3)
	Paranothobranchius SEEGERS, 1985	(1)
	Pronothobranchius RADDA, 1969	(1)
Familie:	**Rivulidae Myers, 1925**	
Gattungen:	*Austrofundulus* MYERS, 1932	(2)
	Campellolebias VAZ-FERREIRA & SIERRA, 1974	(3)
	Cynolebias STEINDACHNER, 1876	(48)
	Cynopoecilus REGAN, 1912	(1)
	Leptolebias MYERS, 1952	(7)
	Maratecoara COSTA, 1995	(2)
	Millerichthys COSTA, 1995	(1)
	Moema COSTA, 1989	(3)
	Neofundulus MYERS, 1924	(4)
	Pituna COSTA, 1989	(1)
	Plesiolebias COSTA, 1990	(5)
	Pterolebias GARMAN, 1895	(11)
	Rachovia MYERS, 1927	(5)
	Renova THOMERSON & THAPHORN, 1995	(1)
	Rivulus POEY, 1860	(90)
	Simpsonichthys CARVALHO, 1959	(3)
	Spectrolebias COSTA & NIELSEN, 1997	(1)
	Stenolebias COSTA, 1995	(2)
	Terranatos TAPHORN & THOMERSON, 1978	(1)
	Trigonectes MYERS, 1925	(4)

were seen separately and there were also founded separate associations for both groups. Only recently, scientists have refrained from this strict division.

At the moment, there is no definite classification of the two groups available. Several American scientists tried to establish the Killifishes within the system of fishgenera in general and to assign different groups of Killifishes to each other, like EIGENMANN, HUBBS, JORDAN or SMITH. The latter (SMITH, 1938) sorted out the confusion in today's Oryzias and Aplocheilus species that had been falsely classified. The American scientist MYERS repeatedly indulged himself into the field of Killifish research. His last classification (MYERS, 1955) was for a long time regarded as

international standard, probably because it was quite easy to comprehend and therefore useful for hobbyists, too. He divided the family of Cyprinodontidae into seven sub-families:

- Cyprinodontinae
- Fundulinae
- Rivulinae
- Oryziatinae
- Procatopodontinae
- Pantanodontinae
- Orestiatinae

A further sub-family that MYERS proposed in 1931 had probably been forgotten on this list: the Lamprichthyinae.

The American scientist SETHI (1960) roughly stuck to this division, but he elavated the sub-families to

independent families. Also, he seperated the European Killifishes from the Northamerican Cyprinodontinae and called them Aphaniidae. When in 1961 the American Killifish Association was founded, scientists as well as hobbyists considered the group of Killifishes as a homogenous one. All sub-families of the Cyprinodontidae family listed above were classified as Killifishes - the Killifish world was still in order.

Since then many new species have been collected, often aquarists searched the tropical woods just to find these particular fish. As a result, new forms were described and species that had only been known from alcohol preserved specimens in the museums now got as live fish into the hands of ichthyologists and hobbyists. Even new genera were discovered which allowed science to work from a broader basis. Consequently the classification needed to be re-arranged according to the findings of the latest Killifish research which had resulted in a vast number of new genera and species. As ichthyology is a 'living' science just like other branches of biology, the scientific classifications always have to be brought into line with the newest research results. Very often the discussion among scientists carries on for several months and sometimes the process of renaming a species goes on for years. Understandibly hobbyists cannot or only hardly follow ongoing discussions - for them often enough simply a familiar fish has yet again another name. The resulting confusion is more than understandable but - unfortunately - cannot be prevented.

The discussion about the latest results of ichthyological research has, of course, also reached the family of Killifishes. The old, well-known scheme of the family of Killis and its sub-families has proved to be inadequate. Especially the controversially received work by PARENTI (1981) has raised many

deutlich gemacht. Insbesondere die in vielen Punkten sehr kontrovers diskutierte Arbeit von PARENTI (1981) hat zu einer Belebung der Diskussion um die Einordnung der verschiedenen Killifischgruppen und ihnen nahe stehender Formen geführt. Heute wird die Zuordnung der Killifische mehrheitlich so gesehen, wie es in der Übersicht auf Seite 6 vorgestellt ist, wobei nicht verschwiegen werden darf, daß die Diskussion noch nicht abgeschlossen ist und manche Wissenschaftler die eine oder andere Zuordnung anders sehen. So werden die *Oryzias*-Arten oder Reiskärpflinge unterschiedlich zugeordnet, sie werden unter anderem auch in die Fischordnungen der Atheriniformes (Ährenfisch-Verwandte) (ROSEN, 1964) oder der Beloniformes (ROSEN & PARENTI, 1981) gestellt, also näher zu den Seehechten. Dieses Buch wendet sich jedoch in erster Linie an Aquarianer, und daher ist die Familie der Reiskärpflinge hier mit aufgeführt, wohl wissend, daß sie, wissenschaftlich betrachtet, hier nicht einzuordnen ist. Aufgrund ihrer äußeren Ähnlichkeit werden sie in diesem Buch vor den Leuchtaugenfischen oder Aplocheilichthyidae vorgestellt. Da einige wenige mit der Gattung *Oryzias* mehr oder weniger nahe verwandte Arten einmal mit diesen in eine gemeinsame Familie gestellt, dann wieder in selbständige Familien eingeordnet werden, sind sie als Adrianichthyidae und Horaichthyidae hier gleich mit aufgeführt. Es sind hochinteressante Fische, über die leider nur wenig bekannt ist. Aquaristisch sind sie bisher kaum in Erscheinung getreten, aber vielleicht entdeckt sie ein Aquarianer anläßlich einer Urlaubsreise und vermag so der Wissenschaft neue Erkenntnisse zu verschaffen.

Wenn wir also heute die Frage stellen, wodurch ein Killifisch definiert wird, so ist diese nicht so leicht zu beantworten. Im wissenschaftlichen Sinne wichtige Kennzeichen des Knochenbaus kann der Aquarianer nicht nachvollziehen. Begnügen wir uns deshalb hier damit, daß die Killifische in der Regel kleine (unter 20 cm Gesamtlänge) Fische mit nur einer ungeteilten Rückenflosse, einer meist abgerundeten und nie gegabelten Schwanzflosse sind, daß sie keine Barteln, jedoch ein vorstülpbares Maul besitzen, und nur Weich- und keine Hartstrahlen haben.

Die Fortpflanzung der Killifische

Die in den Bänden "Killifishes of the World" vorgestellten Killifisch- und *Oryzias*-Verwandten zeigen eine Vielzahl interessanter Verhaltensweisen um für den Fortbestand der Art Sorge zu tragen.

Es gibt wohl keinen Killifisch, der seine Eier auf einmal ablaicht, und schon gar nicht als Freilaicher in das offene Wasser, alle gehören sie zu den "Dauerlaichern", die mehr oder weniger regelmäßig ein bis mehrere Eier an oder in ein Substrat abgeben, es sind also Substratlaicher. Die Geschlechtspartner finden sich dabei vorübergehend, eine Paarbindung ist nicht vorhanden.

Die Haftlaicher setzen ihre Eier an Pflanzen oder zwischen Wurzeln und anderes Material ab, manche "schiessen" ihre Eier regelrecht in Gesteinsspalten. Das Ablaichen erfolgt meist paarweise. Zu den Haftlaichern zählen viele *Aphyosemion*-Arten, *Aplocheilus-*, *Epiplatys-* und verwandte Arten oder die Leuchtaugenfische. Zur Zucht kann der Aquarianer ein Artenbecken einrichten, das mit Ablaichmaterial versehen ist, etwa feinfiedrigen Pflanzen oder einem Ablaichmop (Kunstwollfäden, die an einem Korken befestigt sind). Die Eier können dann abgelesen und in einer Zuchtschale zur Entwicklung gebracht werden. Die meisten Killifischverwandten fressen nach dem Schlüpfen sogleich *Artemia*-Nauplien.

Die *Oryzias*-Verwandten haben eine weitere Stufe zur Brutfürsorge erreicht: Hier tragen die Weibchen ihre mit Fäden versehenen Eier mehr oder weniger lange vor der Afterflosse mit sich herum. *Xenopoecilus oophorus* ist noch weiter gegangen und trägt die Eier in einer Bauchkerbe, wobei sie mit den Flossen festgehalten werden.

Die spezialisierteste Anpassung an ihren Lebensraum haben unter den Killifischen sicher die Saisonfische entwickelt. Sie mußten sich in ihrem Lebenszyklus dem Wechsel von Regen- und Trockenzeiten anpassen. Auch wenn die Übergänge fließend sind, so sind doch die echten Saisonfische alle Bodenlaicher. Einige Gruppen laichen nach Erreichen der Geschlechtsreife paarweise am Bodengrund der Gewässer ab, andere Arten tauchen sogar in diesen zum Ablaichen regelrecht hinein. Zwar zählen auch einige *Aphyosemion*-Arten zu den Bodenlaichern, doch soll das Verhalten dieser Fische sowie ihre Zucht am Beispiel der typischen Saisonfischgattungen *Nothobranchius* bzw. *Cynolebias* in den Folgebänden erläutert werden.

Die *Cyprinodon*-Verwandten betreiben insofern eine Brutfürsorge, als die Männchen ein Revier gründen, das sie gegen Eindringlinge verteidigen. Im Revierzentrum ist ein Ablaichplatz. Schwimmen die Weibchen in ein solches Revier, so werden sie angebalzt und zum Ablaichplatz gelockt. Ist ein Weibchen nicht ablaichbereit, so wird es aus dem Revier vertrieben. Das Männchen kümmert sich um den Nachwuchs nicht. Für diese Fische müssen die Aquarien genügend groß sein und Versteckplätze für die Weibchen aufweisen, sonst können sie getötet werden. Auch hier kann der Aquarianer die Eier ablesen und getrennt zur Entwicklung bringen.

Werden die Geschlechtsprodukte zumeist frei ins Wasser abgegeben, so zeigen zwei Formen hier Abweichungen: *Horaichthys setnai* und *Campellolebias* haben eine innere Befruchtung, die befruchteten Eier werden dann allerdings an Pflanzen bzw. in den Bodengrund abgesetzt.

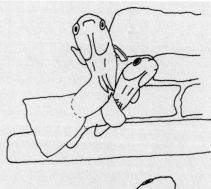

Die bodenlaichenden Saisonfische wie *Pterolebias* (oben) oder *Nothobranchius* (rechts unten) betreiben Brutfürsorge, indem sie die Eier in den Bodengrund abgeben. *Procatopus*-Arten und andere Leuchtaugenfische "schießen" ihre Eier zwischen Pflanzen, Wurzeln oder in Gesteinsspalten.

Seasonal killifishes as Pterolebias *(top) and* Notobranchius *(right, bottom) care for their offspring by spawning the eggs into the soil.* Procatopus *and other lampeyes "shoot" the eggs between plants, roots etc. or in crevices of stones.*

How killifishes spawn and breed

All killifishes and relatives of Oryzias that are shown in the our series "Killifishes of the World" display a wide range of very interesting breeding and brood caring behaviour.

There is probably no killifish that spawns its eggs at once and they never spawn into the open water. Killifishes spawn constantly, they only lay a few eggs at a time throughout the mature life of the fish. These eggs are always placed in a certain substratum: Killifishes are substratum spawners. Male and female meet only for breeding purposes, they don't form pairs for a longer period. Plant spawners spawn their eggs in plants or between roots or similar materials, some literally "shoot" their eggs into cracks in rocks. The fish usually spawn in pairs. Among the plant spawners are many Aphyosemion species, Aplocheilus and Epiplatys and related species, and Lampeyes. For successful breeding, aquarists should set up a breeding tank and furnish it with either plants with many fine leafs or a breeding mop. After spawning, the eggs can be easily removed by hand and put into another tank for hatching. Most of the freshly hatched killifish immediately will take Artemia-nauplii.

Oryzias and their relatives have reached an even higher standard of brood-caring: in these species, the female carries the eggs in front of the anal fin for some time, the eggs being connected to her with threads. Xenopoecilus oophorus has gone even one step further, the female carries the eggs in a notch of its belly, holding them with the fins.

The Killifish species most perfectly adjusted to their environment are certainly the seasonal fishes. They have adapted themselves to the rainy and dry seasons of their biosphere. Although the distinction lines between the different kinds of spawning are fluid, are the true annuals always soil spawners. Some of them spawn pairwise at the bottom of their habitat, others actually dive into the ground to release their eggs. Some of the Aphyosemion species also belong to the group of soil spawners but the behaviour and breeding of these fishes, as well as of the true annual genera Nothobranchius and Cynolebias, will be dealt with thoroughly in the upcoming volumes.

Cyprinodon and their relatives developed a special kind of brood caring: the males set up a territory that is fiercely defended by them. In the centre of this territory a 'spawning site' is chosen. When a female swims into the territory, the male starts courtshipping and leads her to the spawning site. If the female is not willing to spawn, she is immediately driven out of the territory. Hatched-out young are never taken care of by the male. Thus, breeding tanks always have to be big enough to offer the females sufficient hiding places; otherwise they could be killed. The eggs can, like in other killifishes, be collected by hand and hatched in a separate tank.

Usually the eggs and sperms are released into the open water, but two forms are the exception to this rule: Horaichthys setnai and Campellolebias: they perform an internal fertilization. Afterwards, the eggs are (like in all other species) placed in plants or into the ground.

questions that lead to a revival of the discussion about the different forms of the Killifishes and closely related forms. Although the discussion is far from settled and some scientists disagree with some of the classifications, the overview given on page 6 is (at the moment) the most widely accepted one. Still, differences are made, for example, in the classifications of Oryzias species or Ricefish which are sometimes also assigned to the order of Atheriniformes (ROSEN, 1964) or Beloniformes (ROSEN & PARENTI, 1981), that is, closer to the Halfbeaks. AQUALOG - Killis of the World is a book that is intended for hobbyists and therefore the family of Ricefish is included, although we acknowledge that, in scientific terms, they do not belong to the Killifishes. Following external similarities, they are placed in this book in front of the Aplocheilichthyidae. Also taken into consideration are species that are sometimes assigned to the genus of Oryzias; here they are included as the families Adrianichthyidae and Horaichthyidae. They are really interesting fishes but there is little information about them. In the hobby they are hardly recognized - maybe one day a travelling hobbyist discovers them on a holiday trip and thus can help to get an insight into the yet unknown world of the Ricefish.

It should be clear by now that the question how to identify Killifishes is not an easy one to answer. The scientific criteria of bone structure is of little use for the hobbyist. Therefore I would like to propose the following criteria: Killifishes are small (less than 20 cm total length) fishes with an undivided dorsal fin, a mostly rounded but never divided caudal fin, they never have barbels but an outward turnable mouth and only soft, no hard finrays.

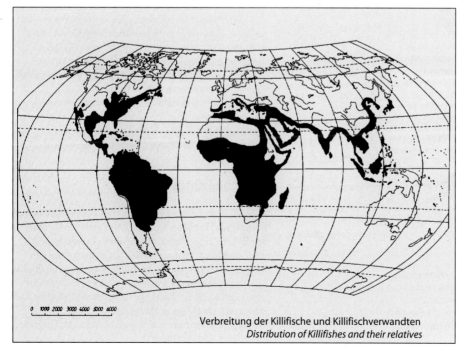

0 1000 2000 3000 4000 5000 6000

Verbreitung der Killifische und Killifischverwandten
Distribution of Killifishes and their relatives

Die Gattungen
The genera

Adrianichthys, Xenopoecilus, Oryzias und Horaichthys

Diese vier Gattungen gehören nach heutiger Auffassung nicht mehr zu den Killifischen (Cyprinodontiformes), sondern in die Ordnung Beloniformes, sie sind also mit den Halbschnabelhechten und den Fliegenden Fischen näher verwandt. Aus historischen Gründen und auch aufgrund ihrer Ähnlichkeit mit den Leuchtaugenfischen werden insbesondere die *Oryzias*-Arten aber bei den Aquarianern den Killifischen zugeordnet. Auch die Killifisch-Gemeinschaften nehmen sich ihrer an. Da dies ein in erster Linie aquaristisch orientiertes Buch ist, wurden die *Oryzias*-Arten und ihre nächsten Verwandten hier mit aufgenommen. Dabei ist sich die Wissenschaft aber noch keineswegs einig, ob die vier Gattungen in eine gemeinsame Familie Oryziidae gehören oder ob drei Familien angebracht sind: Oryziidae mit der einen Gattung *Oryzias*, Adrianichthyidae mit den Gattungen *Adrianichthys* und *Xenopoecilus*, und schließlich Horaichthyidae mit der Gattung *Horaichthys*.

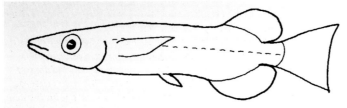

Xenopoecilus sarasinorum

Soweit überhaupt etwas über die Lebensumstände der einzelnen Arten bekannt ist, dürfte *Horaichthys setnai* von der Westküste Indiens die merkwürdigste Art sein. Sie ist die einzige Art der Gattung, besiedelt Brack- bis Süßwasser, wird nur rund 3 cm lang und besitzt ein Begattungsorgan. Von sehr skurrilem Aussehen ist demgegenüber der ebenfalls einzige Vertreter der Gattung, *Adrianichthys kruyti*. Er besitzt eine breite Schnauze in Form eines Entenschnabels. Zu den nur auf Celebes oder Sulawesi vorkommenden Adrianichthyidae gehört als zweite Gattung mit insgesamt drei Arten auch *Xenopoecilus*. Die Gattung *Oryzias* ist gegenüber den vorhergenannten aquaristisch zumindest in einigen Arten gut bekannt. Dennoch können wir davon ausgehen, daß nur ein Teil der zwischen Indien und Japan (jeweils einschließlich) bekannten Arten tatsächlich bekannt und beschrieben ist, denn das Verbreitungsgebiet ist riesig und die Fische sind mehrheitlich relativ klein und unscheinbar. *Oryzias minutillus* aus Thailand gehört sicher zu den kleinsten Fischen überhaupt. Zu den Fortpflanzungsbesonderheiten der Adrianichthyidae, Oryziidae und Horaichthyidae siehe Seite 8.

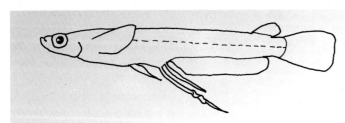

Horaichthys setnai

Aplocheilichthys

Die *Aplocheilichthys*-Arten sind mit etwa 42 Arten von West- bis Ostafrika und vom unteren Nil bis Natal in Südafrika verbreitet. Dabei sind sie recht vielgestaltig. Gattungstypus ist *Aplocheilichthys spilauchen*. Da diese Art in Körpergestalt und Lebensweise etwas von den meisten

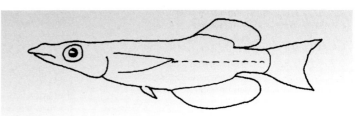

Adrianichthys kruyti

Adrianichthys, Xenopoecilus, Oryzias *and* Horaichthys

Following today's scientific standards, these four genera do not belong to the Killifishes (Cyprinodontiformes), but to the Beloniformes, that is, they are more closely related to the Halfbeaks and the Flying Fishes. For historical reasons, though, and because of the external similarities with the Lampeyes, especially the Oryzias *species are assigned by hobbyists to the family of killifishes. They are also considered by many Killifish associations. As this book is primarily designed for hobbyists we included the* Oryzias *species and their closest relatives. Also, one has to keep in mind that scientists are still not sure whether the four genera belong to one family (Oryziidae) or should be divided into three families: Oryziidae with the genus* Oryzias, *Adrianichthyidae with the genera* Adrianichthys *and* Xenopoecilus, *and Horaichthyidae with the genus* Horaichthys.
As far as anything is known about the living conditions of the species, Horaichthys setnai *from the west coast of India certainly lives under the strangest ones. It is the only species of its*

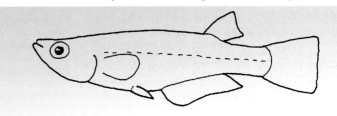

Oryzias latipes

genus and lives in brackish or freshwater. It grows only 3 cm long and the males have a copulative organ. More interesting from a decorative point of view is the comical looking representative of its genus, Adrianichthys kruyti. *It has a broad snout that looks like a duck's bill. The genus* Xenopoecilus *with its three species also belongs to the family of Adrianichthyidae that can only be found on Celebes or Sulawesi. A little bit better known than the fishes described above are some of the species from the genus* Oryzias. *But as the distribution is as wide as the area betweeen India and Japan and most of the* Oryzias *species are small and inconspicuous, most likely the majority of them is not yet discovered or described.* Oryzias minutillus *from Thailand is certainly one of the smallest fishes alive. For more information about the reproduction peculiarities of the genera Oryziidae, Adrianichthyidae and Horaichthyidae, please see page 9.*

Aplocheilichthys

About 42 Aplocheilichthys *species are distributed as wide as from the west to the east coast of Africa and from the lower Nile to Natal in Southafrica. The species' appearance of this genus displays a great variety. The genustype is* Aplocheilichthys spilauchen. *As this particular species deviates from all other species in exterior and behaviour it was proposed to assign only this species to the genus* Aplocheilichthys *and all other species to the genus* Micropanchax MYERS, 1924. *Although this idea has certainly many advantages I will stick*

anderen Leuchtaugenfischen abweicht, wurde verschiedentlich der Vorschlag geäußert, nur sie in der Gattung *Aplocheilichthys* zu belassen, die übrigen Arten jedoch in die Gattung *Micropanchax* MYERS, 1924 zu stellen. Obgleich dieser Vorschlag durchaus etwas für sich hat, soll hier der üblichen Einteilung gefolgt werden bis eine dringend erforderliche Gattungsrevision vorliegt. PARENTI (1981: 510) schlägt eine Aufteilung der Gattung in *Aplocheilichthys* und "*Aplocheilichthys*" vor, wobei letztere Gattungszuordnung auf einer Sammlung undatierten Materials von *A. johnstoni* beruht. Diesem Vorschlag wird hier nicht gefolgt. Zur Benennung der Arten sei festgestellt, daß in diesem Buch *Aplocheilichthys luxophthalmus* BRÜNING, 1929 anstelle von *A. macrophtalmus* MEINKEN, 1933 verwendet wird, ersterer Name hat Priorität. Ferner werden hier die mitunter als selbständige Gattung *Congopanchax* POLL, 1971 betrachteten Leuchtaugenfische - vermutlich umfassen sie nur eine Art - als Untergattung zu *Aplocheilichthys* aufgeführt. *Aplocheilichthys* haben - wie die mit ihnen verwandten Arten - eine leuchtende Augeniris, man sennt sie deshalb auch Leuchtaugenfische. Selten sind sie größer als 5 cm. Die Männchen haben oft ausgezogene Flossen, häufig sind sie intensiver als die Weibchen gefärbt. Bei vielen Arten ist die Unterscheidung aber nicht immer einfach. In zahlreicher Literatur ist zu lesen, daß die *Aplocheilichthys*-Arten Schwarmfische seien. Dies ist jedoch nicht richtig. Vielmehr suchen alle Leuchtaugenfische die Geselligkeit, sie schließen sich oft zu Trupps zusammen. Dennoch braucht jedes Tier genügend Freiraum, in einer Plastiktüte längere Zeit transportierte Fische können sich durchaus gegenseitig beschädigen und sogar töten. Das Aquarium sollte für alle Leuchtaugenfische eher mit gedämpftem Licht versehen sein, Weichwasser ist in jedem Falle angebracht, wenn auch bei manchen Arten nicht erforderlich. Lebendfutter ist vorzuziehen, für manche Arten notwendig. Alle Leuchtaugenfische sind Haftlaicher.

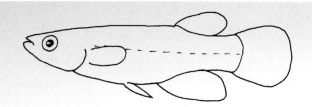

Aplocheilichthys spilauchen

to the common classification until the long overdue revision of the genus has been published. PARENTI (1981:510) suggested the division of the genus into Aplocheilichthys and "Aplocheilichthys", in which the genus assignment of the latter is based on a collection of undated material of A. johnstoni. I do not follow this suggestion either. Concerning the naming of the species I would like to mention that I use A. luxophtalmus BRÜNING, 1929 instead of A. macrophtalmus MEINKEN, 1933 because the first name has priority. Finally I included Congopanchax POLL, 1971 not as a genus (as it is sometimes done) but as a subgenus of Aplocheilichthys.

Aplocheilichthys have - like all species related to them - a shining iris; that is why they are also called Lampeyes. They rarely grow larger than 5 cm. Males often have elongate fins and are more brightly coloured than females but in many species the division of the sexes is not this easy. One can often read in specialist literature that Aplocheilichthys species are usually swarmfish. This is not true. All Lampeyes rather look for company and often join together in groups. But nevertheless each fish needs sufficient space - several fish kept together in a plastic bag for transport might after a while hurt or even kill each other. Aquaria for Lampeyes should be subduedly lighted; soft water is preferred but not necessary in every species. Live food should be favoured, some species require it. The eggs of Lampeyes are preferably spawned between plants, roots or stones.

Hylopanchax *and* Hypsopanchax

The two genera of Lampeyes are usually found in streams of tropical woods. The majority of Hypsopanchax species lives in a ring-like area around the Kongo river basin. Only few species and the monotypical genus Hylopanchax live in the central area of the basin. Care instructions are the same as for all other Lampeyes.

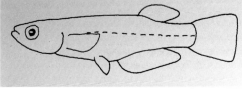

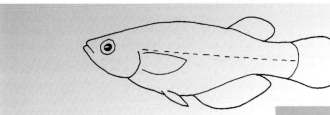

Hylopanchax stictopleuron (oben) und *Hypsopanchax platysternus* /
Hylopanchax stictopleuron (top) and *Hypsopanchax platysternus*

Hylopanchax und *Hypsopanchax*

Beide Gattungen von Leuchtaugenfischen sind vorzugsweise Bewohner von Urwaldbächen, wobei die Mehrheit der *Hypsopanchax*-Arten in einem Kreis um das Kongobecken herum zu finden sind, nur wenige Arten sowie die monotypische Gattung *Hylopanchax* kommen im zentralen Bereich des Kongobeckens selbst vor. Die Pflege erfolgt wie die anderer Leuchtaugenfische.

Laciris und *Lamprichthys*

Beide Gattungen weisen nur jeweils eine Art auf und kommen je in einem See des zentralafrikanischen Grabens vor: *Laciris pelagicus* im Edward-See, *Lamprichthys tanganicanus* im Tanganjika-See. Während über *Laciris* keine Erfahrungen vorliegen, wird *Lamprichthys*, der größte bekannte Leuchtaugenfisch, regelmäßig gezüchtet. Diese Art hat sich als Spaltenlaicher erwiesen, die Eier werden in Spalten und

Laciris pelagicus (oben) und *Lamprichthys tanganicanus* /
Laciris pelagicus (top) and *Lamprichthys tanganicanus*

Laciris *and* Lamprichthys

Both genera have only one species and each is endemic in only one lake of the African Rift Valley: Laciris pelagicus in Lake Edward and Lamprichthys tanganicanus in Lake Tanganyika.

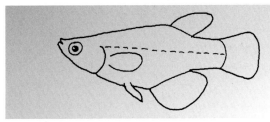

Pantanodon stuhlmanni

Ritzen von Steinen abgelaicht. Die Jungfische schlüpfen vor allem in der Nacht.

Pantanodon

Pantanodon umfaßt zwei Arten, *stuhlmanni* (synonymisiert mit *P. podoxys* in SEEGERS, 1997) und *madagascariensis*, die in schwach salinen bis hypersalinen Gewässern des ostafrikanischen und madegassischen Küsteneinzuges vorkommen, hin und wieder jedoch auch in reinem Süßwasser anzutreffen sind. Insgesamt leben sie nie weit vom Meer entfernt. Besonders in den Salinen des kenianischen Küsteneinzuges findet sich *P. stuhlmanni* in ungeheuren Mengen, die dortige Form hat sich aber auch am empfindlichsten und hinfälligsten gezeigt. Nur *P. stuhlmanni* konnte bisher in Gefangen-

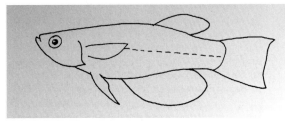

Procatopus nototaenia

schaft gepflegt und zur Nachzucht gebracht werden, die Art hat sich als schwieriger Pflegling erwiesen.

Plataplochilus und Procatopus

Beide Gattungen von Leuchtaugenfischen haben eine ähnliche Lebensweise, sie kommen im Küsteneinzug Zentralafrikas von Nigeria bis Equatorial-Guinea (*Procatopus*) bzw. von Equatorial-Guinea bis Kongo (*Plataplochilus*) vor, wo sie vorzugsweise Bäche und kleinere Fließgewässer bevölkern. Die Vertreter beider Gattungen sehen sich sehr ähnlich, so daß bereits vorgeschlagen wurde, sie in nur einer Gattung *Procatopus* zu vereinen. Beide Gattungen haben überdies gemeinsam, daß die in ihr enthaltenen Formen zur Zeit kaum gegeneinander abzugrenzen sind. CLAUSEN (1959) revidierte die Gattung *Procatopus* und beschrieb 6 neue Arten sowie 2 neue Untergattungen. Insgesamt wurden bisher 10 Arten dieser Gattung beschrieben, davon werden von den Ichthyologen, die sich mit diesen Fischen beschäftigt haben, nur drei Arten als gültig betrachtet. Es kann jedoch kein Zweifel daran bestehen, daß es mehr als diese drei Arten gibt. Ähnliche Konfusion gibt es bezüglich der Gattung *Plataplochilus*. Da also eine tiefgreifende Revision der Gattungen gegenwärtig fehlt, ist die Zuordnung der in diesem Buch gezeigten Phänotypen zu den beschriebenen Arten nicht immer völlig sicher. Die Haltung und Pflege von *Plataplochilus* und *Procatopus* entspricht der der *Aplocheilichthys*-Arten.

Adamas

Adamas ist zur Zeit monotypisch, die Gattung besteht nur aus einer Art. Dieser Fisch gehört zu den Zwergen unter den Killifischen, er zeigt gestaltlich Anklänge an *Aphyosemion*, aber auch an *Epiplatys* und Leuchtaugenfische, obgleich die Art mit den Leuchtaugenfischen sicher nicht näher verwandt ist. Die Pflege verläuft wie die von *Aphyoplatys*.

While there is literally nothing known about Laciris, *is the breeding of* Lamprichthys, *the largest of all known Lampeyes, quite regular. In spawning, this species has proved to place the eggs in crevices in rocks. The eggs hatch preferably in the dark.*

Pantanodon

The genus Pantanodon *has two species,* P. stuhlmanni *(synonymized with* P. podoxys *by* SEEGERS, 1996) *and* P. madagascariensis *which live in slightly salty or hyper salty water of the coastal areas of East Africa and Madagascar. Sometimes they*

Plataplochilus ngaensis

can also be found in freshwater, but they are nevertheless always close to the sea. Only P. stuhlmanni *has been successfully kept in the aquarium and even been bred. But on the whole* Pantanodon *turned out to be extremely difficult fish to keep.*

Plataplochilus *and* Procatopus

Both Lampeyes genera have similar living circumstances. They prefer small streams and other running waters. One can find Procatopus *in the coastal regions of Central Africa, from Nigeria to Equatorial-Guinea and* Plataplochilus *from Equatorial-Guinea to Kongo. The fish of both genera look very similar; consequently it has been proposed to put them together in one single genus,* Procatopus. *The forms in both genera are also hardly to distinguish from each other. In 1959* CLAUSEN *revised the genus* Procatopus *and described six new species and two sub-genera. Altogether ten species have been described so far but only three species have been acknowledged by scientists. Still, there is no doubt that more than three* Procatopus *species exist. A similar confusing situation has occurred in the genus* Plataplochilus. *As obviously a revision of both genera is necessary but not available at the moment I have to point out that the phenotypical assignments to the*

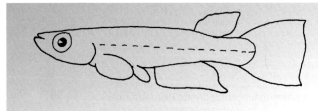

Adamas formosus

depicted species are not definite. Care instructions for both genera are the same as for Aplocheilichthys.

Adamas

The genus Adamas *is at the moment monotypical, that is, it has only one species. This fish is a dwarf among killifishes. Its exterior resembles* Aphyosemion, Epiplatys *and also* Lamp-

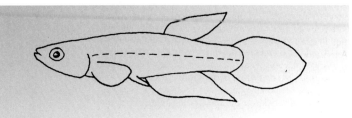

Aphyoplatys duboisi

Aphyoplats

Auch *Aphyoplatys* ist monotypisch, es gibt also nur eine *Aphyoplatys*-Art. Überdies handelt es sich dabei ebenfalls um einen recht kleinen Fisch. Wie *Adamas formosus* besiedelt auch *Aphyoplatys duboisi* den Regenwald-Einzug des westlichen Kongobeckens und beide Arten haben ähnliche ökologische Bedürfnisse. Beide sollten in nicht zu großen und vor allem eher flachen und verkrauteten Aquarien gepflegt werden.

Aphyosemion

Die Gattung *Aphyosemion*, wie sie hier verstanden wird, ist die größte Killifischgattung. Sie nimmt auch in diesem Buch den umfangreichsten Raum ein. Zu ihr gehören außerordentlich farbenprächtige Fische, die in ihren Farbzusammenstellungen an Korallenfische erinnern, so daß die *Aphyosemion*-Arten schon immer bei den Aquarianern großes Interesse erzielten. Es ist allerdings in den letzten Jahren bezüglich der Gattungszuordnung vieler Arten Konfusion eingetreten, und man findet in der Literatur die gleiche Art unter dem Gattungsnamen *Aphyosemion*, aber auch unter *Roloffia*, andere Arten sind einer Gattung *Fundulopanchax* zugeordnet. Es fehlt zur Zeit eine fundierte Revision der gesamten Gattung sowie ihr nahe verwandter Arten. Die Gattungsbezeichnung *Roloffia* ist von der Nomenklatur-

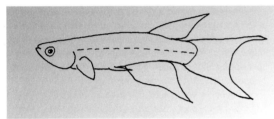

Aphyosemion christyi, eine typische Art der Gattung, laicht vorzugsweise als Haftlaicher zwischen Pflanzen /
Aphyosemion christyi is a typical species of the genus; it prefers to spawn between plants.

kommission verworfen worden, sie kann von ernstzunehmenden Biologen nicht mehr verwendet werden. Die Internationale Nomenklaturkommission wurde von den Biologenverbänden eingesetzt um die Namengebung in der Zoologie zu regeln. Ihre Entscheidungen sind für Biologen bindend, auch wenn sie hier und da nicht glücklich erscheinen mögen. Sich darüber hinwegzusetzen erinnert an einen Autofahrer, der sich entschieden hat, an roten Ampeln nicht zu halten, weil er die entsprechende Verkehrsverordnung für falsch hält. Ob ein derartiges Vorgehen immer glücklich ist, sei dahingestellt. Anstelle der Gattungsbezeichnung *Roloffia* steht *Callopanchax* MYERS, 1933 zur Verfügung, ferner wurden weitere Gattungs- bzw. Untergattungsbezeichnungen für diverse kleine Arten der früheren Sammelgattung *Roloffia* publiziert: *Archiaphyosemion* RADDA, 1977 (Typusart: *Aphyosemion guineense* DAGET, 1954) und *Scriptaphyosemion* RADDA & PÜRZL, 1987 (Typusart: *Aphyosemion guineense gery* LAMBERT, 1958). Bevor jedoch nicht eine grundlegende Revision der Gattung im weiteren Sinne erfolgt ist, seien die fraglichen Arten hier in diese Gattung *Aphyosemion* einbezogen. *Fundulopanchax* wurde von PARENTI (1981) wieder eingeführt. Sie glaubt, grundlegende Unterschiede zwischen der Gruppe der "kleineren Arten" (*Aphyosemion christyi*-Typ) und den "größeren Arten" (*A. sjoestedti*-Typ) gefunden zu haben. Ihre Arbeit ist bezüglich der *Aphyosemion*-Arten jedoch sicher nicht als Revision zu bezeichnen, hat sie doch von den insgesamt 112 derzeit einzuordnenden Arten für ihre Gattung *Aphyosemion* nur ganze 4 Arten berücksichtigt, für die Gattung *Fundulopanchax* in ihrem Sinne nur 5 Arten, worunter sich eine falsch bestimmte Art befindet ("*F. gardneri*: Ghana" muß fehlbestimmt sein, da es die Art dort meines Wissens nicht gibt). Zwischen beiden Gruppen wurden die morphologisch am weitesten auseinanderstehenden Formen herangezogen, die auch ein Laie als extrem

eyes, although this fish is definitely no relative of the latter. It requires the same care as Aphyoplatys.

Aphyoplatys

Like Adamas, *this is a monotypical genus.* Aphyoplatys duboisi *is also very small and has the same ecological requirements as* Adamas formosus. *Both genera can be found in the rainforest areas of the western Kongo River basin.* Adamas *and* Aphyoplatys *should be kept in shallow, densely planted tanks.*

Aphyosemion

Among Killifishes, as they are defined in this book, Aphyosemion *is the most extensive genus and consequently it occupies most of this book.* Aphyosemion *has always been of great interest for aquarists because of its wonderful colouration and its resemblance to Coral Fish. The classification of the species is as confusing and confused as in many other killifish genera. For example, one can find in specialist literature the same fish as a species of* Aphyosemion *but also as* Roloffia *or* Fundulopanchax. *Like I said before: a thourough revision of the genus and its closely related species is long overdue. Serious scientists will not use the name* Roloffia *- the International Commission on Zoological Nomenclature has dimissed this name. This commission was put up by biologist associations on order to settle the name giving processes in zoology. The decisions of the commission are binding for all*

Aphyosemion sjoestedti ist eine recht robuste Art und laicht als Saisonfisch vorzugsweise am Boden ab. /
Aphyosemion sjoestedti is a more robust species and as a seasonal fish it prefers to spawn as a bottom spawner.

biologists although one or the other may be not too happy with some of them. But to ignore these decisions would be like a driver going through a red light because he deemed traffic regulations unnecessary. Callopanchax MYERS, 1933 *has replaced the former genus name* Roloffia *and other genus and sub-genus names have been published replacing the names of some smaller species of the former collective genus* Roloffia: Archiaphyosemion RADDA, 1977 *(genustype:* Aphyosemion guineense DAGET, 1954*) and* Scriptaphyosemion RADDA & PÜRZL, 1987 *(genustype:* Aphyosemion guineense gery LAMBERT, 1958*). Before the genus is not fundamentally revised, the species in question will be assigned to the genus* Aphyosemion.
The name Fundulopanchax *was re-invented by* PARENTI *in 1981. She believes to have found fundamental differences between the "smaller" species (*Aphyosemion christyi *type) and the "bigger" species (*Aphyosemion sjoestedti *type). But her work certainly cannot be regarded as a revision because she took out of 112 relevant species only four of the genus* Aphyosemion *and only five species of the genus* Fundulopanchax *in her sense into consideration. (Among the* Fundulopanchax *she has, in my opinion, one falsely classified species: "*F.gardneri*: Ghana". As far as I am informed, does the species not exist in Ghana.) To distinguish the two groups, those forms were used that differ most from each other in morphological terms - a step that can be very well understood, even by hobbyists. But - species that would be very difficult to be decided on (by the standards* PARENTI *has*

erkennent. Aus dem Bereich der Arten bei denen eine Entscheidung schwer fallen würde (*A. gardneri*-Gruppe, *A. mirabile*-Gruppe, *A. marmoratum*, *A. oeseri*, *A. puerzli* etc.), wurde keine Art berücksichtigt. Ferner gibt die Autorin bezüglich der Artenzusammensetzung ihrer Gattung *Fundulopanchax* nur an "Approximately 50 species ...". Warum welche Art besonders der oben angeführten Arten (-gruppen) *Fundulopanchax* im Sinne PARENTIS zuzuordnen ist, muß daher dem Einfallsreichtum des jeweiligen Betrachters anheimgestellt werden. Es muß also einer wirklichen Gattungsrevision überlassen bleiben, ob und wie die Großgattung *Aphyosemion* aufzugliedern sei. Eine Gattung *Fundulopanchax* wird daher hier nicht verwendet. Damit der Aquarianer jedoch in der Literatur zu findende Gattungszuordnungen hier nachvollziehen kann, ist bei den entsprechenden Arten ein (*F.*) hinter dem Gattungsnamen *Aphyosemion* bzw. seiner Abkürzung zu finden. Außer den bereits genannten (Unter-) Gattungsnamen stehen noch die folgenden zur Verfügung, die bei einer Gattungsrevision zu diskutieren wären: *Chromaphyosemion* RADDA, 1971, *Paraphyosemion* KOTTELAT, 1976, *Raddaella* HUBER, 1977, *Kathetys* HUBER, 1977, *Gularopanchax* RADDA, 1977, *Paludopanchax* RADDA, 1977 und *Mesoaphyosemion* RADDA, 1977. *Chromaphyosemion* scheint die am klarsten umrissene Gruppe darzustellen, doch auch sie zeigt über eine unbeschriebene Art (SEEGERS, 1981, Abb. 11) von Mapan, Kamerun (S. 55 unten), Bezüge zu *A. bamilekorum*, das gemeinhin in die *A. bualanum/elberti*-Gruppe gestellt wird.

Die Pflege der *Aphyosemion*-Arten ist keineswegs einheitlich, wie es in einer Gattung mit so vielen Arten und mit einem so großen Verbreitungsgebiet zu erwarten ist, zumal dieses Verbreitungsgebiet unterschiedliche Landschaftsräume wie Savanne und Regenwald mit umfaßt. Allgemein gilt: *Aphyosemion*-Arten aus Bergländern (z.B. in Gabun) benötigen kühlere Temperaturen (unter 20-22°C), solche aus dem Küsteneinzug brauchen es deutlich wärmer (24-26°C). Die meisten Arten lassen sich sowohl im Torfansatz (Erläuterung siehe *Nothobranchius* in Band II) als auch als Haftlaicher zur Fortpflanzung bringen, wobei im letzteren Falle die Eier aus Pflanzen, Fasern, einem Wollmop oder dergleichen abgelesen und in einer Zuchtschale zur Entwicklung gebracht werden können. Die Jungfische fressen meist sogleich *Artemia*-Nauplien.

set up) are simply left out, e.g. A.gardneri group, A. mirabile group, A. marmoratum, A. oeseri, A. puerzli etc. In terms of species classification, the author only gives a hint, that she assigns "approximately fifty species..." to her genus Fundulopanchax. Unfortunately PARENTI does not say how and why one is supposed to assign a certain species or species-group to the genus Fundulopanchax - that is probably up to the imagination of the reader. Therefore one still has to wait for a fundamental revision of the genus Aphyosemion before it can be decided if and how it should be divided into several genera. Consequently, I will not use the genus name Fundulopanchax. But to make it easier for the user of this book who might have read the name 'Fundulopanchax' in connection to some species, I added the abbreviation (F.) behind the genus names in question. Besides the genus and sub-genus names that have already been mentioned, the following names would have to be taken into consideration in a revision: Chromaphyosemion RADDA, 1971, Paraphyosemion KOTTELAT, 1976, Raddaella HUBER, 1977, Kathetys HUBER, 1977, Gularopanchax RADDA, 1977, Paludopanchax RADDA, 1977, and Mesoaphyosemion RADDA, 1977. Among these, Chromaphyosemion seems to be the most clearly defined group, but one not yet identified species (SEEGERS, 1981, fig. 11) from Mapan, Camerun, connects it with A. bamilekorum which is usually counted among the A. bualanum/elberti group (see p. 55 bottom).

Like one expects from a genus that is as widely spread and diverse as Aphyosemion, care instructions are as varied, especially as Aphysemion lives in environments as diverse as the savanna and the rainforrest. In general, Aphyosemion species from mountainous regions (like in Gabon) need lower temperatures (20 - 22° C), those from coastal regions need higher temperatures (24-26° C). Most species can be bred as soil spawners in peat substratum or as plant spawners that spawn on plants, a sponge or mops where the eggs can easily be removed to a hatching tank. The fry immediately will take brine shrimp nauplii after hatching.

Anmerkungen zum Bildteil:

Die Legenden zu den Bildern enthalten die folgenden Angaben:
- Die AQUALOG-Code-Nummer der Art, gefolgt vom voll ständigen wissenschaftlichen Namen. Seine Bedeutung ist auf Seite 2 erläutert.
- Den deutschen / den englischen populären Namen, soweit vorhanden.
- "ABC 97/1" kennzeichnet den Fundortcode eines Sammlers. Dieser Fundort ist nicht selten in verschiedener Literatur (z.B. DKG-Journal), insbsondere aber in LANGTON (1996) aufgeschlüsselt, oft aber auch (noch)unbekannt. In jedem Fall sollte eine solche Fundortpopulation aber unbedingt rein erhalten und rein weitergezüchtet werden, denn sonst geht in der Aquaristik die Vielfalt der Fundortformen verloren und es bleibt nach einigen Jahren eine Einheitsform einer Art übrig, die mit den Ausgangspopulationen, wie sie in der Natur vorgefunden worden waren, nicht mehr viel gemein hat. Überdies hat sich hin und wieder gezeigt, daß zwei zunächst einer Art zugeordnete Fundortpopulationen sich später als getrennte Arten herausstellten.
- [T.t.] bedeutet: Diese Population stammt vom Typenfundort der Art.
- In der dritten Zeile sind die Fundorte der Population, soweit bekannt, angegeben. Hierzu gilt das oben dargestellte: **Fundortpopulationen stets rein weiterzüchten, nie kreuzen !**
- Die Kürzel in der dritten Zeile und die Bedeutungen der Piktogramme sind auf der vorderen inneren Umschlagklappe erläutert, ausgeklappt erlaubt sie einen unmittelbaren Vergleich.

Some notes concerning the tables:

The captions of the photos contain the following informations:
- *The AQUALOG code-number of the species, followed by the complete scientific name of the species. It is explained on page 2.*
- *The german / english common names as far as available.*
- *"ABC 97/1"designates the collecting code or collecting localities of the different collectors. Such codes are sometimes explained in various literature (as for example the DKG-Journal), but see especially LANGTON (1996). Some codes, however, are not yet published. In any case every population should be truely bred to avoid the loss of the variability of the different strains as they were found in the wild and to avoid the production of hybrids. There could be the danger that within some years the variability of a given species might vanish and then there would only be a type in the hobby which has only little similarity with the wild strain.*
- *[T.t.] means: This population originates from the type locality of the species.*
- *The collecting localities of the respective populations, as far as known, are given in the third line. Please remember:*
  Do never interbreed specimens of different localities !
- *The abbreviations and ideograms of the third and fourth line are explained on the inside of the back cover, please, unfold it.*

Die Arten*
The species*

Adrianichthyidae WEBER, 1913

Adrianichthys WEBER, 1913
A. kruyti WEBER, 1913

Xenopoecilus REGAN, 1911
X. oophorus KOTTELAT, 1990
X. poptae WEBER & DE BEAUFORT, 1922
X. sarasinorum (POPTA, 1905)

Horaichthyidae KULKARNI, 1940

Horaichthys KULKARNI, 1940
H. setnai KULKARNI, 1940

Oryziidae SETHI, 1960
(= Oryziatidae Rosen, 1964)

Oryzias JORDAN & SNYDER, 1906
O. carnaticus (JERDON, 1849)
O. celebensis (WEBER, 1894)
O. curvinotus (NICHOLS & POPE, 1927)
O. javanicus (BLEEKER, 1854)
O. latipes latipes (TEMMINCK & SCHLEGEL, 1850)
O. latipes sinensis CHEN, HIROSHI & CHU, 1989
O. luzonensis (HERRE & ABLAN, 1934)
O. marmoratus (AURICH, 1935)
O. matanensis (AURICH, 1935)
O. mekongensis UWA & MAGTOON, 1986
O. melastigmus (McCLELLAND, 1839)
O. minutillus SMITH, 1945
O. nigrimas KOTTELAT, 1990
O. orthognathus KOTTELAT, 1990
O. profundicola KOTTELAT, 1990
O. timorensis (WEBER & DE BEAUFORT, 1922)

Aplocheilichthyidae SETHI, 1960

Aplocheilichthys BLEEKER, 1863
A. antinorii (VINCIGUERRA, 1883)
A. atripinna (PFEFFER, 1896)
A. bracheti BERKENKAMP, 1983
A. brichardi (POLL, 1971)
A. bukobanus (AHL, 1924)
A. camerunensis RADDA, 1971
A. centralis SEEGERS, 1996
A. ehrichi BERKENKAMP & ETZEL, 1994
A. fuelleborni (AHL, 1924)
A. hutereaui (BOULENGER, 1913)
A. jeanneli (PELLEGRIN, 1935)
A. johnstoni (GÜNTHER, 1893)
A. kabae DAGET, 1962
A. kassenjiensis (AHL, 1924)
A. katangae (BOULENGER, 1912)
A. keilhacki AHL, 1928
A. kingii (BOULENGER, 1913)
A. kongoranensis (AHL, 1924)
A. lamberti DAGET, 1962
A. loati (BOULENGER, 1901)

A. lualabaensis (POLL, 1938)
A. luxophthalmus luxophthalmus BRÜNING, 1929
A. luxophthalmus hannerzi SCHEEL, 1968
A. macrurus (BOULENGER, 1904)
A. maculatus maculatus KLAUSEWITZ, 1957
A. maculatus lacustris SEEGERS, 1984
A. matthesi SEEGERS, 1996
A. mediolateralis POLL, 1967
A. moeruensis (BOULENGER, 1914)
A. myaposae (BOULENGER, 1908)
A. myersi POLL, 1952
A. nigrolateralis POLL, 1967
A. nimbaensis (DAGET, 1948)
A. normani AHL, 1928
A. omoculatus WILDEKAMP, 1977
A. pfaffi DAGET, 1954
A. pumilus (BOULENGER, 1906)
A. rancureli DAGET, 1964
A. rudolfianus (WORTHINGTON, 1932)
A. scheeli ROMAN, 1970
A. schioetzi SCHEEL, 1968
A. spilauchen (DUMÉRIL, 1859)
A. usanguensis WILDEKAMP, 1977
A. vitschumbaensis (AHL, 1924)

Hylopanchax POLL & LAMBERT, 1965
H. stictopleuron (FOWLER, 1949)

Hypsopanchax MYERS, 1924
H. catenatus RADDA, 1981
H. jobaerti POLL & LAMBERT, 1985
H. jubbi POLL & LAMBERT, 1985
H. modestus (PAPPENHEIM & BOULENGER, 1914)
H. platysternus (NICHOLS & GRISCOM, 1917)
H. zebra (PELLEGRIN, 1929)

Laciris HUBER, 1981
L. pelagicus (WORTHINGTON, 1932)

Lamprichthys REGAN, 1911
L. tanganicanus (BOULENGER, 1898)

Pantanodon MYERS, 1955
P. madagascariensis (ARNOULT, 1963)
P. stuhlmanni (AHL, 1924)

Plataplochilus AHL, 1928
P. cabindae (BOULENGER, 1911)
P. chalcopyrus LAMBERT, 1963
P. loemensis (PELLEGRIN, 1924)
P. miltotaenia LAMBERT, 1963
P. ngaensis (AHL, 1924)
P. terveri (HUBER, 1981)

Procatopus BOULENGER, 1904
P. aberrans AHL, 1927
P. nototaenia BOULENGER, 1904
P. similis AHL, 1927

* In der Reihenfolge der Fotos im Bildteil /
* In the same order than in the photo section

Aplocheilidae Bleeker, 1860

Adamas Huber, 1979
A. formosus Huber, 1979

Aphyoplatys Clausen, 1967
A. duboisi (Poll, 1952)

Aphyosemion Myers, 1924
A. ahli Myers, 1933
A. (F.) amieti Radda, 1976
A. amoenum Radda & Pürzl, 1976
A. (F.) arnoldi (Boulenger, 1908)
A. aureum Radda, 1980
A. australe (Rachow, 1921)
A. bamilekorum Radda, 1971
A. (F.) batesii (Boulenger, 1911)
A. bitaeniatum (Ahl, 1924)
A. bivittatum (Lönnberg, 1895)
A. bualanum (Ahl, 1924)
A. buytaerti Radda & Huber, 1978
A. calliurum (Boulenger, 1911)
A. cameronense cameronense (Boulenger, 1903)
A. cameronense haasi Radda & Pürzl, 1976
A. cameronense halleri Radda & Pürzl, 1976
A. cameronense obscurum (Ahl, 1924)
A. caudofasciatum Huber & Radda, 1979
A. cauveti (Romand & Ozouf, 1995)
A. celiae celiae Scheel, 1971
A. celiae winifredae Radda & Scheel, 1975
A. chauchei Huber & Scheel, 1981
A. christyi (Boulenger, 1915)
A. (F.) cinnamomeum Clausen, 1963
A. citrineipinnis Huber & Radda, 1977
A. coeleste Huber & Radda, 1977
A. cognatum Meinken, 1951
A. congicum (Ahl, 1924)
A. dargei Amiet, 1987
A. decorsei (Pellegrin, 1904)
A. (F.) deltaense Radda, 1976
A. edeanum Amiet, 1987
A. elberti (Ahl, 1924)
A. elegans (Boulenger, 1899)
A. escherichi (Ahl, 1924)
A. exigoideum Radda & Huber, 1977
A. exiguum (Boulenger, 1911)
A. (F.) fallax Ahl, 1935
A. ferranti (Boulenger, 1910)
A. (F.) filamentosum (Meinken, 1933)
A. franzwerneri Scheel, 1971
A. gabunense gabunense Radda, 1975
A. gabunense boehmi Radda & Huber, 1977
A. gabunense marginatum Radda & Huber, 1977
A. (F.) gardneri gardneri (Boulenger, 1911)
A. (F.) gardneri lacustre Langton, 1974
A. (F.) gardneri mamfense Radda, 1974
A. (F.) gardneri nigerianum Clausen, 1963
A. geryi Lambert, 1958
A. guignardi (Romand, 1981)
A. guineense Daget, 1954
A. (F.) gulare (Boulenger, 1901)
A. hanneloreae hanneloreae Radda & Pürzl, 1985
A. hanneloreae wuendschi Radda & Pürzl, 1985
A. heinemanni Berkenkamp, 1983
A. herzogi Radda, 1975
A. hofmanni Radda, 1980
A. jeanpoli (Berkenkamp & Etzel, 1979)
A. joergenscheeli Huber & Radda, 1977

A. labarrei Poll, 1951
A. lamberti Radda & Huber, 1977
A. lefiniense Woeltjes, 1984
A. liberiense liberiense (Boulenger, 1908)
A. liberiense schmitti (Romand, 1979)
A. loennbergii (Boulenger, 1903)
A. louessense (Pellegrin, 1931)
A. lugens Amiet, 1991
A. lujae (Boulenger, 1911)
A. maculatum Radda & Pürzl, 1977
A. maeseni Poll, 1941
A. marmoratum Radda, 1973
A. mimbon Huber, 1977
A. (F.) mirabile mirabile Radda, 1970
A. (F.) mirabile intermittens Radda, 1974
A. (F.) mirabile moense Radda, 1970
A. (F.) mirabile traudeae Radda, 1971
A. monroviae (Roloff & Ladiges, 1972)
A. (F.) ndianum Scheel, 1968
A. occidentale Clausen, 1966
A. ocellatum Huber & Radda, 1977
A. oeseri (Schmidt, 1928)
A. ogoense ogoense (Pellegrin, 1930)
A. ogoense ottogartneri Radda, 1980
A. ogoense pyrophore Huber & Radda, 1979
A. pascheni pascheni (Ahl, 1928)
A. pascheni festivum Amiet, 1987
A. passaroi Huber, 1994
A. petersi (Sauvage, 1882)
A. poliaki Amiet, 1991
A. (F.) powelli (van der Zee & Wildekamp, 1994)
A. primigenium Radda & Huber, 1977
A. (F.) puerzli Radda & Scheel, 1974
A. punctatum Radda & Pürzl, 1977
A. raddai Scheel, 1975
A. rectogoense Radda & Huber, 1977
A. riggenbachi (Ahl, 1924)
A. (F.) robertsoni Radda & Scheel, 1974
A. roloffi Roloff, 1936
A. (F.) rubrolabiale Radda, 1973
A. scheeli Radda, 1970
A. schioetzi Huber & Scheel, 1981
A. schluppi Radda & Huber, 1978
A. (F.) sjoestedti (Lönnberg, 1895)
A. splendopleure (Brüning, 1929)
A. (F.) spoorenbergi Berkenkamp, 1976
A. striatum (Boulenger, 1911)
A. thysi Radda & Huber, 1978
A. (F.) toddi Clausen, 1966
A. viride (Ladiges & Roloff, 1973)
A. wachtersi wachtersi Radda & Huber, 1978
A. wachtersi mikeae Radda, 1980
A. (F.) walkeri (Boulenger, 1911)
A. wildekampi Berkenkamp, 1973
A. zygaima Huber, 1981

Adrianichthyidae
Horaichthyidae
Oryziidae

Photo: M. Kottelat

Photo: F. Schäfer

1. Ufer des Poso-Sees, Sulawesi, Biotop von
   Xenopoecilus oophorus.
2. Flußmündung an der Westküste Sumatras,
   hier kommt eine nicht näher bestimmte
   Oryzias-Art vor.
3. Im Towuti-See, Sulawesi, lebt unter anderem
   Oryzias profundicola.

1. *Shore of Lake Poso, Sulawesi. Here* Xenopoecilus oophorus *was collected.*
2. *Mouth of a river on the westcoast of Sumatra,
   where an undetermined* Oryzias *species was
   present.*
3. Oryzias profundicola *lives between the roots
   and trees growing in Lake Towuti, Sulawesi.*

Photo: M. Kottelat

X02855-4 *Adrianichthys kruyti* WEBER, 1913
Entenschnabelkärpfling / Duck-bill Poso Minnow
Lake Poso, Sulawesi bzw. Celebes / Sulawesi or Celebes; W; 16 cm
▷ ⚑ ○ ☺ ☺ ⊞ 🖳 ➤ ⚠ ⬡ ⬜ ⬜ ♂   Photo: M. Kottelat

X97230-4 *Xenopoecilus oophorus* KOTTELAT, 1990
Eitragender Posokärpfling / Egg Carrying Poso Minnow
Lake Poso, Sulawesi bzw. Celebes / Sulawesi or Celebes; W; 8,5 cm
⚠ ⚑ ○ ☺ ☺ ⊞ 🖳 ➤ ⚠ ⬜ ⬜ ♀   Photo: M. Kottelat

X97230-4 *Xenopoecilus oophorus* KOTTELAT, 1990
Eitragender Posokärpfling / Egg Carrying Poso Minnow
Lake Poso, Sulawesi bzw. Celebes / Sulawesi or Celebes; W; 8,5 cm
⚠ ⚑ ○ ☺ ☺ ⊞ 🖳 ➤ ⚠ ⬜ ⬜ ♂   Photo: G. Ott

X97230-4 *Xenopoecilus oophorus* KOTTELAT, 1990
Eitragender Posokärpfling / Egg Carrying Poso Minnow
Lake Poso, Sulawesi bzw. Celebes / Sulawesi or Celebes; W; 8,5 cm
⚠ ⚑ ○ ☺ ☺ ⊞ 🖳 ➤ ⚠ ⬜ ⬜ ♀   Photo: G. Ott

X97233-3 *Xenopoecilus poptae* WEBER & DE BEAUFORT, 1922
Gestreckter Posokärpfling / Elongate Poso Minnow
Lake Poso, Sulawesi bzw. Celebes / Sulawesi or Celebes; W; 18 cm
⚠ ⚑ ○ ☺ ☺ ⊞ 🖳 ➤ ⚠ ⬜ ⬜   Photo: M. Kottelat

X97235-4 *Xenopoecilus sarasinorum* (POPTA, 1905)
Sarasins Schaufelkärpfling / Sarasins Minnow
Lake Lindu, Sulawesi bzw. Celebes / Sulawesi or Celebes; W; 8 cm
⚠ ⚑ ○ ☺ ☺ ⊞ 🖳 ➤ ⚠ ⬜ ⬜ ♂   Photo: M. Kottelat

X97235-3 *Xenopoecilus sarasinorum* (POPTA, 1905)
Sarasins Schaufelkärpfling / Sarasins Minnow
Lake Lindu, Sulawesi bzw. Celebes / Sulawesi or Celebes; W; 8 cm
⚠ ⚑ ○ ☺ ☺ ⊞ 🖳 ➤ ⚠ ⬜ ⬜ ♂   Photo: O. Böhm

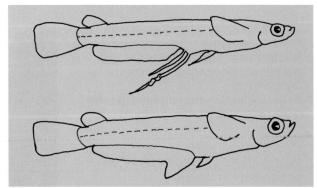

X52935-4 *Horaichthys setnai* KULKARNI, 1940
Indischer Glaskärpfling / Indian Glaskilli
West coast of India around Bombay; W; 2,5 cm
Exact data unknown ⚠ ⚑ ○ ☺ ⊞ 🖳 ➤ ⚠ ⬜ ♂   Drawing: L. Seegers after Kulkarni

X68978-4 *Oryzias celebensis* (WEBER, 1894)
Celebes-Reiskärpfling / Celebes Medaka, Celebes Ricefish
Sulawesi (Celebes) / Sulawesi (Celebes); W; 4,5 cm
▷↑P○☺☺⊞🖼️➡️ ⚠️🔟 ♂ (top), ♀
Photo: M. Kottelat

X69005-4 *Oryzias javanicus* (BLEEKER, 1854)
Java-Reiskärpfling / Javanese Medaka, Javanese Ricefish
Java, Indonesien / Java, Indonesia; B; 4,5 cm
▷↑P○☺☺⊞🖼️➡️ ⚠️🔟 ♂, ♀ (top)
Photo: A. Norman

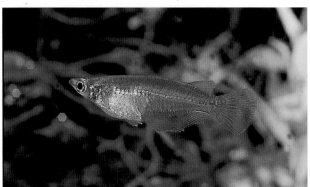

X69015-4 *Oryzias javanicus* (BLEEKER, 1854)
Java-Reiskärpfling / Javanese Medaka, Javanese Ricefish
Kuta, Bali, Indonesien / Kuta, Bali, Indonesia; W; 4,5 cm
▷↑P○☺☺⊞🖼️➡️ ⚠️🔟 ♂
Photo: H.-J. Günther

X69015-4 *Oryzias javanicus* (BLEEKER, 1854)
Java-Reiskärpfling / Javanese Medaka, Javanese Ricefish
Kuta, Bali, Indonesien / Kuta, Bali, Indonesia; W; 4,5 cm
⚠️↑P○☺☺⊞🖼️➡️ ⚠️🔟🔳 ♀
Photo: H.-J. Günther

X69005-4 *Oryzias javanicus* (BLEEKER, 1854)
Java-Reiskärpfling / Javanese Medaka, Javanese Ricefish
Java, Indonesien / Java, Indonesia; W; 4,5 cm
▷↑P○☺☺⊞🖼️➡️ ⚠️🔟 ♂
Photo: M. Kottelat

X69055-4 *Oryzias latipes* (TEMMINCK & SCHLEGEL, 1846)
Japan-Reiskärpfling / Japanese Medaka, Japanese Ricefish
Aquarienstamm / Aquarium strain; B; 3,5 cm
▷↑P○☺☺⊞🖼️➡️ ⚠️🔟 ♂ (top), ♀
Photo: L. Seegers

X69055-4 *Oryzias latipes* (TEMMINCK & SCHLEGEL, 1846)
Japan-Reiskärpfling / Japanese Medaka, Japanese Ricefish
Aquarienstamm / Aquarium strain; B; 3,5 cm
▷↑P○☺☺⊞🖼️➡️ ⚠️🔟 ♂
Photo: L. Seegers

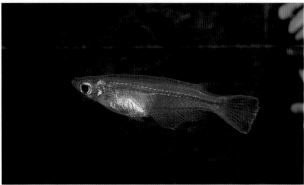

X69055-4 *Oryzias latipes* (TEMMINCK & SCHLEGEL, 1846)
Japan-Reiskärpfling / Japanese Medaka, Japanese Ricefish
Aquarienstamm / Aquarium Strain; B; 3,5 cm
▷↑P○☺☺⊞🖼️➡️ ⚠️🔟 ♂
Photo: L. Seegers

X69065-4 *Oryzias latipes* (Temminck & Schlegel, 1846)
Gold-Reiskärpfling / Golden Medaka, Golden Ricefish
Aquarienstamm / Aquarium strain; B; 3,5 cm
▷🏠○☺☻⊞🗺➡ ⚠🅜 ♂
Photo: L. Seegers

X69065-4 *Oryzias latipes* (Temminck & Schlegel, 1846)
Gold-Reiskärpfling / Golden Medaka, Golden Ricefish
Aquarienstamm / Aquarium strain; B; 3,5 cm
▷🏠○☺☻⊞🗺➡ ⚠🅜 ♂
Photo: L. Seegers

X69075-4 *Oryzias marmoratus* (Aurich, 1935)
Marmor-Reiskärpfling / Marmorated Medaka, Marmorated Ricefish
Lake Wawontoa, Sulawesi (Celebes)/ Sulawesi (Celebes); W; 5 cm
▷⚓P○☺☻⊞🗺➡ ⚠🅜 ♂
Photo: M. Kottelat

X69085-4 *Oryzias matanensis* (Aurich, 1935)
Matano-Reiskärpfling / Matano Medaka, Matano Ricefish
Lake Matano, Sulawesi (Celebes)/ Sulawesi (Celebes); W; 5,5 cm
▷⚓P○☺☻⊞🗺➡ ⚠🅜 ♂
Photo: M. Kottelat

X69115-4 *Oryzias* sp. aff. *melastigma* (McClelland, 1839)
Gefleckter Reiskärpfling / Spotted Medaka, Spotted Ricefish
Satul, Süd-Thailand / Satul, southern Thailand; W; 5 cm
▷⚓P○☺☻⊞🗺➡ ⚠🅜 ♂
Photo: L. Seegers

X69115-4 *Oryzias* sp. aff. *melastigma* (McClelland, 1839)
Gefleckter Reiskärpfling / Spotted Medaka, Spotted Ricefish
Satul, Süd-Thailand / Satul, southern Thailand; W; 5 cm
▷⚓P○☺☻⊞🗺➡ ⚠🅜 ♀ mit Eiern/with eggs
Photo: L. Seegers

X69105-4 *Oryzias melastigma* (McClelland, 1839)
Gefleckter Reiskärpfling / Spotted Medaka, Spotted Ricefish
Aquarienstamm / Aquarium strain; B; 5 cm
▷⚓P○☺☻⊞🗺➡ ⚠🅜 ♂
Photo: L. Seegers

X69105-4 *Oryzias melastigma* (McClelland, 1839)
Gefleckter Reiskärpfling / Spotted Medaka, Spotted Ricefish
Aquarienstamm / Aquarium strain; B; 5 cm
▷⚓P○☺☻⊞🗺➡ ⚠🅜 ♀
Photo: L. Seegers

X69120-4 *Oryzias melastigma* (MᴄCʟᴇʟʟᴀɴᴅ, 1839)
Gefleckter Reiskärpfling / Spotted Medaka, Spotted Ricefish
Kalkutta, Indien / Calcutta, India; W; 5 cm
▷⧈○☺☺⊞🗺➤⚠🔟♂ Photo: L. Seegers

X69120-4 *Oryzias melastigma* (MᴄCʟᴇʟʟᴀɴᴅ, 1839)
Gefleckter Reiskärpfling / Spotted Medaka, Spotted Ricefish
Kalkutta, Indien / Calcutta, India; W; 5 cm
▷⧈○☺☺⊞🗺➤⚠🔟♀ Photo: L. Seegers

X69135-4 *Oryzias minutillus* Sᴍɪᴛʜ, 1945
Zwerg-Reiskärpfling / Dwarf Medaka, Dwarf Ricefish
Bangkok, Thailand / Bangkok, Thailand; W; 2 cm
▷⧈○☺☺⊞🗺➤🛑🔟♂ Photo: L. Seegers

X69135-4 *Oryzias minutillus* Sᴍɪᴛʜ, 1945
Zwerg-Reiskärpfling / Dwarf Medaka, Dwarf Ricefish
Bangkok, Thailand / Bangkok, Thailand; W; 2 cm
▷⧈○☺☺⊞🗺➤🛑🔟♀ Photo: L. Seegers

X69136-4 *Oryzias minutillus* Sᴍɪᴛʜ, 1945
Zwerg-Reiskärpfling / Dwarf Medaka, Dwarf Ricefish
Satul, Süd-Thailand / Satul, southern Thailand; W; 2 cm
▷⧈○☺☺⊞🗺➤🛑🔟♂ Photo: L. Seegers

X69136-4 *Oryzias minutillus* Sᴍɪᴛʜ, 1945
Zwerg-Reiskärpfling / Dwarf Medaka, Dwarf Ricefish
Satul, Süd-Thailand / Satul, southern Thailand; W; 2 cm
▷⧈○☺☺⊞🗺➤🛑🔟♀ Photo: L. Seegers

X69155-4 *Oryzias nigrimas* Kᴏᴛᴛᴇʟᴀᴛ, 1990
Schwarzer Reiskärpfling / Black Medaka, Black Ricefish
Lake Poso, Sulawesi (Celebes) / Lake Poso, Sulawesi; W; 5,5 cm
▷⧈○☺☺⊞🗺➤⚠🔟♂ Photo: M. Kottelat

X69155-4 *Oryzias nigrimas* Kᴏᴛᴛᴇʟᴀᴛ, 1990
Schwarzer Reiskärpfling / Black Medaka, Black Ricefish
Lake Poso, Sulawesi (Celebes) / Lake Poso, Sulawesi; W; 5,5 cm
▷⧈○☺☺⊞🗺➤⚠🔟♂ (top), ♀ Photo: H.-G. Evers

X69156-4 *Oryzias nigrimas* KOTTELAT, 1990
Schwarzer Reiskärpfling / Black Medaka, Black Ricefish
Lake Poso, eastcoast near Tentena, Sulawesi or Celebes; W; 5,5 cm
▷ ⇑P ○ ☺ ☻ ⊞ 🕸➤ ⚠ m ♂
Photo: L. Seegers

X69156-4 *Oryzias nigrimas* KOTTELAT, 1990
Schwarzer Reiskärpfling / Black Medaka, Black Ricefish
Lake Poso, eastcoast near Tentena, Sulawesi or Celebes; W; 5,5 cm
▷ ⇑P ○ ☺ ☻ ⊞ 🕸➤ ⚠ m ♀
Photo: L. Seegers

X69160-4 *Oryzias orthognathus* KOTTELAT, 1990
Spitzkopf-Reiskärpfling / Pointed Head Medaka, Pointed Head Ricefish
Lake Poso, eastcoast near Tentena, Sulawesi or Celebes; W; 6,5 cm
▷ ⇑P ○ ☺ ☻ ⊞ 🕸➤ ⚠ m ♂
Photo: M. Kottelat

X69161-4 *Oryzias profundicola* KOTTELAT, 1990
Gelbflossen-Reiskärpfling / Yellow Finned Medaka or Ricefish
Lake Towuti, 4-7 km east of Timampu, Sulawesi or Celebes; W; 6 cm
▷ ⇑P ○ ☺ ☻ ⊞ 🕸➤ ⚠ m ♂
Photo: M. Kottelat

X69165-4 *Oryzias* spec. "Bentota"
Bentota-Reiskärpfling / Bentota Medaka, Bentota Ricefish
Bentota Fluß, Sri Lanka / Bentota River, Sri Lanka; W; 4,0 cm
▷ ⇑P ○ ☺ ☻ ⊞ 🕸➤ ⚠ m ♂
Photo: L. Seegers

X69165-4 *Oryzias* spec. "Bentota"
Bentota-Reiskärpfling / Bentota Medaka, Bentota Ricefish
Bentota Fluß, Sri Lanka / Bentota River, Sri Lanka; W; 4,0 cm
▷ ⇑P ○ ☺ ☻ ⊞ 🕸➤ ⚠ m ♀
Photo: L. Seegers

X69168-4 *Oryzias* spec. "China" (*sinensis* CHEN, HIROSHI & CHU, 1989?)
China-Reiskärpfling / Chinese Medaka, Chinese Ricefish
Südchina / Southern China; W; 3,0-3,5 cm
▷ ⇑P ○ ☺ ☻ ⊞ 🕸➤ ⚠ m ♂
Photo: L. Seegers

X69168-4 *Oryzias* spec. "China" (*sinensis* CHEN, HIROSHI & CHU, 1989?)
China-Reiskärpfling / Chinese Medaka, Chinese Ricefish
Südchina / Southern China; W; 3,0-3,5 cm
▷ ⇑P ○ ☺ ☻ ⊞ 🕸➤ ⚠ m ♀
Photo: L. Seegers

Photo: L. Seegers

Photo: E. Pürzl

Photo: L. Seegers

1. Gewässer südlich von Dar es Salaam, Tanzania, Biotop mit *Aplocheilichthys kongoranensis* und *A. maculatus lacustris*.
2. Bach südwestlich von Lambarene, Gabun, Fundort von *Plataplochilus miltotaenia*.
3. Lake George, Uganda. Hier findet sich *Aplocheilichthys vitschumbaensis*.

1. *Water south of Dar es Salaam, Tanzania, habitat of* Aplocheilichthys kongoranensis *and* A. maculatus lacustris.
2. *Brook southwest of Lambarene, Gabon, collecting locality of* Plataplochilus miltotaenia.
3. *L ake George, Uganda. Here* Aplocheilichthys vitschumbaensis *can be found.*

A04565-4 *Aplocheilichthys antinorii* (Vinciguerra, 1883)
Schwarzer Leuchtaugenfisch / Black Lampeye
Abiyata-See, Äthiopien / Lake Abiyata, Ethiopia; W; 4,0-4,5 cm
▷⫯P○☺☹⊞🔅➡🛑▥ ♂   Photo: L. Seegers

A04565-4 *Aplocheilichthys antinorii* (Vinciguerra, 1883)
Schwarzer Leuchtaugenfisch / Black Lampeye
Abiyata-See, Äthiopien / Lake Abiyata, Ethiopia; W; 4,0-4,5 cm
▷⫯P○☺☹⊞🔅➡🛑▥ ♀   Photo: L. Seegers

A04566-4 *Aplocheilichthys (Congopanchax) brichardi* (Poll, 1971)
Brichards Leuchtaugenfisch / Brichard's Lampeye
Mbandaka, Zaïre / Mbandaka, Zaïre; W; 3,0 cm
⚠P◑☺☹⊞⬆🔅➡🛑▥ ♂   Photo: L. Seegers

A04566-4 *Aplocheilichthys (Congopanchax) brichardi* (Poll, 1971)
Brichards Leuchtaugenfisch / Brichard's Lampeye
Mbandaka, Zaïre / Mbandaka, Zaïre; W; 3,0 cm
⚠P◑☺☹⊞⬆🔅➡🛑▥ ♂   Photo: E. Schraml

A04558-4 *Aplocheilichthys bukobanus* (Ahl, 1924)
Bukoba-Leuchtaugenfisch / Bukoba Lampeye, rötliche/reddish Form
Bukoba, Viktoriasee, Tansania / Lake Victoria, Tanzania; W; 4,0-4,5 cm
▷🦞○◑☺☹⊞⬆🔅➡⚠▥ ♂   Photo: L. Seegers

A04559-4 *Aplocheilichthys bukobanus* (Ahl, 1924)
Bukoba-Leuchtaugenfisch / Bukoba Lampeye, schwärzliche/blackish Form
Bukoba, Viktoriasee, Tansania / Lake Victoria, Tanzania; W; 4,0-4,5 cm
▷🦞○◑☺☹⊞⬆🔅➡⚠▥ ♂   Photo: L. Seegers

A04550-4 *Aplocheilichthys bukobanus* (Ahl, 1924)
Bukoba-Leuchtaugenfisch / Bukoba Lampeye," K 83/17"
Kaloleni SO Kisumu, Viktoriasee, Kenia / Lake Victoria, Kenya; W; 4,0-4,5 cm
▷🦞○◑☺☹⊞⬆🔅➡⚠▥ ♂   Photo: L. Seegers

A04551-4 *Aplocheilichthys bukobanus* (Ahl, 1924)
Bukoba-Leuchtaugenfisch / Bukoba Lampeye
Entebbe, Viktoriasee, Uganda / Lake Victoria, Uganda; W; 4,0-4,5 cm
▷🦞○◑☺☹⊞⬆🔅➡⚠▥ ♂   Photo: L. Seegers

A04572-4 *Aplocheilichthys bukobanus* (AHL, 1924)
Bukoba-Leuchtaugenfisch / Bukoba Lampeye," U 88/1"
Mpugwe NO Masaka, Viktoriasee / L. Victoria, Uganda; W; 4,0-4,5 cm
▷ ₽ ○ ◐ ☺ ☺ ⊞ ⬆ 🔲 ➤ ⚠ m ♂   Photo: L. Seegers

A04573-4 *Aplocheilichthys bukobanus* (AHL, 1924)
Bukoba-Leuchtaugenfisch / Bukoba Lampeye," U 88/17"
13 km SO Masindi, Uganda / 13 km SE Masindi, Uganda; W; 4,0-4,5 cm
▷ ₽ ○ ◐ ☺ ☺ ⊞ ⬆ 🔲 ➤ ⚠ m ♀   Photo: L. Seegers

A04574-4 *Aplocheilichthys bukobanus* (AHL, 1924)
Bukoba-Leuchtaugenfisch / Bukoba Lampeye
" UG 14", Lake Wamala, Uganda; W; 4,0-4,5 cm
▷ ₽ ○ ☺ ☺ ⊞ ⬆ 🔲 ➤ ⚠ m ♂   Photo: L. Seegers

A04575-4 *Aplocheilichthys bukobanus* (AHL, 1924)
Bukoba-Leuchtaugenfisch / Bukoba Lampeye
Butiaba, Lake Albert, Uganda; W; 4,0-4,5 cm
▷ ₽ ○ ◐ ☺ ☺ ⊞ ⬆ 🔲 ➤ ⚠ m ♂   Photo: L. Seegers

A04567-4 *Aplocheilichthys camerunensis* RADDA, 1971
Kamerun-Leuchtaugenfisch / Cameroon Lampeye [T.t.]
8 km S Sangmelima, Kamerun / Cameroon; W; 3,0 cm
◁ ▷ ₽ ◐ ☺ ☺ ⊞ ⬆ 🔲 ➤ ⚠ m ♂   Photo: E. Pürzl

A04567-4 *Aplocheilichthys camerunensis* RADDA, 1971
Kamerun-Leuchtaugenfisch / Cameroon Lampeye [T.t.]
8 km S Sangmelima, Kamerun / Cameroon; W; 3,0 cm
◁ ▷ ₽ ◐ ☺ ☺ ⊞ ⬆ 🔲 ➤ ⚠ m ♀   Photo: E. Pürzl

A04567-4 *Aplocheilichthys camerunensis* RADDA, 1971
Kamerun-Leuchtaugenfisch / Cameroon Lampeye [T.t.]
8 km S Sangmelima, Kamerun / Cameroon; B; 3,0 cm
◁ ▷ ₽ ◐ ☺ ☺ ⊞ ⬆ 🔲 ➤ ⚠ m ♂   Photo: L. Seegers

A04576-4 *Aplocheilichthys camerunensis* RADDA, 1971
Kamerun-Leuchtaugenfisch / Cameroon Lampeye
Kamerun / Cameroon; B; 3,0 cm
◁ ▷ ₽ ◐ ☺ ☺ ⊞ ⬆ 🔲 ➤ ⚠ m ♂   Photo: E. Pürzl

A04568-4 *Aplocheilichthys centralis* SEEGERS, 1996, Holotypus
Zentralafrikanischer Leuchtaugenfisch / Central African Lampeye
"TZ 94/105", Wogo River, Rukwa drainage, Tanzania; W; 3,3 cm
Photo: L. Seegers

A04569-3 *Aplocheilichthys centralis* SEEGERS, 1996
Zentralafrikanischer Leuchtaugenfisch / Central African Lampeye
"TZ 91/115", Iwanga, NW Lake Rukwa, Tanzania; W; 3,0-3,5 cm
Photo: L. Seegers

A04570-4 *Aplocheilichthys centralis* SEEGERS, 1996
Zentralafrikanischer Leuchtaugenfisch / Central African Lampeye
"TZ 91/135", Kasama, S Lake Victoria drainage, Tanzania; W; 3,0-3,5 cm
Photo: L. Seegers

A04570-4 *Aplocheilichthys centralis* SEEGERS, 1996
Zentralafrikanischer Leuchtaugenfisch / Central African Lampeye
"TZ 91/135", Kasama, S Lake Victoria drainage, Tanzania; W; 3,0-3,5 cm
Photo: L. Seegers

A04571-3 *Aplocheilichthys centralis* SEEGERS, 1996
Zentralafrikanischer Leuchtaugenfisch / Central African Lampeye
"U 88/5", 27 km W Mbarara, 6 km O Kabwohe, Uganda; W; 3,0-3,5 cm
Photo: L. Seegers

A04571-4 *Aplocheilichthys centralis* SEEGERS, 1996
Zentralafrikanischer Leuchtaugenfisch / Central African Lampeye
"U 88/5", 27 km W Mbarara, 6 km O Kabwohe, Uganda; W; 3,0-3,5 cm
Photo: L. Seegers

A04552-3 *Aplocheilichthys* cf. *centralis* SEEGERS, 1996
Zentralafrikanischer Leuchtaugenfisch / Central African Lampeye
"U 88/17", 13 km O Masindi, Uganda; W; 3,0-3,5 cm
Photo: L. Seegers

A04552-4 *Aplocheilichthys* cf. *centralis* SEEGERS, 1996
Zentralafrikanischer Leuchtaugenfisch / Central African Lampeye
"U 88/17", 13 km O Masindi, Uganda; W; 3,0-3,5 cm
Photo: L. Seegers

A04553-4 *Aplocheilichthys fuelleborni* (AHL, 1924)
Fülleborns Leuchtaugenfisch / Fuelleborn's Lampeye, "TZ 91/115"
Iwanga, NW shore of Lake Rukwa, Tanzania; W; 3,5 cm
▷♬○☺☻⊞⬆🐟➡ ⚠🅜 ♀   Photo: L. Seegers

A04554-4 *Aplocheilichthys fuelleborni* (AHL, 1924)
Fülleborns Leuchtaugenfisch / Fuelleborn's Lampeye, "TZ 87/9"
Nkululu River, Malagarasi drainage, Tanzania; W; 3,5 cm
▷♬○☺☻⊞⬆🐟➡ ⚠🅜 ♀   Photo: L. Seegers

A04555-4 *Aplocheilichthys fuelleborni* (AHL, 1924)
Fülleborns Leuchtaugenfisch / Fuelleborn's Lampeye, "TZ 91/11"
Rungwa drainage, Lake Rukwa basin, Tanzania; W; 3,5 cm
▷♬○☺☻⊞⬆🐟➡ ⚠🅜 ♂   Photo: L. Seegers

A04556-4 *Aplocheilichthys fuelleborni* (AHL, 1924)
Fülleborns Leuchtaugenfisch / Fuelleborn's Lampeye, "TZ 92/3"
Kigwa, 64 km E Tabora, Wala, Malagarasi system, Tanzania; W; 3,5 cm
▷♬○☺☻⊞⬆🐟➡ ⚠🅜 ♂   Photo: L. Seegers

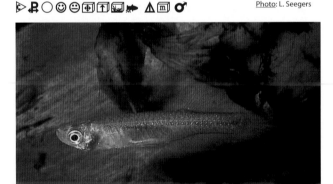

A04578-4 *Aplocheilichthys* cf. *fuelleborni* (AHL, 1924)
Fülleborns Leuchtaugenfisch / Fuelleborn's Lampeye
Lower Wembere River near Sekenke, Tanzania; W; 3,5 cm
▷♬○☺☻⊞⬆🐟➡ ⚠🅜 ♀   Photo: L. Seegers

A04579-4 *Aplocheilichthys* cf. *fuelleborni* (AHL, 1924)
Fülleborns Leuchtaugenfisch / Fuelleborn's Lampeye
Lake Chaya, upper Wembere system, Tanzania; W; 3,5 cm
▷♬○☺☻⊞⬆🐟➡ ⚠🅜 ♀   Photo: L. Seegers

A04588-4 *Aplocheilichthys hutereaui* (BOULENGER, 1913)
Hutereaus Leuchtaugenfisch / Hutereau's Lampeye
Shaba, südliches Zaïre / Shaba province, southern Zaïre; W; 3,5 cm
▷♬○◐☺☻⊞⬆🐟➡ ⚠🅜 ♂   Photo: L. Seegers

A04588-4 *Aplocheilichthys hutereaui* (BOULENGER, 1913)
Hutereaus Leuchtaugenfisch / Hutereau's Lampeye
Shaba, südliches Zaïre / Shaba province, southern Zaïre; W; 3,5 cm
▷♬○◐☺☻⊞⬆🐟➡ ⚠🅜 ♀   Photo: L. Seegers

A04589-4 *Aplocheilichthys* sp. aff. *hutereaui* (BOULENGER, 1913)
Hutereaus Leuchtaugenfisch / Hutereau's Lampeye, "TZ 92/145"
Kalunga River on Kasama - Isoka road, northern Zambia; W; 2,5 cm
▷♫○◑☺☻⊞⬆⛶➠ ⚠ⓜ♂   Photo: L. Seegers

A04580-4 *Aplocheilichthys* sp. aff. *hutereaui* (BOULENGER, 1913)
Chambeshi-Zwergleuchtaugenfisch / Chambeshi Dwarf Lampeye
Chisimba Falls, Nord-Sambia / northern Zambia; B; 2,0 cm
▷♫○◑☺☻⊞⬆⛶➠ ⚠ⓜ♂   Photo: L. Seegers

A04581-4 *Aplocheilichthys jeanneli* (PELLEGRIN, 1935)
Omo-Leuchtaugenfisch / Omo Lampeye
Ferguson's Bay, Lake Turkana, Kenya; W; 3,5 cm
▷♫○◑☺☻⊞⬆⛶➠ ⚠ⓜ♂   Photo: L. Seegers

A04590-4 *Aplocheilichthys johnstoni* (GÜNTHER, 1893)
Johnstons Leuchtaugenfisch / Johnston's Lampeye, "TZ 92/144"
59 km E Kasama, Kalunga drainage, northern Zambia; W; 8,5 cm
▷♫○◑☺☻⊞⬆⛶➠ ⚠ⓜ♂   Photo: L. Seegers

A04591-4 *Aplocheilichthys johnstoni* (GÜNTHER, 1893)
Johnstons Leuchtaugenfisch / Johnston's Lampeye
Dikuluwe River, N Bunkeya, Shaba, southern Zaïre; W; 8,5 cm
▷♫○◑☺☻⊞⬆⛶➠ ⚠ⓜ♂   Photo: L. Seegers

A04591-4 *Aplocheilichthys johnstoni* (GÜNTHER, 1893)
Johnstons Leuchtaugenfisch / Johnston's Lampeye
Dikuluwe River, N Bunkeya, Shaba, southern Zaïre; W; 8,5 cm
▷♫○◑☺☻⊞⬆⛶➠ ⚠ⓜ♀   Photo: L. Seegers

A04592-4 *Aplocheilichthys johnstoni* (GÜNTHER, 1893)
Johnstons Leuchtaugenfisch / Johnston's Lampeye
Harare, Simbabwe / Harare, Zimbabwe; W; 8,5 cm
▷♫○◑☺☻⊞⬆⛶➠ ⚠ⓜ♂   Photo: L. Seegers

A04592-4 *Aplocheilichthys johnstoni* (GÜNTHER, 1893)
Johnstons Leuchtaugenfisch / Johnston's Lampeye
Harare, Simbabwe / Harare, Zimbabwe; W; 8,5 cm
▷♫○◑☺☻⊞⬆⛶➠ ⚠ⓜ♀   Photo: L. Seegers

A04593-4 *Aplocheilichthys* cf. *johnstoni* (GÜNTHER, 1893)
Johnstons Leuchtaugenfisch / Johnston's Lampeye, "TZ 88/14"
Kyela, Malawi-Einzug, Tansania / Malawi drainage, Tanzania; W; 5 cm
▷♀○◐◑☺☻⊞⬆⬆⬇⬅ ⚠m♂   Photo: L. Seegers

A04593-4 *Aplocheilichthys* cf. *johnstoni* (GÜNTHER, 1893)
Johnstons Leuchtaugenfisch / Johnston's Lampeye, "TZ 88/14"
Kyela, Malawi-Einzug, Tansania / Malawi drainage, Tanzania; W; 5 cm
▷♀○◐◑☺☻⊞⬆⬆⬇⬅ ⚠m♀   Photo: L. Seegers

A04582-4 *Aplocheilichthys* sp. aff. *johnstoni* (GÜNTHER, 1893)
Johnstons Leuchtaugenfisch / Johnston's Lampeye
Aquaristikimport / Aquarium import of unknown origin; W; 5 cm
▷♀○◐◑☺☻⊞⬆⬆⬇⬅ ⚠m♂   Photo: L. Seegers

A04594-4 ? *Aplocheilichthys kassenjiensis* (AHL, 1924)
Albertsee-Leuchtaugenfisch / Lake Albert Lampeye
Butiaba, Albertsee, Uganda / Lake Albert, Uganda; W; 3,5 cm
▷♀○◐◑☺☻⊞⬆⬇⬅ ⚠m♂   Photo: L. Seegers

A04595-4 *Aplocheilichthys katangae* (BOULENGER, 1912)
Katanga-Leuchtaugenfisch / Blackstripe Lampeye
Molapitse River, Lebowa, N Südafrika / N South Africa; W; 4,5 cm
▷♀○◐☺☻⊞⬆⬇⬅ ⚠m♂   Photo: L. Seegers

A04595-4 *Aplocheilichthys katangae* (BOULENGER, 1912)
Katanga-Leuchtaugenfisch / Blackstripe Lampeye
Molapitse River, Lebowa, N Südafrika / N South Africa; W; 4,5 cm
▷♀○◐◑☺☻⊞⬆⬇⬅ ⚠m♀   Photo: L. Seegers

A04596-4 *Aplocheilichthys kongoranensis* (AHL, 1924)
Kongoro-Leuchtaugenfisch / Kongoro Lampeye
Kibiti, 140 km südl. Dar es Salaam, Tansania / Tanzania; W; 4,0 cm
⚠♀○◐◑☺☻⊞⬆⬇⬅ ⚠m♂   Photo: L. Seegers

A04596-4 *Aplocheilichthys kongoranensis* (AHL, 1924)
Kongoro-Leuchtaugenfisch / Kongoro Lampeye
Kibiti, 140 km südl. Dar es Salaam, Tansania / Tanzania; W; 4,0 cm
⚠♀○◐◑☺☻⊞⬆⬇⬅ ⚠m♀   Photo: L. Seegers

A04583-4 *Aplocheilichthys kongoranensis* (AHL, 1924)
Kongoro-Leuchtaugenfisch / Kongoro Lampeye
Rufiji drainage, Selous Game Reserve, Tansania / Tanzania; W; 4,0 cm
Photo: L. Seegers

A04584-4 *Aplocheilichthys kongoranensis* (AHL, 1924)
Kongoro-Leuchtaugenfisch / Kongoro Lampeye
Mbezi River, 50 km südl. Dar es Salaam, Tansania / Tanzania; W; 4,0 cm
Photo: L. Seegers

A04586-4 *Aplocheilichthys kongoranensis* (AHL, 1924)
Kongoro-Leuchtaugenfisch / Kongoro Lampeye, "TZ 89/116"
14 km S Dar es Salaam, Tansania / Tanzania; W; 4,0 cm
Photo: L. Seegers

A04601-4 *Aplocheilichthys* cf. *lamberti* DAGET, 1962
Lamberts Leuchtaugenfisch / Lambert's Lampeye
Aquaristik-Import, Guinea / Aquarium import, Guinea; W; 4,5 cm
Photo: L. Seegers

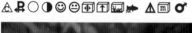

A04600-4 *Aplocheilichthys lamberti* DAGET, 1962
Lamberts Leuchtaugenfisch / Lambert's Lampeye
Aquaristik-Import, Guinea / Aquarium import, Guinea; W; 4,5 cm
Photo: L. Seegers

A04600-4 *Aplocheilichthys lamberti* DAGET, 1962
Lamberts Leuchtaugenfisch / Lambert's Lampeye
Aquaristik-Import, Guinea / Aquarium import, Guinea; W; 4,5 cm
Photo: H.-G. Evers

A04602-4 *Aplocheilichthys luxophth. luxophthalmus* (BRÜNING, 1929)
Roter Leuchtaugenfisch / Big Eye Lampeye, Lamp Eyed Panchax
Aquaristik-Import, Kamerun / Aquarium import, Cameroon; W; 3,5 cm
Photo: L. Seegers

A04602-4 *Aplocheilichthys luxophth. luxophthalmus* (BRÜNING, 1929)
Roter Leuchtaugenfisch / Big Eye Lampeye, Lamp Eyed Panchax
Aquaristik-Import, Kamerun / Aquarium import, Cameroon; B; 3,5 cm
Photo: L. Seegers

A04603-4 *Aplocheilichthys luxophth. luxophthalmus* (BRÜNING, 1929)
Roter Leuchtaugenfisch / Big Eye Lampeye, Lamp Eyed Panchax
Kribi, SW Kamerun / Kribi, SW Cameroon; W; 3,5 cm

⚠️🅱️◐🌓☺️😐⊞⬆️🖼️🐌➧ ⚠️🔳 ♂   Photo: E. Pürzl

A04604-4 *Aplocheilichthys luxophth. luxophthalmus* (BRÜNING, 1929)
Roter Leuchtaugenfisch / Big Eye Lampeye, Lamp Eyed Panchax
Nigerdelta, Nigeria; W; 3,5 cm

⚠️🅱️◐🌓☺️😐⊞⬆️🖼️➧ ⚠️🔳 ♂   Photo: E. Pürzl

A04604-4 *Aplocheilichthys luxophth. luxophthalmus* (BRÜNING, 1929)
Roter Leuchtaugenfisch / Big Eye Lampeye, Lamp Eyed Panchax
Nigerdelta, Nigeria; W; 3,5 cm

⚠️🅱️◐🌓☺️😐⊞⬆️🖼️➧ ⚠️🔳 ♂   Photo: E. Pürzl

A04605-4 *Aplocheilichthys luxophth. luxophthalmus* (BRÜNING, 1929)
Roter Leuchtaugenfisch / Big Eye Lampeye, Lamp Eyed Panchax
Süd-Togo / Southern Togo; W; 3,5 cm

⚠️🅱️◐🌓☺️😐⊞⬆️🖼️➧ ⚠️🔳 ♂   Photo: E. Pürzl

A04606-4 *Aplocheilichthys luxophthalmus hannerzi* SCHEEL, 1968
Hannerz' Leuchtaugenfisch / Hannerz' Lampeye
Einzug des unteren Cross River / Lower Cross River drainage, Nigeria; W; 3,5 cm

⚠️🅱️◐🌓☺️😐⊞⬆️🖼️➧ ⚠️🔳 ♂   Photo: L. Seegers

A04606-4 *Aplocheilichthys luxophthalmus hannerzi* SCHEEL, 1968
Hannerz' Leuchtaugenfisch / Hannerz' Lampeye
Einzug des unteren Cross River / Lower Cross River drainage, Nigeria; W; 3,5 cm

⚠️🅱️◐🌓☺️😐⊞⬆️🖼️➧ ⚠️🔳 ♀   Photo: L. Seegers

A04608-4 *Aplocheilichthys maculatus maculatus* KLAUSEWITZ, 1957
Gelber Leuchtaugenfisch / Spotted Lampeye, "TZ 88/1"
10 km südlich Bagamoyo, Tansania / Tanzania; W; 3,5 cm

⚠️🅱️◐🌓☺️😐⊞⬆️🖼️➧ ⚠️🔳 ♂   Photo: L. Seegers

A04607-4 *Aplocheilichthys maculatus maculatus* KLAUSEWITZ, 1957
Gelber Leuchtaugenfisch / Spotted Lampeye, "TZ 89/101"
Bagamoyo, Tansania / Bagamoyo, Tanzania; W; 3,5 cm

⚠️🅱️◐🌓☺️😐⊞⬆️🖼️➧ ⚠️🔳 ♂   Photo: L. Seegers

A04598-4 *Aplocheilichthys maculatus lacustris* SEEGERS, 1984
Kibiti-Leuchtaugenfisch / Kibiti Lampeye [T.t.]
Kibiti, 140 km S Dar es Salaam, Tansania / Tanzania; W; 4,0 cm
⚠🔟○◑☺☻⊞⬆🔲🐾➡ ⚠🔲 ♂   Photo: L. Seegers

A04599-4 *Aplocheilichthys maculatus lacustris* SEEGERS, 1984
Kibiti-Leuchtaugenfisch / Kibiti Lampeye, "TZ 89/116"
40 km S Dar es Salaam, Tansania / Tanzania; W; 4,0 cm
⚠🔟○◑☺☻⊞⬆🔲🐾➡ ⚠🔲 ♂   Photo: L. Seegers

A04621-4 *Aplocheilichthys matthesi* SEEGERS, 1996
Matthes' Leuchtaugenfisch / Matthes' Lampeye, "TZ 93/26"
Kamuzwadsi R., upper Saisi R., L. Rukwa drainage, Zambia; W; 4,0 cm
▷🔟○◑☺☻⊞⬆🔲🐾➡ ⚠🔲 ♂   Photo: L. Seegers

A04621-4 *Aplocheilichthys matthesi* SEEGERS, 1996
Matthes' Leuchtaugenfisch / Matthes' Lampeye, "TZ 93/26"
Kamuzwadsi R., upper Saisi R., L. Rukwa drainage, Zambia; W; 4,0 cm
▷🔟○◑☺☻⊞⬆🔲🐾➡ ⚠🔲 ♀   Photo: L. Seegers

A04612-4 *Aplocheilichthys moeruensis* (BOULENGER, 1914)
Moeru-Leuchtaugenfisch / Mweru Lampeye
Lake Mweru Wantipa, Zambia; W; 3,5 cm
▷🔟○◑☺☻⊞⬆🔲🐾➡ ⚠🔲 ♂   Photo: L. Seegers

A04612-4 *Aplocheilichthys moeruensis* (BOULENGER, 1914)
Moeru-Leuchtaugenfisch / Mweru Lampeye
Lake Mweru Wantipa, Zambia; W; 3,5 cm
▷🔟○◑☺☻⊞⬆🔲🐾➡ ⚠🔲 ♀   Photo: L. Seegers

A04614-4 *Aplocheilichthys* aff. *moeruensis* (BOULENGER, 1914)
Moeru-Leuchtaugenfisch / Mweru Lampeye
Momba River, Lake Rukwa drainage, Tanzania; W; 3,5 cm
▷🔟○◑☺☻⊞⬆🔲🐾➡ ⚠🔲 ♂   Photo: L. Seegers

A04614-4 *Aplocheilichthys* aff. *moeruensis* (BOULENGER, 1914)
Moeru-Leuchtaugenfisch / Mweru Lampeye
Momba River, Lake Rukwa drainage, Tanzania; W; 3,5 cm
▷🔟○◑☺☻⊞⬆🔲🐾➡ ⚠🔲 ♀   Photo: L. Seegers

A04613-4 *Aplocheilichthys myaposae* (BOULENGER, 1908)
Natal-Leuchtaugenfisch / Natal Lampeye
Natal, Südafrika / Natal, South Africa; W; 5,5 cm

◁ ▷ ₿ ◑ ☺ ☻ ⊞ ⬆ 🖼 ➡ ⚠ ▥ ♂   Photo: L. Seegers

A04613-4 *Aplocheilichthys myaposae* (BOULENGER, 1908)
Natal-Leuchtaugenfisch / Natal Lampeye
Natal, Südafrika / Natal, South Africa; W; 5,5 cm

◁ ▷ ₿ ◑ ☺ ☻ ⊞ ⬆ 🖼 ➡ ⚠ ▥ ♀   Photo: L. Seegers

A04610-4 *Aplocheilichthys (Congopanchax) myersi* POLL, 1952
Kolibri-Leuchtaugenfisch / Hummingbird Lampeye
Aquaristik-Import, Kinshasa, Zaïre; W; 2,5 cm

▷ ℞ ◑ ☺ ☻ ⊞ ⬆ 🖼 ➡ 🐌 ⑤ ♂   Photo: E. Pürzl

A04610-4 *Aplocheilichthys (Congopanchax) myersi* POLL, 1952
Kolibri-Leuchtaugenfisch / Hummingbird Lampeye
Aquaristik-Import, Kinshasa, Zaïre; W; 2,5 cm

▷ ℞ ◑ ☺ ☻ ⊞ ⬆ 🖼 ➡ 🐌 ⑤ ♀   Photo: L. Seegers

A04611-4 *Aplocheilichthys nimbaensis* (DAGET, 1948)
Nimba-Leuchtaugenfisch / Mt. Nimba Lampeye
Nimba-Berge, nordöstliches Liberia / NE Liberia; W; 4,5 cm

◁ ₿ ◑ ☺ ☻ ⊞ ⬆ 🖼 ➡ ⚠ ▥ ♂   Photo: L. Seegers

A04611-4 *Aplocheilichthys nimbaensis* (DAGET, 1948)
Nimba-Leuchtaugenfisch / Mt. Nimba Lampeye
Nimba-Berge, nordöstliches Liberia / NE Liberia; W; 4,5 cm

◁ ₿ ◑ ☺ ☻ ⊞ ⬆ 🖼 ➡ ⚠ ▥ ♀   Photo: L. Seegers

A04611-4 *Aplocheilichthys nimbaensis* (DAGET, 1948)
Nimba-Leuchtaugenfisch / Mt. Nimba Lampeye
Nimba-Berge, nordöstliches Liberia / NE Liberia; W; 4,5 cm

◁ ₿ ◑ ☺ ☻ ⊞ ⬆ 🖼 ➡ ⚠ ▥ ♂   Photo: L. Seegers

A04611-4 *Aplocheilichthys nimbaensis* (DAGET, 1948)
Nimba-Leuchtaugenfisch / Mt. Nimba Lampeye
Nimba-Berge, nordöstliches Liberia / NE Liberia; W; 4,5 cm

◁ ₿ ◑ ☺ ☻ ⊞ ⬆ 🖼 ➡ ⚠ ▥ ♂   Photo: L. Seegers

A04615-4 *Aplocheilichthys normani* AHL, 1928
Normans Leuchtaugenfisch, Blauauge / Norman's Lampeye, Blue-eye
Gambia; W; 4,0 cm
▷ ♫ ◑ ☺ ☺ ⊞ ⬆ 🔲➤ ⚠ 🔲 ♂
Photo: L. Seegers

A04615-4 *Aplocheilichthys normani* AHL, 1928
Normans Leuchtaugenfisch, Blauauge / Norman's Lampeye, Blue-eye
Gambia; W; 4,0 cm
▷ ♫ ◑ ☺ ☺ ⊞ ⬆ 🔲➤ ⚠ 🔲 ♀
Photo: L. Seegers

A04616-4 *Aplocheilichthys normani* AHL, 1928
Normans Leuchtaugenfisch, Blauauge / Norman's Lampeye, Blue-eye
Robertsfield, Liberia; W; 4,0 cm
▷ ♫ ◑ ☺ ☺ ⊞ ⬆ 🔲➤ ⚠ 🔲 ♂
Photo: L. Seegers

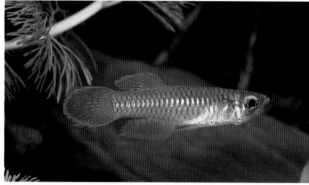

A04546-4 *Aplocheilichthys normani* AHL, 1928
Normans Leuchtaugenfisch, Blauauge / Norman's Lampeye, Blue-eye
Tabili River, Guinea; W; 4,0 cm
▷ ♫ ◑ ☺ ☺ ⊞ ⬆ 🔲➤ ⚠ 🔲 ♂
Photo: L. Seegers

A04617-3 *Aplocheilichthys omoculatus* WILDEKAMP, 1977
Schulterfleck-Leuchtaugenfisch / Ruaha Lampeye
Little Ruaha, Sao Hills, Tanzania; W; 3,5 cm
◁ ▷ ♫ ○ ◑ ☺ ☺ ⊞ ⬆ 🔲➤ ⚠ 🔲 ♂
Photo: L. Seegers

A04622-4 *Aplocheilichthys omoculatus* WILDEKAMP, 1977
Schulterfleck-Leuchtaugenfisch / Ruaha Lampeye, "TZ 93/37"
Brook W Ifunda, on road to Mbeya, Tanzania; W; 3,5 cm
◁ ▷ ♫ ○ ◑ ☺ ☺ ⊞ ⬆ 🔲➤ ⚠ 🔲 ♂
Photo: L. Seegers

A04623-4 *Aplocheilichthys omoculatus* WILDEKAMP, 1977
Schulterfleck-Leuchtaugenfisch / Ruaha Lampeye
Kinaha, Little Ruaha drainage, Tanzania; W; 3,5 cm
◁ ▷ ♫ ○ ◑ ☺ ☺ ⊞ ⬆ 🔲➤ ⚠ 🔲 ♂
Photo: L. Seegers

A04623-4 *Aplocheilichthys omoculatus* WILDEKAMP, 1977
Schulterfleck-Leuchtaugenfisch / Ruaha Lampeye
Kinaha, Little Ruaha drainage, Tanzania; W; 3,5 cm
◁ ▷ ♫ ○ ◑ ☺ ☺ ⊞ ⬆ 🔲➤ ⚠ 🔲 ♀
Photo: L. Seegers

A04618-4 *Aplocheilichthys pfaffi* DAGET, 1954
Pfaffs Leuchtaugenfisch / Pfaff's Lampeye
Ouagadougou, Burkina Faso; W; 3,0 (3,5?) cm
▷♫○◐☺☻⊞⏏⬆🐾 ⚠ⓢ🅜 ♂   Photo: L. Seegers

A04620-4 *Aplocheilichthys pumilus* (BOULENGER, 1906)
Kleiner Tanganjika-Leuchtaugenfisch / Tanganyika Lampeye
Aquarienstamm / Aquarium strain; B; 5,5 cm
▷♫⑀○◐☺☻⊞⏏⬆🐾 ⚠🅜 ♂   Photo: L. Seegers

A04540-4 *Aplocheilichthys pumilus* (BOULENGER, 1906)
Kleiner Tanganjika-Leuchtaugenfisch / Tanganyika Lampeye, "TZ 92/21"
Hafen von Ujiji, Tanganjikasee, Tansania /Ujiji harbour, Tanzania; W; 5,5 cm
▷♫⑀◐☺☻⊞⏏⬆🐾 ⚠ⓢ🅜 ♀   Photo: L. Seegers

A04625-4 *Aplocheilichthys rancureli* DAGET, 1964
Rancurels Leuchtaugenfisch / Rancurel's Lampeye
Elfenbeinküste / Ivory Coast; W; 4,0 cm
▷♫⑀○◐☺☻⊞⏏⬆🐾 ⚠🅜 ♂   Photo: E. Pürzl

A04626-4 *Aplocheilichthys rancureli* DAGET, 1964
Rancurels Leuchtaugenfisch / Rancurel's Lampeye
Tweakpoloe River, Ghana; W; 4,0 cm
▷♫⑀◐☺☻⊞⏏⬆🐾 ⚠ⓢ🅜 ♂   Photo: L. Seegers

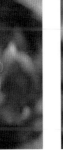

A04626-4 *Aplocheilichthys rancureli* DAGET, 1964
Rancurels Leuchtaugenfisch / Rancurel's Lampeye
Tweakpoloe River, Ghana; W; 4,0 cm
▷♫⑀◐☺☻⊞⏏⬆🐾 ⚠ⓢ🅜 ♀   Photo: L. Seegers

A04627-4 *Aplocheilichthys rudolfianus* (WORTHINGTON, 1932)
Rudolfsee- oder Turkana-Leuchtaugenfisch / Lake Rudolf Lampeye
"K 96/9", Loyangalani, Lake Turkana, Kenia / Kenya; W; 3,0 cm
▷⑀○◐☺☻⊞⏏🐾 ⚠🅜 ♂   Photo: L. Seegers

A04627-4 *Aplocheilichthys rudolfianus* (WORTHINGTON, 1932)
Rudolfsee- oder Turkana-Leuchtaugenfisch / Lake Rudolf Lampeye
"K 86/4", Loyangalani, Lake Turkana, Kenia / Kenya; W; 3,0 cm
▷⑀○◐☺☻⊞⏏🐾 ⚠🅜 ♀   Photo: L. Seegers

A04630-4 *Aplocheilichthys scheeli* ROMAN, 1970
Scheels Leuchtaugenfisch / Scheel's Lampeye
Aquaristik-Import, Süd-Kamerun / Southern Cameroon; W; 3,5 cm
▷⌀🄿🄿🄿◑☺☻⊞⬆🖼➤ ⚠ⓈⓂ ♂   Photo: L. Seegers

A04630-4 *Aplocheilichthys scheeli* ROMAN, 1970
Scheels Leuchtaugenfisch / Scheel's Lampeye
Aquaristik-Import, Süd-Kamerun / Southern Cameroon; W; 3,5 cm
▷⌀🄿🄿🄿◑☺☻⊞⬆🖼➤ ⚠ⓈⓂ ♀   Photo: D. Bork

A04631-4 *Aplocheilichthys scheeli* ROMAN, 1970
Scheels Leuchtaugenfisch / Scheel's Lampeye
Dizangue, Kamerun / Dizangue, Cameroon; W; 3,5 cm
▷⌀🄿🄿🄿◑☺☻⊞⬆🖼➤ ⚠ⓈⓂ ♂   Photo: E. Pürzl

A04632-4 *Aplocheilichthys scheeli* ROMAN, 1970
Scheels Leuchtaugenfisch / Scheel's Lampeye
Kribi, Süd-Kamerun / Kribi, southern Cameroon; W; 3,5 cm
▷⌀🄿🄿◑☺☻⊞⬆🖼➤ ⚠ⓈⓂ ♂   Photo: E. Pürzl

A04635-4 *Aplocheilichthys schioetzi* SCHEEL, 1968
Schiötz' Leuchtaugenfisch / Schiötz' Lampeye
"G 88/1", Südost-Guinea / Southeastern Guinea; W; 3,5 cm
▷⌀🄿◑☺☻⊞⬆🖼➤ ⚠Ⓜ ♂   Photo: L. Seegers

A04635-4 *Aplocheilichthys schioetzi* SCHEEL, 1968
Schiötz' Leuchtaugenfisch / Schiötz' Lampeye
"G 88/1", Südost-Guinea / Southeastern Guinea; W; 3,5 cm
▷⌀🄿◑☺☻⊞⬆🖼➤ ⚠Ⓜ ♀   Photo: L. Seegers

A04636-4 *Aplocheilichthys* cf. *schioetzi* SCHEEL, 1968
Schiötz' Leuchtaugenfisch / Schiötz' Lampeye
Grenze Guinea-Senegal / Guinea-Senegal border; W; 3,5 cm
▷⌀🄿◑☺☻⊞⬆🖼➤ ⚠Ⓜ ♂   Photo: L. Seegers

A04638-4 *Aplocheilichthys schioetzi* SCHEEL, 1968
Schiötz' Leuchtaugenfisch / Schiötz' Lampeye
Ost-Liberia / Eastern Liberia; W; 3,5 cm
▷⌀🄿◑☺☻⊞⬆🖼➤ ⚠Ⓜ ♀   Photo: L. Seegers

A04640-4 *Aplocheilichthys spilauchen* (DUMÉRIL, 1861)
Nackenfleck-Leuchtaugenfisch / Banded Lampeye
Gambia; W; 6,5 cm
▷⚠🏴‍☠️P○◑☺☻⊞⬆🔲🐾➡ ⚠m♂
Photo: L. Seegers

A04641-4 *Aplocheilichthys spilauchen* (DUMÉRIL, 1861)
Nackenfleck-Leuchtaugenfisch / Banded Lampeye
Aquaristik-Import aus Westafrika / Import from Westafrica; W; 6,5
▷⚠🏴‍☠️P○◑☺☻⊞⬆🔲🐾➡ ⚠m♂
Photo: L. Seegers

A04642-4 *Aplocheilichthys spilauchen* (DUMÉRIL, 1861)
Nackenfleck-Leuchtaugenfisch / Banded Lampeye
Robertsfield, Liberia; W; 6,5 cm
▷⚠🏴‍☠️P○◑☺☻⊞⬆🔲🐾➡ ⚠m♂
Photo: L. Seegers

A04642-4 *Aplocheilichthys spilauchen* (DUMÉRIL, 1861)
Nackenfleck-Leuchtaugenfisch / Banded Lampeye
Robertsfield, Liberia; W; 6,5 cm
▷⚠🏴‍☠️P○◑☺☻⊞⬆🔲🐾➡ ⚠m♀
Photo: L. Seegers

A4643-4 *Aplocheilichthys spilauchen* (DUMÉRIL, 1861)
Nackenfleck-Leuchtaugenfisch / Banded Lampeye
Aquarienstamm / Aquarium strain; W?; 6,5 cm
▷⚠🏴‍☠️P○◑☺☻⊞⬆🔲🐾➡ ⚠m♂
Photo: E. Schraml

A04643-4 *Aplocheilichthys spilauchen* (DUMÉRIL, 1861)
Nackenfleck-Leuchtaugenfisch / Banded Lampeye
Aquarienstamm / Aquarium strain; W?; 6,5 cm
▷⚠🏴‍☠️P○◑☺☻⊞⬆🔲🐾➡ ⚠m♂
Photo: A. Cánovas

A04644-4 *Aplocheilichthys spilauchen* (DUMÉRIL, 1861)
Nackenfleck-Leuchtaugenfisch / Banded Lampeye
Nördl. Rio Lifune, N. Angola / North of Rio Lifune, N. Angola; W; 6,5 cm
▷⚠🏴‍☠️P○◑☺☻⊞⬆🔲🐾➡ ⚠m♂
Photo: L. Seegers

A04644-4 *Aplocheilichthys spilauchen* (DUMÉRIL, 1861)
Nackenfleck-Leuchtaugenfisch / Banded Lampeye
Nördl. Rio Lifune, N. Angola / North of Rio Lifune, N. Angola; W; 6,5 cm
▷⚠🏴‍☠️P○◑☺☻⊞⬆🔲🐾➡ ⚠m♀
Photo: L. Seegers

A04650-4 *Aplocheilichthys usanguensis* WILDEKAMP, 1977
Usangu-Leuchtaugenfisch / Usangu Lampeye
Usangu Flats, Great Ruaha drainage, Tanzania; W; 3,0 cm
◁ ▷ ℟ ○ ◑ ☺ ☻ ⊞ ⬆ 🐛 ➤ ⚠ Ⓢ Ⓜ ♂ Photo: L. Seegers

A04650-4 *Aplocheilichthys usanguensis* WILDEKAMP, 1977
Usangu-Leuchtaugenfisch / Usangu Lampeye
Usangu Flats, Great Ruaha drainage, Tanzania; W; 3,0 cm
◁ ▷ ℟ ○ ◑ ☺ ☻ ⊞ ⬆ 🐛 ➤ ⚠ Ⓢ Ⓜ ♀ Photo: L. Seegers

A04660-4 *Aplocheilichthys vitschumbaensis* (AHL, 1924)
Bitschumbi-Leuchtaugenfisch / Bitschumbi Lampeye, "U 88/7"
Kazinga Channel near Mweya, Uganda; W; 4,5-5,0 cm
⚠ ℟ ⇅P ○ ◑ ☺ ☻ ⊞ ⬆ 🐛 ➤ ⚠ Ⓜ ♂ Photo: L. Seegers

A04660-4 *Aplocheilichthys vitschumbaensis* (AHL, 1924)
Bitschumbi-Leuchtaugenfisch / Bitschumbi Lampeye, "U 88/7"
Kazinga Channel near Mweya, Uganda; W; 4,5-5,0 cm
⚠ ℟ ⇅P ○ ◑ ☺ ☻ ⊞ ⬆ 🐛 ➤ ⚠ Ⓜ ♀ Photo: L. Seegers

A04661-3 *Aplocheilichthys* cf. *vitschumbaensis* (AHL, 1924)
Bitschumbi-Leuchtaugenfisch / Bitschumbi Lampeye
Bitschumbi, Edwardsee, Zaïre / Lake Edward, Zaïre; W; 4,5-5,0 cm
⚠ ℟ ⇅P ○ ◑ ☺ ☻ ⊞ ⬆ 🐛 ➤ ⚠ Ⓜ ♂ Photo: L. Seegers

A04541-4 *Aplocheilichthys* cf. *vitschumbaensis* (AHL, 1924)
Bitschumbi-Leuchtaugenfisch / Bitschumbi Lampeye
Kenyoro, Kiogasee, Uganda / Lake Kioga, Uganda; W; 4,5-5,0 cm
⚠ ℟ ○ ◑ ☺ ☻ ⊞ ⬆ 🐛 ➤ ⚠ Ⓜ ♂ Photo: L. Seegers

A04701-4 *Aplocheilichthys* spec. "TZ 91/126"
Makere River, am Weg Kasulu - Kibondo, Tansania /
Makere River on Kasulu - Kibondo road, Tanzania; W; 4,5-5,0 cm
⚠ ℟ ○ ◑ ☺ ☻ ⊞ ⬆ 🐛 ➤ ⚠ Ⓜ ♂ Photo: L. Seegers

A04702-4 *Aplocheilichthys* spec. "TZ 91/128"
6 km nördlich des Malagarasi River am Weg nach Kibondo, Tansania /
6 km N Malagarasi River on road to Kibondo, Tanzania; W; 4,0-4,5 cm
⚠ ℟ ○ ◑ ☺ ☻ ⊞ ⬆ 🐛 ➤ ⚠ Ⓜ ♂ Photo: L. Seegers

A04703-4 *Aplocheilichthys* spec. "TZ 92/144"
60 km östlich Kasama, Kalunga-Einzug, Sambia /
60 km east of Kasama, Kalunga drainage, Zambia; W; 4,0-4,5 cm
⚠🅱○◐☺☹⊞⬆🔤➡ ⚠🔳 ♂   Photo: L. Seegers

A04704-4 *Aplocheilichthys* spec. "TZ 92/131"
Gumba River, am Weg Tunduma - Mbala, Sambia /
Gumba River on Tunduma - Mbala road, Zambia; W; 4,5-5,0 cm
⚠🅱○◐☺☹⊞⬆🔤➡ ⚠🔳 ♀   Photo: L. Seegers

A04705-4 *Aplocheilichthys* spec. "Kasundu"
Kasundu, Malawi; W; 4,0-4,5 cm

⚠🅱○◐☺☹⊞⬆🔤➡ ⚠🔳 ♂   Photo: E. Pürzl

A04706-4 *Aplocheilichthys* spec. "TZ 89/14"
Malagarasi-Leuchtauge / Malagarasi Lampeye
Malagarasi-Einzug / Malagarasi Drainage, Tanzania; W; 4,0-4,5 cm
⚠🅱○◐☺☹⊞⬆🔤➡ ⚠🔳 ♂   Photo: L. Seegers

A04706-4 *Aplocheilichthys* spec. "TZ 89/14"
Malagarasi-Leuchtauge / Malagarasi Lampeye
Malagarasi-Einzug / Malagarasi Drainage, Tanzania; W; 4,0-4,5 cm
⚠🅱○◐☺☹⊞⬆🔤➡ ⚠🔳 ♂   Photo: L. Seegers

A04706-4 *Aplocheilichthys* spec. "TZ 89/14"
Malagarasi-Leuchtauge / Malagarasi Lampeye
Malagarasi-Einzug / Malagarasi Drainage, Tanzania; W; 4,0-4,5 cm
⚠🅱○◐☺☹⊞⬆🔤➡ ⚠🔳 ♀   Photo: L. Seegers

A04707-4 *Aplocheilichthys* sp. aff. *maculatus*, "K 86/1"
Baringo-Leuchtauge / Baringo Lampeye
Molo River, Baringosee, Kenia / Lake Baringo, Kenya; W; 3,5-4,0 cm
⚠🅱↑P○◐☺☹⊞⬆🔤➡ ⚠🔳 ♂   Photo: L. Seegers

A04707-4 *Aplocheilichthys* sp. aff. *maculatus*, "K 83/26"
Baringo-Leuchtauge / Baringo Lampeye
Baringosee, Kenia / Lake Baringo, Kenya; W; 3,5-4,0 cm
⚠🅱↑P○◐☺☹⊞⬆🔤➡ ⚠🔳 ♀   Photo: L. Seegers

A37775-4 *Hylopanchax stictopleuron* (FOWLER, 1949)
Blauer Leuchtaugenfisch / Blue Lampeye
Makokou, Gabun / Makokou, Gabon; W; 3,5 cm
▷♫⳩◑☺☹⊞↥🖼🐟 🐝 s̄m̄ ♂   Photo: L. Seegers

A37775-4 *Hylopanchax stictopleuron* (FOWLER, 1949)
Blauer Leuchtaugenfisch / Blue Lampeye
Makokou, Gabun / Makokou, Gabon; W; 3,5 cm
▷♫⳩◑☺☹⊞↥🖼🐟 🐝 s̄m̄ ♀   Photo: L. Seegers

A37776-4 *Hylopanchax stictopleuron* (FOWLER, 1949)
Blauer Leuchtaugenfisch / Blue Lampeye
Equateur, Zaïre; W; 3,5 cm
▷♫⳩◑☺☹⊞↥🖼🐟 🐝 s̄m̄ ♂   Photo: L. Seegers

A38000-4 *Hypsopanchax catenatus* RADDA, 1981
Ketten-Leuchtaugenfisch / Chain Lampeye
60 km S Franceville on road to Boumango, Gabon; W; 6,0 cm
◁ ♫◑☺☹⊞↥🖼🐟 ⚠m̄ ♂   Photo: E. Pürzl

A38005-4 *Hypsopanchax modestus* (PAPPENHEIM in PAPPENHEIM &
Ruwenzori-Leuchtaugenfisch / Ruwenzori Lampeye   BOULENGER, 1914)
"U 88/10", Rwimi River, 44 km W Fort Portal, Uganda; W; 6,0 cm
◁▷♫◑☺☹⊞↥🖼🐟 ⚠m̄ ♂   Photo: L. Seegers

A38005-4 *Hypsopanchax modestus* (PAPPENHEIM in PAPPENHEIM &
Ruwenzori-Leuchtaugenfisch / Ruwenzori Lampeye   BOULENGER, 1914)
"U 88/10", Rwimi River, 44 km W Fort Portal, Uganda; W; 6,0 cm
◁▷♫◑☺☹⊞↥🖼🐟 ⚠m̄ ♀   Photo: L. Seegers

A38006-4 *Hypsopanchax modestus* (PAPPENHEIM in PAPPENHEIM &
Ruwenzori-Leuchtaugenfisch / Ruwenzori Lampeye   BOULENGER, 1914)
"U 88/12", 12 km W Fort Portal, Uganda; W; 6,0 cm
◁▷♫◑☺☹⊞↥🖼🐟 ⚠m̄ ♂   Photo: L. Seegers

A38006-4 *Hypsopanchax modestus* (PAPPENHEIM in PAPPENHEIM &
Ruwenzori-Leuchtaugenfisch / Ruwenzori Lampeye   BOULENGER, 1914)
"U 88/12", 12 km W Fort Portal, Uganda; W; 6,0 cm
◁▷♫◑☺☹⊞↥🖼🐟 ⚠m̄ ♀   Photo: L. Seegers

A38010-4 *Hypsopanchax platysternus* (NICHOLS & GRISCOM, 1917)
Zaïre-Leuchtaugenfisch / Zaïre Lampeye, "HZ 25/85"
Zaïre; W; 5,5 cm
▷♫ℙ◑☺☹⊞⬆🖼➾ ⚠🔲 ♂
Photo: E. Pürzl

A38010-4 *Hypsopanchax platysternus* (NICHOLS & GRISCOM, 1917)
Zaïre-Leuchtaugenfisch / Zaïre Lampeye, "HZ 25/85"
Zaïre; W; 5,5 cm
▷♫ℙ◑☺☹⊞⬆🖼➾ ⚠🔲 ♀
Photo: E. Pürzl

A38011-4 *Hypsopanchax platysternus* (NICHOLS & GRISCOM, 1917)
Zaïre-Leuchtaugenfisch / Zaïre Lampeye, "HZ 26/85"
Kindu, Zaïre; W; 5,5 cm
▷♫ℙ◑☺☹⊞⬆🖼➾ ⚠🔲 ♂
Photo: L. Seegers

A38015-4 *Hypsopanchax zebra* (PELLEGRIN, 1929)
Zebra-Leuchtaugenfisch / Zebra Lampeye
Kongo; W; 5,5 cm
▷♫ℙ◑☺☹⊞⬆🖼➾ ⚠🔲 ♂
Photo: R. Wildekamp

A40400-4 *Lamprichthys tanganicanus* (BOULENGER, 1898)
Großer Tanganjika-Leuchtaugenfisch / Tanganyikan Pearl Killifish
Tanganjikasee / Lake Tanganyika; W; 12 cm
▷♫ℙ○◑☺☹⊞🖼➾ ⚠🔲 ♂♂
Photo: M.P. & C. Piednoir

A40400-4 *Lamprichthys tanganicanus* (BOULENGER, 1898)
Großer Tanganjika-Leuchtaugenfisch / Tanganyikan Pearl Killifish
Tanganjikasee / Lake Tanganyika; W; 12 cm
▷♫ℙ○◑☺☹⊞🖼➾ ⚠🔲 ♂
Photo: H.J. Mayland

A40400-4 *Lamprichthys tanganicanus* (BOULENGER, 1898)
Großer Tanganjika-Leuchtaugenfisch / Tanganyikan Pearl Killifish
Tanganjikasee / Lake Tanganyika; W; 12 cm
▷♫ℙ○◑☺☹⊞🖼➾ ⚠🔲 ♂♂
Photo: A. Norman

A40400-4 *Lamprichthys tanganicanus* (BOULENGER, 1898)
Großer Tanganjika-Leuchtaugenfisch / Tanganyikan Pearl Killifish
Tanganjikasee / Lake Tanganyika; W; 12 cm
▷♫ℙ○◑☺☹⊞🖼➾ ⚠🔲 ♀
Photo: M.P. & C. Piednoir

A51956-4 *Pantanodon stuhlmanni* (Ahl, 1924)
Ostküsten-Leuchtaugenfisch / Eastcoast Lampeye, "TZ 83/1"
Dar es Salaam, Tanzania; W; 5,0 cm
Photo: L. Seegers

A51956-4 *Pantanodon stuhlmanni* (Ahl, 1924)
Ostküsten-Leuchtaugenfisch / Eastcoast Lampeye, "TZ 83/1"
Dar es Salaam, Tanzania; W; 5,0 cm
Photo: L. Seegers

A51957-4 *Pantanodon stuhlmanni* (Ahl, 1924)
Ostküsten-Leuchtaugenfisch / Eastcoast Lampeye, "TZ 94/5"
16 km north of Tanga on road to Mombasa, Tanzania; W; 5,0 cm
Photo: L. Seegers

A51957-4 *Pantanodon stuhlmanni* (Ahl, 1924)
Ostküsten-Leuchtaugenfisch / Eastcoast Lampeye, "TZ 94/5"
16 km north of Tanga on road to Mombasa, Tanzania; W; 5,0 cm
Photo: L. Seegers

A61203-4 *Plataplochilus* cf. *cabindae* (Boulenger, 1911)
Cabinda-Leuchtaugenfisch / Cabinda Lampeye
Lebamba, Gabun / Lebamba, Gabon; W; 5 cm
Photo: E. Pürzl

A61204-4 *Plataplochilus* cf. *cabindae* (Boulenger, 1911)
Cabinda-Leuchtaugenfisch / Cabinda Lampeye
Mayombe Nationalpark, Kongo / Mayombe National Park; W; 5 cm
Photo: E. Pürzl

A61206-4 *Plataplochilus* cf. *cabindae* (Boulenger, 1911)
Cabinda-Leuchtaugenfisch / Cabinda Lampeye
Moabi, Gabun / Moabi, Gabon; W; 5 cm
Photo: E. Pürzl

A61207-4 *Plataplochilus* cf. *cabindae* (Boulenger, 1911)
Cabinda-Leuchtaugenfisch / Cabinda Lampeye
Ndende, Gabun / Ndende, Gabon; W; 5 cm
Photo: E. Pürzl

A61210-4 *Plataplochilus loemensis* (PELLEGRIN, 1924)
Loeme-Leuchtaugenfisch / Loeme Lampeye
Gamba, Gabun / Gamba, Gabon; W; 6,0 cm
▷♫◑☺☻⊞⬆🐛➡ ⚠🅜 ♂   Photo: L. Seegers

A61210-4 *Plataplochilus loemensis* (PELLEGRIN, 1924)
Loeme-Leuchtaugenfisch / Loeme Lampeye
Gamba, Gabun / Gamba, Gabon; W; 6,0 cm
▷♫◑☺☻⊞⬆🐛➡ ⚠🅜 ♀   Photo: L. Seegers

A61215-4 *Plataplochilus miltotaenia* LAMBERT, 1963
Rotstreifen-Leuchtaugenfisch / Red Striped Lampeye
Lambarene, Gabun / Lambarene, Gabon; W; 5,0 cm
▷♫◑☺☻⊞⬆🐛➡ ⚠🅜 ♂   Photo: E. Pürzl

A61215-4 *Plataplochilus miltotaenia* LAMBERT, 1963
Rotstreifen-Leuchtaugenfisch / Red Striped Lampeye
Lambarene, Gabun / Lambarene, Gabon; W; 5,0 cm
▷♫◑☺☻⊞⬆🐛➡ ⚠🅜 ♀   Photo: E. Pürzl

A61216-4 *Plataplochilus miltotaenia* LAMBERT, 1963
Rotstreifen-Leuchtaugenfisch / Red Striped Lampeye
Aquarienstamm von Lambarene, Gabun / Gabon; W; 5,0 cm
▷♫◑☺☻⊞⬆🐛➡ ⚠🅜 ♂   Photo: L. Seegers

A61216-3 *Plataplochilus miltotaenia* LAMBERT, 1963
Rotstreifen-Leuchtaugenfisch / Red Striped Lampeye
Aquarienstamm von Lambarene, Gabun / Gabon; W; 5,0 cm
▷♫◑☺☻⊞⬆🐛➡ ⚠🅜 ♀   Photo: L. Seegers

A61218-4 ? *Plataplochilus mimus* LAMBERT, 1963
Gelbflossen-Plataplochilus / Yellow Finned Lampeye
Gabun / Gabon; W; 5,0 cm
▷♫◑☺☻⊞⬆🐛➡ ⚠🅜 ♂   Photo: E. Pürzl

A61218-4 ? *Plataplochilus mimus* LAMBERT, 1963
Gelbflossen-Plataplochilus / Yellow Finned Lampeye
Gabun / Gabon; W; 5,0 cm
▷♫◑☺☻⊞⬆🐛➡ ⚠🅜 ♀   Photo: E. Pürzl

A61219-4 ? *Plataplochilus* cf. *mimus* Lambert, 1963
Gelbflossen-Plataplochilus / Yellow Finned Lampeye
Kinguele, Gabun / Kinguele, Gabon; W; 5,0 cm
▷ ⚓ ◐ ☺ ☻ ⊞ ⬆ ▦ ➡ ⚠ m ♂
Photo: E. Pürzl

A61219-4 ? *Plataplochilus* cf. *mimus* Lambert, 1963
Gelbflossen-Plataplochilus / Yellow Finned Lampeye
Kinguele, Gabun / Kinguele, Gabon; W; 5,0 cm
▷ ⚓ ◐ ☺ ☻ ⊞ ⬆ ▦ ➡ ⚠ m ♀
Photo: E. Pürzl

A61220-4 *Plataplochilus ngaensis* (Ahl, 1924)
Nga-Leuchtaugenfisch / Nga Lampeye
Kristallberge, nördlich Akonolinga, NW-Gabun / NW Gabon; W; 5,0 cm
▷ ⚓ ◐ ☺ ☻ ⊞ ⬆ ▦ ➡ ⚠ m ♂
Photo: L. Seegers

A61220-4 *Plataplochilus ngaensis* (Ahl, 1924)
Nga-Leuchtaugenfisch / Nga Lampeye
Kristallberge, nördlich Akonolinga, NW-Gabun / NW Gabon; W; 5,0 cm
▷ ⚓ ◐ ☺ ☻ ⊞ ⬆ ▦ ➡ ⚠ m ♀
Photo: L. Seegers

A61225-4 *Plataplochilus* sp. aff. *ngaensis* (Ahl, 1924)
Nga-Leuchtaugenfisch / Nga Lampeye, "GWW 86/31"
NW-Gabun / NW Gabon; W; 5,0 cm
▷ ⚓ ◐ ☺ ☻ ⊞ ⬆ ▦ ➡ ⚠ m ♂
Photo: L. Seegers

A61226-4 *Plataplochilus* sp. aff. *ngaensis* (Ahl, 1924)
Nga-Leuchtaugenfisch / Nga Lampeye
Cap Esterias, NW-Gabun / NW Gabon; W; 5,0 cm
▷ ⚓ ◐ ☺ ☻ ⊞ ⬆ ▦ ➡ ⚠ m ♂
Photo: E. Pürzl

A61227-4 *Plataplochilus terveri* Huber, 1981
Tervers Leuchtaugenfisch / Terver's Lampeye
Mpassa River, Upper Ogooué, SE Gabon; W; 5,0 cm
◁ ⚓ ◐ ☺ ☻ ⊞ ⬆ ▦ ➡ ⚠ m ♂
Photo: E. Pürzl

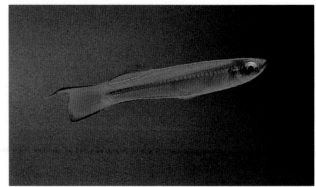

A61228-4 *Plataplochilus* spec.
Mouila-Leuchtaugenfisch / Mouila Lampeye
Mouila, Gabun / Mouila, Gabon; W; 4,0 cm
▷ ⚓ ◐ ☺ ☻ ⊞ ⬆ ▦ ➡ ⚠ m ♂
Photo: E. Pürzl

A74020-4 *Procatopus aberrans* Ahl, 1927
Blaugrüner Leuchtaugenfisch / Bluegreen Lampeye
Aquarienstamm, Kamerun / Aquarium strain, Cameroon; B; 6,0 cm
▷♬◑☺☹⊞⬆🐟➥ ⚠m♂   Photo: H.J. Mayland

A74020-4 *Procatopus aberrans* Ahl, 1927
Blaugrüner Leuchtaugenfisch / Bluegreen Lampeye
Aquarienstamm, Kamerun / Aquarium strain, Cameroon; B; 6,0 cm
▷♬◑☺☹⊞⬆🐟➥ ⚠m♂   Photo: L. Seegers

A74021-4 *Procatopus* cf. *aberrans* Ahl, 1927
Blaugrüner Leuchtaugenfisch / Bluegreen Lampeye
West-Kamerun / W Cameroon; W; 5,0 cm
▷♬◑☺☹⊞⬆🐟➥ ⚠m♂   Photo: L. Seegers

A74021-4 *Procatopus* cf. *aberrans* Ahl, 1927
Blaugrüner Leuchtaugenfisch / Bluegreen Lampeye
West-Kamerun / W Cameroon; W; 5,0 cm
▷♬◑☺☹⊞⬆🐟➥ ⚠m♀   Photo: L. Seegers

A74020-4 *Procatopus aberrans* Ahl, 1927
Blaugrüner Leuchtaugenfisch / Bluegreen Lampeye
Aquarienstamm, Kamerun / Aquarium strain, Cameroon; B; 6,0 cm
▷♬◑☺☹⊞⬆🐟➥ ⚠m♂♀   Photo: L. Seegers

A74060-4 *Procatopus nototaenia* Boulenger, 1904
Breitflossiger Leuchtaugenfisch / Large Finned Lampeye
Kribi, Südwest-Kamerun / Kribi, southwestern Cameroon; W; 6,0 cm
▷♬◑☺☹⊞⬆🐟➥ ⚠m♂   Photo: E. Pürzl

A74061-4 *Procatopus nototaenia* Boulenger, 1904
Breitflossiger Leuchtaugenfisch / Large Finned Lampeye
Aquaristikimport, Kamerun / Aquarium import, Cameroon; W; 6,0 cm
▷♬◑☺☹⊞⬆🐟➥ ⚠m♂   Photo: L. Seegers

A74062-4 *Procatopus nototaenia* Boulenger, 1904
Breitflossiger Leuchtaugenfisch / Large Finned Lampeye
Yabassi, Kamerun / Yabassi Cameroon; W; 6,0 cm
▷♬◑☺☹⊞⬆🐟➥ ⚠m♂   Photo: L. Seegers

A74100-4 *Procatopus similis* Aʜʟ, 1927
Variabler Leuchtaugenfisch / Variable Lampeye
West-Kamerun / Western Cameroon; W; 6,0 cm

▷𝄐❶◐☺☻⊞⬆🖼➡ ⚠🔲 ♂
Photo: L. Seegers

A74101-4 *Procatopus similis* Aʜʟ, 1927
Variabler Leuchtaugenfisch / Variable Lampeye
Aquaristik-Import, Kamerun / Aquariumimport, Cameroon; W; 6,0 cm

▷𝄐❶◐☺☻⊞⬆🖼➡ ⚠🔲 ♂
Photo: L. Seegers

A74102-4 *Procatopus similis* Aʜʟ, 1927
Variabler Leuchtaugenfisch / Variable Lampeye
Kamerun / Cameroon; W; 6,0 cm

▷𝄐❶◐☺☻⊞⬆🖼➡ ⚠🔲 ♂
Photo: E. Pürzl

A74103-4 *Procatopus similis* Aʜʟ, 1927
Variabler Leuchtaugenfisch / Variable Lampeye
Kumba, Kamerun / Kumba, Cameroon; W; 6,0 cm

▷𝄐❶◐☺☻⊞⬆🖼➡ ⚠🔲 ♂
Photo: E. Pürzl

A74104-4 *Procatopus similis* Aʜʟ, 1927
Variabler Leuchtaugenfisch / Variable Lampeye
Muyuka, Kamerun / Muyuka, Cameroon; W; 6,0 cm

▷𝄐❶◐☺☻⊞⬆🖼➡ ⚠🔲 ♂
Photo: E. Pürzl

A74104-4 *Procatopus similis* Aʜʟ, 1927
Variabler Leuchtaugenfisch / Variable Lampeye
Muyuka, Kamerun / Muyuka, Cameroon; W; 6,0 cm

▷𝄐❶◐☺☻⊞⬆🖼➡ ⚠🔲 ♀
Photo: E. Pürzl

A74105-4 *Procatopus similis* Aʜʟ, 1927
Variabler Leuchtaugenfisch / Variable Lampeye
Edea, Kamerun / Edea, Cameroon; W; 6,0 cm

▷𝄐❶◐☺☻⊞⬆🖼➡ ⚠🔲 ♂
Photo: E. Pürzl

A74105-4 *Procatopus similis* Aʜʟ, 1927
Variabler Leuchtaugenfisch / Variable Lampeye
Edea, Kamerun / Edea, Cameroon; W; 6,0 cm

▷𝄐❶◐☺☻⊞⬆🖼➡ ⚠🔲 ♀
Photo: E. Pürzl

Photo: L. Seegers

1. *Cynolebias fulminantis*
2. *Nothobranchius* sp. "Odienya", Lake Victoria
   drainage, Kenya

Diese und alle anderen in
These and all others in

Photo: L. Seegers

Aqualog Killifishes of the World

reference fish of the world

Old World Killifishes II
and
New World Killifishes

Aplocheilidae

Photo: E. Pürzl

1. Lebamba, Gabun. Typenfundort von *Aphyo-semion primigenium* und Lebensraum einer *Plataplochilus*-Art.
2. Cocobeach, Gabun, Fundort von *Aphyose-mion striatum* und *Plataplochilus ngaensis*.
3. Takundi, Zaïre (Z 17/82). Zwischen den Pflan-zen fanden sich *Aphyosemion congicum*.

1. Lebamba, Gabun. Type locality of *Aphyosemion primi-genium* and habitat of a *Plataplochilus* species.
2. Cocobeach, Gabun. Collecting locality of *Aphyose-mion striatum* and *Plataplochilus ngaensis*.
3. Takundi, Zaïre (Z 17/82). Between the water plants *Aphyosemion congicum* was collected.

Photo:
E. Pürzl

Photo: E. Pürzl

A00075-4 *Adamas formosus* Huber, 1979
Zwerg-Prachtkärpfling / Starhead Killi
Aquarienstamm / Aquarium strain; B; 3,0 cm
▷🐟♨◑☺☻⊞⬆🖼➡ ⚠Ⓢ♂
Photo: E. Pürzl

A00075-4 *Adamas formosus* Huber, 1979
Zwerg-Prachtkärpfling / Starhead Killi
Aquarienstamm / Aquarium strain; B; 3,0 cm
▷🐟♨◑☺☻⊞⬆🖼➡ ⚠Ⓢ♀
Photo: E. Pürzl

A00076-4 *Adamas formosus* Huber, 1979
Zwerg-Prachtkärpfling / Starhead Killi
Pool Malebo, Zaïre; W; 3,0 cm
▷🐟♨◑☺☻⊞⬆🖼➡ ⚠Ⓢ♂
Photo: L. Seegers

A00077-4 *Adamas formosus* Huber, 1979
Zwerg-Prachtkärpfling / Starhead Killi
Tchicapika, Kongo; W; 3,0 cm
▷🐟♨◑☺☻⊞⬆🖼➡ ⚠Ⓢ♂
Photo: L. Seegers

A00077-4 *Adamas formosus* Huber, 1979
Zwerg-Prachtkärpfling / Starhead Killi; Tchicapika, Kongo; W; 3,0 cm
mit Glanzschuppen auf dem Kopf / showing its brillant scales on head
▷🐟♨◑☺☻⊞⬆🖼➡ ⚠Ⓢ♂
Photo: L. Seegers

A02506-4 *Aphyoplatys duboisi* (Poll, 1952)
Zwerg-Kongohechtling / Dubois' Panchax
Aquarienstamm / Aquarium strain; B; 3,0 cm
▷🐟♨◑☺☻⊞⬆🖼➡ ⚠Ⓢ♂
Photo: E. Pürzl

A02505-4 *Aphyoplatys duboisi* (Poll, 1952)
Zwerg-Kongohechtling / Dubois' Panchax
Oyo, Ost-Kongo / Oyo, eastern Congo; B; 3,0 cm
▷🐟♨◑☺☻⊞⬆🖼➡ ⚠Ⓢ♂
Photo: S. Hellner-

A02505-4 *Aphyoplatys duboisi* (Poll, 1952)
Zwerg-Kongohechtling / Dubois' Panchax
Oyo, Ost-Kongo / Oyo, eastern Congo; B; 3,0 cm
▷🐟♨◑☺☻⊞⬆🖼➡ ⚠Ⓢ♀
Photo: L. Seegers

A03205-4 *Aphyosemion ahli* MYERS, 1933
Ahls Prachtkärpfling / Ahl's Lyretail, Blue Calliurum
Bipade, Südwest-Kamerun / Bipade, SW-Cameroon; B; 5,0 cm
▷⚑⚠❦◖◑☺☹⊞🗇🐌➤ ⚠ⓜ♂   Photo: H.J. Mayland

A03206-4 *Aphyosemion ahli* MYERS, 1933
Ahls Prachtkärpfling / Ahl's Lyretail, Blue Calliurum
Edea, Südwest-Kamerun / Edea, SW-Cameroon; W; 5,0 cm
▷⚑⚠❦◖◑☺☹⊞🗇🐌➤ ⚠ⓜ♂   Photo: E. Pürzl

A03207-4 *Aphyosemion ahli* MYERS, 1933
Ahls Prachtkärpfling / Ahl's Lyretail, Blue Calliurum
Kribi, Südwest-Kamerun / Kribi, SW-Cameroon; W; 5,0 cm
▷⚑⚠❦◖◑☺☹⊞🗇🐌➤ ⚠ⓜ♂   Photo: E. Pürzl

A03208-4 *Aphyosemion ahli* MYERS, 1933
Ahls Prachtkärpfling / Ahl's Lyretail, Blue Calliurum, "CCMP 84/1"
Mayukka, Südwest-Kamerun / Mayukka, SW-Cameroon; W; 5,0 cm
▷⚑⚠❦◖◑☺☹⊞🗇🐌➤ ⚠ⓜ♂   Photo: L. Seegers

A03209-4 *Aphyosemion ahli* MYERS, 1933
Ahls Prachtkärpfling / Ahl's Lyretail, Blue Calliurum
Lobé, Südwest-Kamerun / Lobé, SW Cameroon; W; 5,0 cm
▷⚑⚠❦◖◑☺☹⊞🗇🐌➤ ⚠ⓜ♂♀   Photo: L. Seegers

A03211-4 *Aphyosemion ahli* MYERS, 1933
Ahls Prachtkärpfling / Ahl's Lyretail, Blue Calliurum
Londji, Südwest-Kamerun / Londji, SW-Cameroon; B; 5,0 cm
▷⚑⚠❦◖◑☺☹⊞🗇🐌➤ ⚠ⓜ♂   Photo: S. Hellner

A03212-4 *Aphyosemion ahli* MYERS, 1933
Ahls Prachtkärpfling / Ahl's Lyretail, Blue Calliurum
Südwest-Kamerun / SW Cameroon; W; 5,0 cm
▷⚑⚠❦◖◑☺☹⊞🗇🐌➤ ⚠ⓜ♂   Photo: L. Seegers

A03212-4 *Aphyosemion ahli* MYERS, 1933
Ahls Prachtkärpfling / Ahl's Lyretail, Blue Calliurum
Südwest-Kamerun / SW Cameroon; B; 5,0 cm
▷⚑⚠❦◖◑☺☹⊞🗇🐌➤ ⚠ⓜ♂   Photo: L. Seegers

A03210-4 *Aphyosemion (F?) amieti* RADDA, 1976
Amiets Prachtkärpfling / Amiet's Lyretail [T.t.]
Somakak, West-Kamerun / Somakak, West Cameroon; W; 7,0 cm
♂ Photo: E. Pürzl

A03110-4 *Aphyosemion (F?) amieti* RADDA, 1976
Amiets Prachtkärpfling / Amiet's Lyretail
Somakak, West-Kamerun / Somakak, West Cameroon; B; 7,0 cm
♀ Photo: L. Seegers

A03110-4 *Aphyosemion (F?) amieti* RADDA, 1976
Amiets Prachtkärpfling / Amiet's Lyretail
Somakak, West-Kamerun / Somakak, West Cameroon; B; 7,0 cm
♂ Photo: L. Seegers

A03112-4 *Aphyosemion (F?) amieti* RADDA, 1976
Amiets Prachtkärpfling / Amiet's Lyretail, "HJRK 92/18"
Somakak, West-Kamerun / Somakak, West Cameroon; B; 7,0 cm
♂ Photo: W. Eigelshofen

A03215-4 *Aphyosemion amoenum* RADDA & PÜRZL, 1976
Rotflossen-Prachtkärpfling / Red-Finned Killi
Ndoupé near Sonbo, Kelle/Nyong system, Cameroon; B; 5,0 cm
♂ Photo: L. Seegers

A03215-4 *Aphyosemion amoenum* RADDA & PÜRZL, 1976
Rotflossen-Prachtkärpfling / Red-Finned Killi
Ndoupé near Sonbo, Kelle/Nyong system, Cameroon; B; 5,0 cm
♂ Photo: L. Seegers

A03215-4 *Aphyosemion amoenum* RADDA & PÜRZL, 1976
Rotflossen-Prachtkärpfling / Red-Finned Killi
Ndoupé near Sonbo, Kelle/Nyong system, Cameroon; B; 5,0 cm
♂ Photo: L. Seegers

A03215-4 *Aphyosemion amoenum* RADDA & PÜRZL, 1976
Rotflossen-Prachtkärpfling / Red-Finned Killi
Ndoupé near Sonbo, Kelle/Nyong system, Cameroon; B; 5,0 cm
♀ Photo: L. Seegers

A03217-4 *Aphyosemion amoenum* Radda & Pürzl, 1976
Rotflossen-Prachtkärpfling / Red-Finned Killi
Dibang, Kamerun / Cameroon; B; 5,0 cm
Photo: R. Lütje

A03216-4 *Aphyosemion amoenum* Radda & Pürzl, 1976
Rotflossen-Prachtkärpfling / Red-Finned Killi, "EMS 90/10"
Ndoupé near Sonbo, Kelle/Nyong system, Cameroon; B; 5,0 cm
Photo: S. Hellner

A03117-4 *Aphyosemion amoenum* Radda & Pürzl, 1976
Rotflossen-Prachtkärpfling / Red-Finned Killi, "CGE 91/13"
Dibang, Kamerun / Cameroon; W; 5,0 cm
Photo: R. Lütje

A03218-4 *Aphyosemion amoenum* Radda & Pürzl, 1976
Rotflossen-Prachtkärpfling / Red-Finned Killi, "C 89/22"
Nkonga, Kamerun / Cameroon; B; 5,0 cm
Photo: S. Hellner

A03219-4 *Aphyosemion amoenum* Radda & Pürzl, 1976
Rotflossen-Prachtkärpfling / Red-Finned Killi
Pouma, Kamerun / Cameroon; B; 5,0 cm
Photo: R. Lütje

A03213-4 *Aphyosemion amoenum* Radda & Pürzl, 1976
Rotflossen-Prachtkärpfling / Red-Finned Killi, "EMS 90/9"
Log Bako `o, 5 km E Pouma, Kamerun / Cameroon; B; 5,0 cm
Photo: R. Lütje

A03214-4 *Aphyosemion amoenum* Radda & Pürzl, 1976
Rotflossen-Prachtkärpfling / Red-Finned Killi, "EMS 90/8"
San Mayo, Kamerun / Cameroon; B; 5,0 cm
Photo: S. Hellner

A03981-4 *Aphyosemion* sp. aff. *amoenum* Radda & Pürzl, 1976
Rotflossen-Prachtkärpfling / Red-Finned Killi
Kamerun / Cameroon; W; 5,0 cm
Photo: L. Seegers
Bako `o

A03220-3 *Aphyosemion (F.) arnoldi* (BOULENGER, 1908)
Arnolds Prachtkärpfling / Arnold's Killi
Südwest-Nigeria / SW Nigeria; B; 5,0 cm
▷♬⚑◑☺☹⊞🖼🐟 ⚠🅼 ♂   Photo: E. Pürzl

A03221-4 *Aphyosemion (F.) arnoldi* (BOULENGER, 1908)
Arnolds Prachtkärpfling / Arnold's Killi
Sapele, Südwest-Nigeria / Sapele, SW Nigeria; W; 5,0 cm
▷♬⚑◑☺☹⊞🖼🐟 ⚠🅼 ♂   Photo: E. Pürzl

A03223-4 *Aphyosemion (F.) arnoldi* (BOULENGER, 1908)
Arnolds Prachtkärpfling / Arnold's Killi
Warri, Südwest-Nigeria / Warri, SW Nigeria; B; 5,0 cm
▷♬⚑◑☺☹⊞🖼🐟 ⚠🅼 ♂   Photo: L. Seegers

A03223-4 *Aphyosemion (F.) arnoldi* (BOULENGER, 1908)
Arnolds Prachtkärpfling / Arnold's Killi
Warri, Südwest-Nigeria / Warri, SW Nigeria; B; 5,0 cm
▷♬⚑◑☺☹⊞🖼🐟 ⚠🅼 ♀   Photo: L. Seegers

A03223-4 *Aphyosemion (F.) arnoldi* (BOULENGER, 1908)
Arnolds Prachtkärpfling / Arnold's Killi
Warri, Südwest-Nigeria / Warri, SW Nigeria; B; 5,0 cm
▷♬⚑◑☺☹⊞🖼🐟 ⚠🅼 ♂   Photo: L. Seegers

A03224-3 *Aphyosemion (F.) arnoldi* (BOULENGER, 1908)
Arnolds Prachtkärpfling / Arnold's Killi
Aquarienstamm, SW-Nigeria / Aquarium strain, SW Nigeria; B; 5,0 cm
▷♬⚑◑☺☹⊞🖼🐟 ⚠🅼 ♂   Photo: L. Seegers

A03224-4 *Aphyosemion (F.) arnoldi* (BOULENGER, 1908)
Arnolds Prachtkärpfling / Arnold's Killi
Aquarienstamm, SW-Nigeria / Aquarium strain, SW Nigeria; B; 5,0 cm
▷♬⚑◑☺☹⊞🖼🐟 ⚠🅼 ♂   Photo: L. Seegers

A03224-4 *Aphyosemion (F.) arnoldi* (BOULENGER, 1908)
Arnolds Prachtkärpfling / Arnold's Killi
Aquarienstamm, SW-Nigeria / Aquarium strain, SW Nigeria; B; 5,0 cm
▷♬⚑◑☺☹⊞🖼🐟 ⚠🅼 ♀   Photo: L. Seegers

A03222-4 *Aphyosemion aureum* RADDA, 1980
Goldprachtkärpfling / Golden Killi, "GHP 80/7" [T.t.]
Mouila, 47 km SW Koulamoutou, Gabun / Gabon; W; 5,0 cm
◁ ♫♥ℙ◑☺☻⊞🐟➡ ⚠🔲 ♂   Photo: E. Pürzl

A03222-4 *Aphyosemion aureum* RADDA, 1980
Goldprachtkärpfling / Golden Killi, "GHP 80/7" [T.t.]
Mouila, 47 km SW Koulamoutou, Gabun / Gabon; W; 5,0 cm
◁ ♫♥ℙ◑☺☻⊞🐟➡ ⚠🔲 ♀   Photo: E. Pürzl

A03122-4 *Aphyosemion aureum* RADDA, 1980
Goldprachtkärpfling / Golden Killi, "GHP 80/7"
Mouila, 47 km SW Koulamoutou, Gabun / Gabon; B; 5,0 cm
◁ ♫♥ℙ◑☺☻⊞🐟➡ ⚠🔲 ♂   Photo: L. Seegers

A03122-4 *Aphyosemion aureum* RADDA, 1980
Goldprachtkärpfling / Golden Killi, "GHP 80/7"
Mouila, 47 km SW Koulamoutou, Gabun / Gabon; B; 5,0 cm
◁ ♫♥ℙ◑☺☻⊞🐟➡ ⚠🔲 ♂   Photo: S. Hellner-

A03225-3 *Aphyosemion australe* (RACHOW, 1921)
Kap Lopez / Chocolate Lyretail
Cap Esterias, Gabun / Cap Esterias, Gabon; W; 5,0 cm
▷♫♥ℙ◑☺☻⊞🐟➡ ◇⚠🔲 ♂   Photo: E. Pürzl

A03225-4 *Aphyosemion australe* (RACHOW, 1921)
Kap Lopez / Chocolate Lyretail
Cap Esterias, Gabun / Cap Esterias, Gabon; W; 5,0 cm
▷♫♥ℙ◑☺☻⊞🐟➡ ◇⚠🔲 ♀   Photo: E. Pürzl

A03226-4 *Aphyosemion australe* (RACHOW, 1921)
Kap Lopez / Chocolate Lyretail
Mayumba, Süd-Kongo / Mayumba, Southern Congo; B; 5,0 cm
▷♫♥ℙ◑☺☻⊞🐟➡ ◇⚠🔲 ♂   Photo: L. Seegers

A03226-4 *Aphyosemion australe* (RACHOW, 1921)
Kap Lopez / Chocolate Lyretail
Mayumba, Süd-Kongo / Mayumba, Southern Congo; B; 5,0 cm
▷♫♥ℙ◑☺☻⊞🐟➡ ◇⚠🔲 ♀   Photo: L. Seegers

A03227-4 *Aphyosemion australe* (RACHOW, 1921)
Kap Lopez / Chocolate Lyretail
Aquarienstamm (Kap Lopez, Gabun ?) / Aquarium strain; B; 5,0 cm
▷ ♫ ❶ ☺ ☹ ⊞ 🖵 ➡ ◈ ⚠ m ♂   Photo: L. Seegers

A03230-4 *Aphyosemion australe* (RACHOW, 1921)
Gold-Kap Lopez / Golden Lyretail
Aquarienstamm, Zuchtform / Aquarium strain; Z; 5,0 cm
▷ ♫ ❶ ☺ ☹ ⊞ 🖵 ➡ ◈ ⚠ m ♂   Photo: J. Glaser

A03231-4 *Aphyosemion australe* (RACHOW, 1921)
Rotkäppchen-Gold-Kap Lopez / Golden Lyretail
Aquarienstamm, Mutante / Aquarium strain; Z; 5,0 cm
▷ ♫ ❶ ☺ ☹ ⊞ 🖵 ➡ ◈ ⚠ m ♂   Photo: H.J. Mayland

A03232-4 *Aphyosemion bamilekorum* RADDA, 1971
Bamileke-Prachtkärpfling / Bamileke Killi
Mbouda, Kamerun / Mbouda, Cameroon; B; 4,0 cm
◁ ♫ ❶ ☺ ☹ ⊞ ⬇ 🖵 ➡ ◈ ⚠ m ♂   Photo: R. Lütje

A03229-4 *Aphyosemion bamilekorum* RADDA, 1971
Bamileke-Prachtkärpfling / Bamileke Killi
Bafoussam, Kamerun / Bafoussam, Cameroon; B; 4,0 cm
◁ ♫ ❶ ☺ ☹ ⊞ ⬇ 🖵 ➡ ◈ ⚠ m ♂   Photo: L. Seegers

A03229-4 *Aphyosemion bamilekorum* RADDA, 1971
Bamileke-Prachtkärpfling / Bamileke Killi
Bafoussam, Kamerun / Bafoussam, Cameroon; B; 4,0 cm
◁ ♫ ❶ ☺ ☹ ⊞ ⬇ 🖵 ➡ ◈ ⚠ m ♀   Photo: L. Seegers

A03228-4 *Aphyosemion bamilekorum* RADDA, 1971
Bamileke-Prachtkärpfling / Bamileke Killi, "GPE 90/4"
9 km NW Bafoussam, Kamerun / Cameroon; W; 4,0 cm
◁ ♫ ❶ ☺ ☹ ⊞ ⬇ 🖵 ➡ ◈ ⚠ m ♂   Photo: E. Pürzl

A03982-4 *Aphyosemion* sp. aff. *bamilekorum*
Brauner Prachtkärpfling / Brown Killi
Mapan, Kamerun / Mapan, Cameroon; W; 4,5 cm
◁ ▷ ♫ ❶ ☺ ☹ ⊞ ⬇ 🖵 ➡ ◈ ⚠ m ♂   Photo: L. Seegers

A03234-4 *Aphyosemion (F.) batesii* (Boulenger, 1911)
Bates Prachtkärpfling / Bates' Killi
Ayos, Kamerun / Ayos, Cameroon; W; 7,0 cm
Photo: E. Pürzl

A03735-4 *Aphyosemion (F.) batesii* (Boulenger, 1911)
Bates Prachtkärpfling / Bates' Killi
Djoum, Kamerun / Djoum, Cameroon; W; 7,0 cm
Photo: E. Pürzl

A03736-4 *Aphyosemion (F.) batesii* (Boulenger, 1911)
Bates Prachtkärpfling / Bates' Killi
M'bandjok, Kamerun / M'bandjok, Cameroon; W; 7,0 cm
Photo: E. Pürzl

A03737-4 *Aphyosemion (F.) batesii* (Boulenger, 1911)
Bates Prachtkärpfling / Bates' Killi
Sangmelima, Kamerun / Sangmelima, Cameroon; W; 7,0 cm
Photo: E. Pürzl

A03737-4 *Aphyosemion (F.) batesii* (Boulenger, 1911)
Bates Prachtkärpfling / Bates' Killi
Sangmelima, Kamerun / Sangmelima, Cameroon; W; 7,0 cm
Photo: L. Seegers

A03738-4 *Aphyosemion (F.) batesii* (Boulenger, 1911)
Bates Prachtkärpfling / Bates' Killi
30 km westlich Sangmelima, Kamerun / Cameroon; W; 7,0 cm
Photo: L. Seegers

A03739-3 *Aphyosemion (F.) batesii* (Boulenger, 1911)
Bates Prachtkärpfling / Bates' Killi, "PEG 94/20"
Gabun / Gabon; W; 7,0 cm
Photo: R. Lütje

A03740-4 *Aphyosemion (F.) batesii* (Boulenger, 1911)
Bates Prachtkärpfling / Bates' Killi
Koumameyong, Gabun / Koumameyong, Gabon; W; 7,0 cm
Photo: E. Pürzl

A03738-4 *Aphyosemion (F.) batesii* (BOULENGER, 1911)
Bates Prachtkärpfling / Bates' Killi
Umgebung von Sangmelima, Kamerun / From near Sangmelima, Cameroon; W; 7,0 cm

Photo: L. Seegers

A03741-4 *Aphyosemion (F.) batesii* (BOULENGER, 1911) (*A. splendidum/kunzi*-Phänotyp)
Bates Prachtkärpfling, ablaichendes Paar / Bates' Killi, spawning pair
Nördlich von Oyem, Gabun / North of Oyem, Gabon; W; 7,0 cm

Photo: L. Seegers

A03742-4 *Aphyosemion batesii* (Boulenger, 1911)
Bates Prachtkärpfling / Bates' Killi
Makokou, Gabun / Makokou, Gabon; W; 7,0 cm
◁ ▷ ₿ ⏚ ◑ ☺ ☺ ⊞ 🖼 ➥ ⚠ 🔲 ♂   Photo: E. Pürzl

A03742-4 *Aphyosemion batesii* (Boulenger, 1911)
Bates Prachtkärpfling / Bates' Killi
Makokou, Gabun / Makokou, Gabon; W; 7,0 cm
◁ ▷ ₿ ⏚ ◑ ☺ ☺ ⊞ 🖼 ➥ ⚠ 🔲 ♂   Photo: L. Seegers

A03743-3 *Aphyosemion batesii* (Boulenger, 1911)
Bates Prachtkärpfling / Bates' Killi
Ehombitio, Gabun / Ehombitio, Gabon; B; 7,0 cm
◁ ▷ ₿ ⏚ ◑ ☺ ☺ ⊞ 🖼 ➥ ⚠ 🔲 ♂   Photo: L. Seegers

A03744-4 *Aphyosemion batesii* (Boulenger, 1911)
Bates Prachtkärpfling / Bates' Killi, "GBG 93/13"
Gabun / Gabon; W; 7,0 cm
◁ ▷ ₿ ⏚ ◑ ☺ ☺ ⊞ 🖼 ➥ ⚠ 🔲 ♂   Photo: R. Lütje

A03745-3 *Aphyosemion batesii* (Boulenger, 1911)
Bates Prachtkärpfling / Bates' Killi
Aquarienstamm, Gabun / Aquarium strain, Gabon; B; 7,0 cm
◁ ▷ ₿ ⏚ ◑ ☺ ☺ ⊞ 🖼 ➥ ⚠ 🔲 ♂   Photo: L. Seegers

A03745-4 *Aphyosemion batesii* (Boulenger, 1911)
Bates Prachtkärpfling / Bates' Killi
Aquarienstamm, Gabun / Aquarium strain, Gabon; B; 7,0 cm
◁ ▷ ₿ ⏚ ◑ ☺ ☺ ⊞ 🖼 ➥ ⚠ 🔲 ♂   Photo: L. Seegers

A03746-4 *Aphyosemion batesii* (Boulenger, 1911)
Bates Prachtkärpfling / Bates' Killi
Equateur, West-Zaïre; W; 7,0 cm
▷ ₿ ⏚ ◑ ☺ ☺ ⊞ 🖼 ➥ ⚠ 🔲 ♂   Photo: L. Seegers

A03746-4 *Aphyosemion batesii* (Boulenger, 1911)
Bates Prachtkärpfling / Bates' Killi
Equateur, West-Zaïre; W; 7,0 cm
▷ ₿ ⏚ ◑ ☺ ☺ ⊞ 🖼 ➥ ⚠ 🔲 ♀   Photo: L. Seegers

A03235-4 *Aphyosemion bertholdi* (ROLOFF, 1965) [= *A. liberiense*?]
Bertholds Prachtkärpfling / Berthold's Killi
Liberia; B; 4,0 cm
▷♨⚓◑☺☹⊞🖼➥ ◈ⓜ♂   Photo: S. Hellner

A03241-4 *Aphyosemion bitaeniatum* (AHL, 1924)
Glanz-oder Zweistreifen-Prachtkärpfling / Two-striped Aphyosemion
Togo; W; 4,5 cm
▷♨⚓◑☺☹⊞🖼➥ ◈ⓜ♂   Photo: E. Pürzl

A03240-4 *Aphyosemion bitaeniatum* (AHL, 1924)
Glanz-oder Zweistreifen-Prachtkärpfling / Two-striped Aphyosemion
Benin; W; 4,5 cm
▷♨⚓◑☺☹⊞🖼➥ ◈ⓜ♂   Photo: E. Pürzl

A03240-4 *Aphyosemion bitaeniatum* (AHL, 1924)
Glanz-oder Zweistreifen-Prachtkärpfling / Two-striped Aphyosemion
Benin; B; 4,5 cm
▷♨⚓◑☺☹⊞🖼➥ ◈ⓜ♂   Photo: E. Pürzl

A03242-4 *Aphyosemion bitaeniatum* (AHL, 1924)
Glanz-oder Zweistreifen-Prachtkärpfling / Two-striped Aphyosemion
Ikpenle, Benin; B; 4,5 cm
▷♨⚓◑☺☹⊞🖼➥ ◈ⓜ♂   Photo: L. Seegers

A03242-4 *Aphyosemion bitaeniatum* (AHL, 1924)
Glanz-oder Zweistreifen-Prachtkärpfling / Two-striped Aphyosemion
Ikpenle, Benin; B; 4,5 cm
▷♨⚓◑☺☹⊞🖼➥ ◈ⓜ♀   Photo: L. Seegers

A03243-4 *Aphyosemion bitaeniatum* (AHL, 1924)
Glanz-oder Zweistreifen-Prachtkärpfling / Two-striped Aphyosemion
Igolo, Benin; B; 4,5 cm
▷♨⚓◑☺☹⊞🖼➥ ◈ⓜ♂   Photo: L. Seegers

A03244-4 *Aphyosemion bitaeniatum* (AHL, 1924)
Glanz-oder Zweistreifen-Prachtkärpfling / Two-striped Aphyosemion
Takou, Benin; B; 4,5 cm
▷♨⚓◑☺☹⊞🖼➥ ◈ⓜ♂   Photo: L. Seegers

A03747-4 *Aphyosemion bitaeniatum* (AHL, 1924)
Glanz-oder Zweistreifen-Prachtkärpfling / Two-striped Aphyosemion
Zienvie, Benin; B; 4,5 cm
▷ ♣ ⅃P ◑ ☺ ☹ ⊞ ▦ ➤ ◈ m ♂   Photo: L. Seegers

A03748-4 *Aphyosemion bitaeniatum* (AHL, 1924)
Glanz-oder Zweistreifen-Prachtkärpfling / Two-striped Aphyosemion
Ijebu Ode, Nigeria; B; 4,5 cm
▷ ♣ ⅃P ◑ ☺ ☹ ⊞ ▦ ➤ ◈ m ♂   Photo: S. Hellner

A03749-4 *Aphyosemion bitaeniatum* (AHL, 1924)
Glanz-oder Zweistreifen-Prachtkärpfling / Two-striped Aphyosemion
Iwere, Nigeria; B; 4,5 cm
▷ ♣ ⅃P ◑ ☺ ☹ ⊞ ▦ ➤ ◈ m ♂   Photo: L. Seegers

A03750-4 *Aphyosemion bitaeniatum* (AHL, 1924)
Glanz-oder Zweistreifen-Prachtkärpfling / Two-striped Aphyosemion
Lagos, Nigeria; B; 4,5 cm
▷ ♣ ⅃P ◑ ☺ ☹ ⊞ ▦ ➤ ◈ m ♂   Photo: S. Hellner-

A03750-4 *Aphyosemion bitaeniatum* (AHL, 1924)
Glanz-oder Zweistreifen-Prachtkärpfling / Two-striped Aphyosemion
Lagos, Nigeria; B; 4,5 cm
▷ ♣ ⅃P ◑ ☺ ☹ ⊞ ▦ ➤ ◈ m ♂   Photo: L. Seegers

A03750-4 *Aphyosemion bitaeniatum* (AHL, 1924)
Glanz-oder Zweistreifen-Prachtkärpfling / Two-striped Aphyosemion
Lagos, Nigeria; B; 4,5 cm
▷ ♣ ⅃P ◑ ☺ ☹ ⊞ ▦ ➤ ◈ m ♂   Photo: E. Pürzl

A03750-4 *Aphyosemion bitaeniatum* (AHL, 1924)
Glanz-oder Zweistreifen-Prachtkärpfling / Two-striped Aphyosemion
Lagos, Nigeria; B; 4,5 cm
▷ ♣ ⅃P ◑ ☺ ☹ ⊞ ▦ ➤ ◈ m ♂   Photo: L. Seegers

A03751-4 *Aphyosemion bitaeniatum* (AHL, 1924)
Glanz-oder Zweistreifen-Prachtkärpfling / Two-striped Aphyosemion
Aquarienstamm, Nigeria / Aquarium strain, Nigeria; B; 4,5 cm
▷ ♣ ⅃P ◑ ☺ ☹ ⊞ ▦ ➤ ◈ m ♂   Photo: L. Seegers

A03752-4 *Aphyosemion bitaeniatum* (Ahl, 1924)
Glanz-oder Zweistreifen-Prachtkärpfling / Two-striped Aphyosemion
Umudike, Nigeria; B; 4,5 cm
▷♫↕℗◑☺☻⊞▦➡ ◈m ♂   Photo: L. Seegers

A03752-4 *Aphyosemion bitaeniatum* (Ahl, 1924)
Glanz-oder Zweistreifen-Prachtkärpfling / Two-striped Aphyosemion
Umudike, Nigeria; B; 4,5 cm
▷♫↕℗◑☺☻⊞▦➡ ◈m ♂   Photo: S. Hellner-

A03245-4 *Aphyosemion bivittatum* (Lönnberg, 1895)
Gebänderter Prachtkärpfling / Two-banded Killi
Biafra, Nigeria; B; 4,0 cm
▷♫↕℗◑☺☻⊞▦➡ ◈m ♂   Photo: L. Seegers

A03970-4 *Aphyosemion bivittatum* (Lönnberg, 1895)
Gebänderter Prachtkärpfling / Two-banded Killi
Funge, West-Kamerun / Funge, western Cameroon; W; 4,0 cm
▷♫↕℗◑☺☻⊞▦➡ ◈m ♂   Photo: L. Seegers

A03246-4 *Aphyosemion bivittatum* (Lönnberg, 1895)
Gebänderter Prachtkärpfling / Two-banded Killi
Funge, West-Kamerun / Funge, western Cameroon; B; 4,0 cm
▷♫↕℗◑☺☻⊞▦➡ ◈m ♂   Photo: E. Pürzl

A03246-4 *Aphyosemion bivittatum* (Lönnberg, 1895)
Gebänderter Prachtkärpfling / Two-banded Killi
Funge, West-Kamerun / Funge, western Cameroon; B; 4,0 cm
▷♫↕℗◑☺☻⊞▦➡ ◈m ♀   Photo: E. Pürzl

A03146-4 *Aphyosemion bivittatum* (Lönnberg, 1895)
Gebänderter Prachtkärpfling / Two-banded Killi, partly xanthoristic
Funge, West-Kamerun / Funge, western Cameroon; F1; 4,0 cm
▷♫↕℗◑☺☻⊞▦➡ ◈m ♂   Photo: L. Seegers

A03246-4 *Aphyosemion bivittatum* (Lönnberg, 1895)
Gebänderter Prachtkärpfling / Two-banded Killi
Funge, West-Kamerun / Funge, western Cameroon; B; 4,0 cm
▷♫↕℗◑☺☻⊞▦➡ ◈m ♂   Photo: S. Hellner-

A03250-4 *Aphyosemion brueningi* (ROLOFF, 1971) [= *A. liberiense*?]
Brünings Prachtkärpfling / Bruening's Killi, "RL 93"
Liberia; B; 6,0 cm

▷ ♫ ⏸ ◑ ☺ ☹ ⊞ 🖼 ➤ ◈ m ♂
Photo: L. Seegers

A03251-4 *Aphyosemion brueningi* (ROLOFF, 1971) [= *A. liberiense*?]
Brünings Prachtkärpfling / Bruening's Killi
Giema, Sierra Leone; W; 6,0 cm

▷ ♫ ⏸ ◑ ☺ ☹ ⊞ 🖼 ➤ ◈ m ♂
Photo: S. Hellner

A03258-4 *Aphyosemion buytaerti* RADDA & HUBER, 1978
Buytaerts Prachtkärpfling / Buytaert's Killi, "RPC 28"
Ékouma River bei Ogouée, Kongo / Congo; W; 4,0 cm

◁ ♫ ⏸ ◑ ☺ ☹ ⊞ 🖼 ➤ ⚠ m ♂
Photo: J. Buytaert

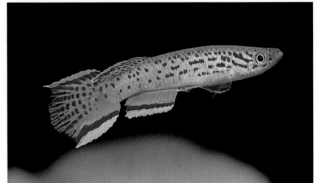

A03266-4 *Aphyosemion calliurum* (BOULENGER, 1911)
Rotsaumprachtkärpfling / Banner Lyretail
Benin; B; 4,5 cm

▷ ♫ ⏸ ◑ ☺ ☹ ⊞ 🖼 ➤ ◈ m ♂
Photo: E. Pürzl

A03261-4 *Aphyosemion calliurum* (BOULENGER, 1911)
Rotsaumprachtkärpfling / Banner Lyretail
Nigerdelta, Nigeria / Niger Delta, Nigeria; W; 4,5 cm

▷ ♫ ⏸ ◑ ☺ ☹ ⊞ 🖼 ➤ ◈ m ♂
Photo: E. Pürzl

A03262-4 *Aphyosemion calliurum* (BOULENGER, 1911)
Rotsaumprachtkärpfling / Banner Lyretail
Funge, Kamerun / Funge, Cameroon; W; 4,5 cm

▷ ♫ ⏸ ◑ ☺ ☹ ⊞ 🖼 ➤ ◈ m ♂
Photo: L. Seegers

A03263-4 *Aphyosemion calliurum* (BOULENGER, 1911)
Rotsaumprachtkärpfling / Banner Lyretail
Monea, Kamerun / Monea, Cameroon; B; 4,5 cm

▷ ♫ ⏸ ◑ ☺ ☹ ⊞ 🖼 ➤ ◈ m ♂
Photo: S. Hellner-

A03264-4 *Aphyosemion calliurum* (BOULENGER, 1911)
Rotsaumprachtkärpfling / Banner Lyretail
Campo, Kamerun / Campo, Cameroon; B; 4,5 cm

▷ ♫ ⏸ ◑ ☺ ☹ ⊞ 🖼 ➤ ◈ m ♂
Photo: S. Hellner

A03265-4 *Aphyosemion cameronense cameronense* (Boulenger, 1911)
Kamerun-Prachtkärpfling / Cameroon Killi
Bengbis, Kamerun / Bengbis, Cameroon; W; 4,5 cm
◁▷♬⑫①☺☹✛▨� ◈⚠▥♂   Photo: E. Pürzl

A03753-4 *Aphyosemion cameronense cameronense* (Boulenger, 1911)
Kamerun-Prachtkärpfling / Cameroon Killi
Djoum, Kamerun / Djoum, Cameroon; W; 4,5 cm
◁▷♬⑫①☺☹✛▨➥ ◈⚠▥♂   Photo: E. Pürzl

A03754-4 *Aphyosemion cameronense cameronense* (Boulenger, 1911)
Kamerun-Prachtkärpfling / Cameroon Killi
Sangmelima, Kamerun / Sangmelima, Cameroon; W; 4,5 cm
◁▷♬⑫①☺☹✛▨➥ ◈⚠▥♂   Photo: E. Pürzl

A03755-4 *Aphyosemion cameronense cameronense* (Boulenger, 1911)
Kamerun-Prachtkärpfling / Cameroon Killi, "HJRK 92/7"
Mfoumou, 14-33 km east of Ma'an, Cameroon; B; 4,5 cm
◁▷♬⑫①☺☹✛▨➥ ◈⚠▥♂   Photo: R. Lütje

A03756-4 *Aphyosemion cameronense cameronense* (Boulenger, 1911)
Kamerun-Prachtkärpfling / Cameroon Killi, "HJRK 92/11"
82 km W Ebolowa, Cameroon; B; 4,5 cm
◁▷♬⑫①☺☹✛▨➥ ◈⚠▥♂   Photo: S. Hellner

A03756-4 *Aphyosemion cameronense cameronense* (Boulenger, 1911)
Kamerun-Prachtkärpfling / Cameroon Killi, "HJRK 92/11"
82 km W Ebolowa, Cameroon; B; 4,5 cm
◁▷♬⑫①☺☹✛▨➥ ◈⚠▥♀   Photo: S. Hellner

A03757-4 *Aphyosemion cameronense cameronense* (Boulenger, 1911)
Kamerun-Prachtkärpfling / Cameroon Killi, "CGE 91/8"
Meuban I, 29 km S Djoum, southern Cameroon; B; 4,5 cm
◁▷♬⑫①☺☹✛▨➥ ◈⚠▥♂   Photo: R. Lütje

A03758-4 *Aphyosemion cameronense cameronense* (Boulenger, 1911)
Kamerun-Prachtkärpfling / Cameroon Killi, "CGE 91/9"
Mébassa, 99 km from Djoum on the Endengué road, Cameroon; B; 4,5 cm
◁▷♬⑫①☺☹✛▨➥ ◈⚠▥♂   Photo: R. Lütje

A03759-4 *Aphyosemion cameronense cameronense* (Boulenger, 1911)
Kamerun-Prachtkärpfling / Cameroon Killi
Rio Ecucu, Equatorial Guinea; B; 4,5 cm

◁ ▷ ♣♌ ◑ ☺ ☺ ⊞▦🐛➡ ◈ ⚠ m ♂   Photo: L. Seegers

A03760-4 *Aphyosemion cameronense cameronense* (Boulenger, 1911)
Kamerun-Prachtkärpfling / Cameroon Killi
Ovan, N-Gabun / Ovan, N-Gabon; B; 4,5 cm

◁ ▷ ♣♌ ◑ ☺ ☺ ⊞▦🐛➡ ◈ ⚠ m ♂   Photo: E. Pürzl

A03761-4 *Aphyosemion cameronense cameronense* (Boulenger, 1911)
Kamerun-Prachtkärpfling / Cameroon Killi
Abelaissi, Nord-Gabun / Abelaissi, northern Gabon; B; 4,5 cm

◁ ▷ ♣♌ ◑ ☺ ☺ ⊞▦🐛➡ ◈ ⚠ m ♂   Photo: R. Lütje

A03762-4 *Aphyosemion cameronense cameronense* (Boulenger, 1911)
Kamerun-Prachtkärpfling / Cameroon Killi
Melen, Nord-Gabun / Melen, northern Gabon; B; 4,5 cm

◁ ▷ ♣♌ ◑ ☺ ☺ ⊞▦🐛➡ ◈ ⚠ m ♂   Photo: R. Lütje

A03763-4 *Aphyosemion cameronense cameronense* (Boulenger, 1911)
Kamerun-Prachtkärpfling / Cameroon Killi, "GWW 86/2"
Latta, Nord-Gabun / Latta, northern Gabon; B; 4,5 cm

◁ ▷ ♣♌ ◑ ☺ ☺ ⊞▦🐛➡ ◈ ⚠ m ♂   Photo: R. Lütje

A03764-4 *Aphyosemion cameronense cameronense* (Boulenger, 1911)
Kamerun-Prachtkärpfling / Cameroon Killi, "EMS 90/3"
Mebandi, Nord-Gabun / Mebandi, northern Gabon; B; 4,5 cm

◁ ▷ ♣♌ ◑ ☺ ☺ ⊞▦🐛➡ ◈ ⚠ m ♂   Photo: R. Lütje

A03765-4 *Aphyosemion cameronense cameronense* (Boulenger, 1911)
Kamerun-Prachtkärpfling / Cameroon Killi, "GAB 10/90"
39 km S Mitzic on Lalara road, northern Gabon; B; 4,5 cm

◁ ▷ ♣♌ ◑ ☺ ☺ ⊞▦🐛➡ ◈ ⚠ m ♂   Photo: R. Lütje

A03766-4 *Aphyosemion cameronense cameronense* (Boulenger, 1911)
Kamerun-Prachtkärpfling / Cameroon Killi, "CGE 91/11"
Nguem, 7 km W Ngomedzap, northern Gabon; B; 4,5 cm

◁ ▷ ♣♌ ◑ ☺ ☺ ⊞▦🐛➡ ◈ ⚠ m ♂   Photo: R. Lütje

A03767-4 *Aphyosemion cameronense cameronense* (Boulenger, 1911)
Kamerun-Prachtkärpfling / Cameroon Killi, "LEC 93/3"
N Ebé, 8 km W Ovan, northern Gabon; W; 4,5 cm

 Photo: R. Lütje

A03768-4 *Aphyosemion cameronense cameronense* (Boulenger, 1911)
Kamerun-Prachtkärpfling / Cameroon Killi, "LEC 93/11"
Ayol, 5 km W Ovan, northern Gabon; W; 4,5 cm

Photo: R. Lütje

A03769-4 *Aphyosemion cameronense cameronense* (Boulenger, 1911)
Kamerun-Prachtkärpfling / Cameroon Killi, "LEC 93/15"
48 km W Mitzic on road to Sam, northern Gabon; W; 4,5 cm

Photo: R. Lütje

A03770-4 *Aphyosemion cameronense cameronense* (Boulenger, 1911)
Kamerun-Prachtkärpfling / Cameroon Killi, "LEC 93/16"
Sam, Nord-Gabun / Sam, northern Gabon; B; 4,5 cm

Photo: S. Hellner

A03771-4 *Aphyosemion cameronense cameronense* (Boulenger, 1911)
Kamerun-Prachtkärpfling / Cameroon Killi, "PEG 93/16"
NW Zomoko, northern Gabon; B; 4,5 cm

Photo: R. Lütje

A03772-4 *Aphyosemion cameronense cameronense* (Boulenger, 1911)
Kamerun-Prachtkärpfling / Cameroon Killi, "PEG 94/36"
Mbomo, 20 km NW Oyem, northern Gabon; B; 4,5 cm

Photo: R. Lütje

A03773-4 *Aphyosemion cameronense cameronense* (Boulenger, 1911)
Kamerun-Prachtkärpfling / Cameroon Killi, "PEG 94/37"
Between Yoss and Mégoga, N Oyem, northern Gabon; W; 4,5 cm

Photo: R. Lütje

A03774-4 *Aphyosemion cameronense cameronense* (Boulenger, 1911)
Kamerun-Prachtkärpfling / Cameroon Killi, "PEG 94/38"
Adzap, 31 km NW Oyem, northern Gabon; W; 4,5 cm

Photo: R. Lütje

A03780-4 *Aphyosemion* sp. aff. *cameronense* [Pop. 1]
Kamerun-Prachtkärpfling / Cameroon Killi, "CGE 91/12"
Mvilé, Süd-Kamerun / Mvilé, southern Cameroon; B; 4,5 cm
◁ ▷ ♬ ♭ ◐ ☺ ☻ ⊞ 🖳 ➡ ◈ ⚠ 🅼 ♂   Photo: R. Lütje

A03781-4 *Aphyosemion* sp. aff. *cameronense* [Pop. 2]
Kamerun-Prachtkärpfling / Cameroon Killi, "HJRK 92/10"
N Ambam, Süd-Kamerun / Southern Cameroon; W; 4,5 cm
◁ ▷ ♬ ♭ ◐ ☺ ☻ ⊞ 🖳 ➡ ◈ ⚠ 🅼 ♂   Photo: R. Lütje

A03782-4 *Aphyosemion* sp. aff. *cameronense* [Pop. 3]
Kamerun-Prachtkärpfling / Cameroon Killi, "CGE 91/6"
Efoulan, east of Djoum, southern Cameroon; B; 4,5 cm
◁ ▷ ♬ ♭ ◐ ☺ ☻ ⊞ 🖳 ➡ ◈ ⚠ 🅼 ♂   Photo: R. Lütje

A03783-4 *Aphyosemion* sp. aff. *cameronense* [Pop. 4]
Kamerun-Prachtkärpfling / Cameroon Killi
Belinga, Nord-Gabun / Belinga, northern Gabon; B; 4,5 cm
◁ ▷ ♬ ♭ ◐ ☺ ☻ ⊞ 🖳 ➡ ◈ ⚠ 🅼 ♂   Photo: R. Lütje

A03784-4 *Aphyosemion* sp. aff. *cameronense* [Pop. 5]
Kamerun-Prachtkärpfling / Cameroon Killi, "GJP 80/14"
Beleme, Nord-Gabun / Beleme, northern Gabon; B; 4,5 cm
◁ ▷ ♬ ♭ ◐ ☺ ☻ ⊞ 🖳 ➡ ◈ ⚠ 🅼 ♂   Photo: L. Seegers

A03784-4 *Aphyosemion* sp. aff. *cameronense* [Pop. 5]
Kamerun-Prachtkärpfling / Cameroon Killi, "LEC 93/12"
Koumameyong, northern Gabon; B; 4,5 cm
◁ ▷ ♬ ♭ ◐ ☺ ☻ ⊞ 🖳 ➡ ◈ ⚠ 🅼 ♂   Photo: R. Lütje

A03786-4 *Aphyosemion* sp. aff. *cameronense* [Pop. 6]
Kamerun-Prachtkärpfling / Cameroon Killi, "LEC 93/21"
Assok, Nord-Gabun / Assok, northern Gabon; W; 4,5 cm
◁ ▷ ♬ ♭ ◐ ☺ ☻ ⊞ 🖳 ➡ ◈ ⚠ 🅼 ♂   Photo: R. Lütje

A03786-4 *Aphyosemion* sp. aff. *cameronense* [Pop. 6]
Kamerun-Prachtkärpfling / Cameroon Killi, "LEC 93/22"
Song, Nord-Gabun / Song, northern Gabon; W; 4,5 cm
◁ ▷ ♬ ♭ ◐ ☺ ☻ ⊞ 🖳 ➡ ◈ ⚠ 🅼 ♂   Photo: R. Lütje

A03786-4 *Aphyosemion* sp. aff. *cameronense* [Pop. 6]
Kamerun-Prachtkärpfling / Cameroon Killi, "GEB 94/24"
Etsam, Nord-Gabun / Etsam, northern Gabon; W; 4,5 cm

◁ ▷ ß⋔ ◑ ☺ ☺ ⊞▦⋙ ◈ ⚠ ▥ ♂   Photo: R. Lütje

A03787-4 *Aphyosemion* sp. aff. *cameronense* [Pop. 7]
Kamerun-Prachtkärpfling / Cameroon Killi, "LEC 93/7"
W Ebegna, 48 km W Makokou, northern Gabon; W; 4,5 cm

◁ ▷ ß⋔ ◑ ☺ ☺ ⊞▦⋙ ◈ ⚠ ▥ ♂   Photo: R. Lütje

A03788-4 *Aphyosemion* sp. aff. *cameronense* [Pop. 8]
Kamerun-Prachtkärpfling / Cameroon Killi, "LEC 93/14"
PK 14 west of Mitzic, northern Gabon; W; 4,5 cm

◁ ▷ ß⋔ ◑ ☺ ☺ ⊞▦⋙ ◈ ⚠ ▥ ♂   Photo: R. Lütje

A03788-4 *Aphyosemion* sp. aff. *cameronense* [Pop. 8]
Kamerun-Prachtkärpfling / Cameroon Killi, "LEC 93/14"
PK 14 west of Mitzic, northern Gabon; W; 4,5 cm

◁ ▷ ß⋔ ◑ ☺ ☺ ⊞▦⋙ ◈ ⚠ ▥ ♂   Photo: R. Lütje

A03789-4 *Aphyosemion* sp. aff. *cameronense* [Pop. 9]
Kamerun-Prachtkärpfling / Cameroon Killi, "EMS 90/2"
Ngoyang, Mbyada, southern Cameroon; W; 4,5 cm

◁ ▷ ß⋔ ◑ ☺ ☺ ⊞▦⋙ ◈ ⚠ ▥ ♂   Photo: R. Lütje

A03789-4 *Aphyosemion* sp. aff. *cameronense* [Pop. 9]
Kamerun-Prachtkärpfling / Cameroon Killi
Ngoyang (Chantier), southern Cameroon; B; 4,5 cm

◁ ▷ ß⋔ ◑ ☺ ☺ ⊞▦⋙ ◈ ⚠ ▥ ♂   Photo: S. Hellner

A03266-4 *Aphyosemion cameronense haasi* RADDA & PÜRZL, 1976
Haas' Kamerun-Prachtkärpfling / Haas' Cameroon Killi
27 km NW Zomoko, affl. of Amvené, N Lalara, N Gabon; W; 4,5 cm

◁ ▷ ß⋔ ◑ ☺ ☺ ⊞▦⋙ ◈ ⚠ ▥ ♂   Photo: E. Pürzl

A03790-4 *Aphyosemion cameronense* cf. *haasi* RADDA & PÜRZL, 1976
Haas' Kamerun-Prachtkärpfling / Haas' Cameroon Killi
Süd-Kamerun / Southern Cameroon; W; 4,5 cm

◁ ▷ ß⋔ ◑ ☺ ☺ ⊞▦⋙ ◈ ⚠ ▥ ♂   Photo: L. Seegers

A03710-4 *Aphyosemion cameronense halleri* RADDA & PÜRZL, 1976
Hallers Kamerun-Prachtkärpfling / Haller's Cameroon Killi
Catholic Mission of Ambam, southern Cameroon; B; 4,5 cm
◁ ▷ ₿ ℙ ◑ ☺ ☺ ⊞ ▦⟶ ◈ ⚠ ⊡ ♂   Photo: L. Seegers

A03705-4 *Aphyosemion cameronense halleri* RADDA & PÜRZL, 1976
Hallers Kamerun-Prachtkärpfling / Haller's Cameroon Killi
Catholic Mission of Ambam, southern Cameroon; W; 4,5 cm
◁ ▷ ₿ ℙ ◑ ☺ ☺ ⊞ ▦⟶ ◈ ⚠ ⊡ ♀   Photo: E. Pürzl

A03705-4 *Aphyosemion cameronense halleri* RADDA & PÜRZL, 1976
Hallers Kamerun-Prachtkärpfling / Haller's Cameroon Killi, "LEC 93/7"
Catholic Mission of Ambam, southern Cameroon; W; 4,5 cm
◁ ▷ ₿ ℙ ◑ ☺ ☺ ⊞ ▦⟶ ◈ ⚠ ⊡ ♂   Photo: R. Lütje

A03708-4 *Aphyosemion cameronense halleri* RADDA & PÜRZL, 1976
Hallers Kamerun-Prachtkärpfling / Haller's Cameroon Killi, "LEC 93/6"
Bikong, Süd-Kamerun / Bikong, southern Cameroon; W; 4,5 cm
◁ ▷ ₿ ℙ ◑ ☺ ☺ ⊞ ▦⟶ ◈ ⚠ ⊡ ♂   Photo: R. Lütje

A03708-4 *Aphyosemion cameronense halleri* RADDA & PÜRZL, 1976
Hallers Kamerun-Prachtkärpfling / Haller's Cameroon Killi, "LEC 93/6"
Bikong, Süd-Kamerun / Bikong, southern Cameroon; W; 4,5 cm
◁ ▷ ₿ ℙ ◑ ☺ ☺ ⊞ ▦⟶ ◈ ⚠ ⊡ ♂   Photo: R. Lütje

A03709-4 *Aphyosemion cameronense halleri* RADDA & PÜRZL, 1976
Hallers Kamerun-Prachtkärpfling / Haller's Cameroon Killi, "GBL 85/21"
Billi, Nord-Gabun / Billi, northern Gabon; W; 4,5 cm
◁ ▷ ₿ ℙ ◑ ☺ ☺ ⊞ ▦⟶ ◈ ⚠ ⊡ ♂   Photo: L. Seegers

A03706-4 *Aphyosemion cameronense obscurum* (AHL, 1924)
Punktierter Kamerun-Prachtkärpfling / Spotted Cameroon Killi, "EMS 8"
Matomb, Kamerun / Matomb, Cameroon; W; 4,5 cm
◁ ▷ ₿ ℙ ◑ ☺ ☺ ⊞ ▦⟶ ◈ ⚠ ⊡ ♂   Photo: S. Hellner

A03706-4 *Aphyosemion cameronense obscurum* (AHL, 1924)
Punktierter Kamerun-Prachtkärpfling / Spotted Cameroon Killi, "EMS 90/13"
Matomb, Kamerun / Matomb, Cameroon; W; 4,5 cm
◁ ▷ ₿ ℙ ◑ ☺ ☺ ⊞ ▦⟶ ◈ ⚠ ⊡ ♂   Photo: R. Lütje

A03267-4 *Aphyosemion caudofasciatum* Huber & Radda, 1979
Schwanzstreifen-Prachtkärpfling / Caudal-stripe Killi, "RPC 28"
Ekouma bei Ogouée / Ekouma River near Ogouée, Congo; B; 5,0 cm
▷₿⫙❶☺☺⊞🖳➽ ◈⚠🔟♂
Photo: L. Seegers

A03267-4 *Aphyosemion caudofasciatum* Huber & Radda, 1979
Schwanzstreifen-Prachtkärpfling / Caudal-stripe Killi, "RPC 28"
Ekouma bei Ogouée / Ekouma River near Ogouée, Congo; B; 5,0 cm
▷₿⫙❶☺☺⊞🖳➽ ◈⚠🔟♂
Photo: R. Lütje

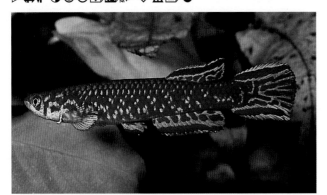

A03268-4 *Aphyosemion cauveti* (Romand & Ozouf, 1995)
Kindia-Prachtkärpfling / Kindia Killi
Kindia, Guinea / Kindia, Guinea; B; 5,0 cm
▷₿❶☺☺⊞🖳➽ ⚠🔟♂
Photo: W. Eigelshofen

A03270-4 *Aphyosemion celiae celiae* Scheel, 1971
Celias Prachtkärpfling / Celia's Aphyosemion
Badouma, West-Kamerun / Badouma, western Cameroon; W; 5,0 cm
▷₿⫙❶☺☺⊞🖳➽ ◈⚠🔟♂
Photo: E. Pürzl

A03271-3 *Aphyosemion celiae celiae* Scheel, 1971
Celias Prachtkärpfling / Celia's Aphyosemion
Eboni, West-Kamerun / Eboni, western Cameroon; F₁; 5,0 cm
▷₿⫙❶☺☺⊞🖳➽ ◈⚠🔟♂
Photo: L. Seegers

A03272-4 *Aphyosemion celiae celiae* Scheel, 1971
Celias Prachtkärpfling / Celia's Aphyosemion
West-Kamerun / Western Cameroon; W; 5,0 cm
▷₿⫙❶☺☺⊞🖳➽ ◈⚠🔟♂
Photo: L. Seegers

A03273-4 *Aphyosemion celiae winifredae* Radda & Scheel, 1975
Winifreds Prachtkärpfling / Winifred's Aphyosemion [T.t.]
New Butu, 17 km N junct. Kumba-Bekondo-L. Soden, Cameroon; W; 5,0 cm
▷₿⫙❶☺☺⊞🖳➽ ◈⚠🔟♂
Photo: E. Pürzl

A03274-4 *Aphyosemion celiae winifredae* Radda & Scheel, 1975
Winifreds Prachtkärpfling / Winifred's Aphyosemion
Aquarienstamm, W Kamerun / Aquarium strain, W Cameroon; W; 5,0 cm
▷₿⫙❶☺☺⊞🖳➽ ◈⚠🔟♂
Photo: L. Seegers

A03707-4 *Aphyosemion chauchei* HUBER & SCHEEL, 1981
Chauches Prachtkärpfling / Chauche's Aphyosemion
Equateur, Zaïre; W; 5,0 cm
▷ ♫ ⑆ ◑ ☺ ☺ ☺ ⊞ 🕮 ➤ ⚠ 🔟 ♂

A03707-4 *Aphyosemion chauchei* HUBER & SCHEEL, 1981
Chauches Prachtkärpfling / Chauche's Aphyosemion
Equateur, Zaïre; W; 5,0 cm
▷ ♫ ⑆ ◑ ☺ ☺ ☺ ⊞ 🕮 ➤ ⚠ 🔟 ♀

A03275-4 *Aphyosemion chaytori* (ROLOFF, 1971) [= *A. roloffi*?]
Chaytors Prachtkärpfling / Chaytor's Aphyosemion
Ngabu, Sierra Leone; W; 5,0 cm
▷ ♫ ⑆ ◑ ☺ ☺ ☺ ⊞ 🕮 ➤ ◈ ⚠ 🔟 ♂

A03288-4 *Aphyosemion* cf. *christyi* (BOULENGER, 1915)
Christys Prachtkärpfling / Christy's Lyretail
Oyo, Kongo / Oyo, Congo; B; 5,0 cm
▷ ♫ ⑆ ◑ ☺ ☺ ☺ ⊞ 🕮 ➤ ◈ ⚠ 🔟 ♂

A03280-4 *Aphyosemion christyi* (BOULENGER, 1915)
Christys Prachtkärpfling / Christy's Lyretail, "HZ 85/8"
Nördlich Kisangani, Zaïre / North of Kisangani, Zaïre; F1; 5,0 cm
▷ ♫ ⑆ ◑ ☺ ☺ ☺ ⊞ 🕮 ➤ ◈ ⚠ 🔟 ♂

A03280-4 *Aphyosemion christyi* (BOULENGER, 1915)
Christys Prachtkärpfling / Christy's Lyretail, "HZ 85/8"
Nördlich Kisangani, Zaïre / North of Kisangani, Zaïre; F1; 5,0 cm
▷ ♫ ⑆ ◑ ☺ ☺ ☺ ⊞ 🕮 ➤ ◈ ⚠ 🔟 ♀

A03281-4 *Aphyosemion christyi* (BOULENGER, 1915)
Christys Prachtkärpfling / Christy's Lyretail
Umgebung von Kisangani, Zaïre / Vicinity of Kisangani, Zaïre; B; 5,0 cm
▷ ♫ ⑆ ◑ ☺ ☺ ☺ ⊞ 🕮 ➤ ◈ ⚠ 🔟 ♂

A03281-4 *Aphyosemion christyi* (BOULENGER, 1915)
Christys Prachtkärpfling / Christy's Lyretail
Umgebung von Kisangani, Zaïre / Vicinity of Kisangani, Zaïre; B; 5,0 cm
▷ ♫ ⑆ ◑ ☺ ☺ ☺ ⊞ 🕮 ➤ ◈ ⚠ 🔟 ♂

A03282-4 *Aphyosemion christyi* (BOULENGER, 1915)
Christys Prachtkärpfling / Christy's Lyretail, "KCF 5"
Zentralafrikanische Republik / Central African Republic; B; 5,0 cm
▷♫❗️🌓☺️😊⊞🖥️➤ ◈⚠️ⓜ♂ Photo: L. Seegers

A03282-4 *Aphyosemion christyi* (BOULENGER, 1915)
Christys Prachtkärpfling / Christy's Lyretail, "KCF 5"
Zentralafrikanische Republik / Central African Republic; B; 5,0 cm
▷♫❗️🌓☺️😊⊞🖥️➤ ◈⚠️ⓜ♀ Photo: L. Seegers

A03283-4 *Aphyosemion christyi* (BOULENGER, 1915)
Christys Prachtkärpfling / Christy's Lyretail
Equateur, Zaïre / Equateur, Zaïre; W; 5,0 cm
▷♫❗️🌓☺️😊⊞🖥️➤ ◈⚠️ⓜ♂ Photo: L. Seegers

A03284-4 *Aphyosemion christyi* (BOULENGER, 1915)
Christys Prachtkärpfling / Christy's Lyretail
Bangui, Central African Republic; B; 5,0 cm
▷♫❗️🌓☺️😊⊞🖥️➤ ◈⚠️ⓜ♂ Photo: L. Seegers

A03284-4 *Aphyosemion christyi* (BOULENGER, 1915)
Christys Prachtkärpfling / Christy's Lyretail
Bangui, Central African Republic; B; 5,0 cm
▷♫❗️🌓☺️😊⊞🖥️➤ ◈⚠️ⓜ♂ Photo: E. Pürzl

A03285-4 *Aphyosemion christyi* (BOULENGER, 1915)
Christys Prachtkärpfling / Christy's Lyretail, "RCA 83/2"
Zentralafrikanische Republik / Central African Republic; B; 5,0 cm
▷♫❗️🌓☺️😊⊞🖥️➤ ◈⚠️ⓜ♂ Photo: S. Hellner-

A03286-4 *Aphyosemion christyi* (BOULENGER, 1915)
Christys Prachtkärpfling / Christy's Lyretail
5 km north of N'jili, Kinshasa Airport, Zaïre; W; 5,0 cm
▷♫❗️🌓☺️😊⊞🖥️➤ ◈⚠️ⓜ♂ Photo: E. Pürzl

A03287-4 *Aphyosemion christyi* (BOULENGER, 1915)
Christys Prachtkärpfling / Christy's Lyretail
Nord-Zaïre / Northern Zaïre; B; 5,0 cm
▷♫❗️🌓☺️😊⊞🖥️➤ ◈⚠️ⓜ♂ Photo: E. Pürzl

A03290-4 *Aphyosemion (F.) cinnamomeum* CLAUSEN, 1963
Zimt-Prachtkärpfling / Cinnamon Killi
S Manyemen, Kamerun / South of Manyemen, Cameroon; W; 6,0 cm
▷♫⚘♪①☺☻⊞▱➡ ◈⚠ⓜ ♂   Photo: L. Seegers

A03290-4 *Aphyosemion (F.) cinnamomeum* CLAUSEN, 1963
Zimt-Prachtkärpfling / Cinnamon Killi
S Manyemen, Kamerun / South of Manyemen, Cameroon; W; 6,0 cm
▷♫⚘♪①☺☻⊞▱➡ ◈⚠ⓜ ♀   Photo: L. Seegers

A03791-4 *Aphyosemion (F.) cinnamomeum* CLAUSEN, 1963
Zimt-Prachtkärpfling / Cinnamon Killi
West-Kamerun / Western Cameroon; W; 6,0 cm
▷♫⚘♪①☺☻⊞▱➡ ◈⚠ⓜ ♂   Photo: L. Seegers

A03792-4 *Aphyosemion (F.) cinnamomeum* CLAUSEN, 1963
Zimt-Prachtkärpfling / Cinnamon Killi
Kumba, West-Kamerun / Kumba, western Cameroon; B; 6,0 cm
▷♫⚘♪①☺☻⊞▱➡ ◈⚠ⓜ ♂   Photo: E. Pürzl

A03291-4 *Aphyosemion citrineipinnis* HUBER & RADDA, 1977
Zitronenflossen-Prachtkärpfling / Lemon-finned Killi "G 21/76" [T.t.]
Yéno, Mogambi, Ngounié River system, S Gabon; W; 4,5 cm
◁♫⚘♪①☺☻⊞▱➡ ⚠ⓜ ♂   Photo: E. Pürzl

A03291-3 *Aphyosemion citrineipinnis* HUBER & RADDA, 1977
Zitronenflossen-Prachtkärpfling / Lemon-finned Killi "G 21/76"
Yéno, Mogambi, Ngounié River system, S Gabon; B; 4,5 cm
◁♫⚘♪①☺☻⊞▱➡ ⚠ⓜ ♂   Photo: E. Pürzl

A03793-4 *Aphyosemion citrineipinnis* HUBER & RADDA, 1977
Zitronenflossen-Prachtkärpfling / Lemon-finned Killi "G 21/76"
Yéno, Mogambi, Ngounié River system, S Gabon; B; 4,5 cm
◁♫⚘♪①☺☻⊞▱➡ ⚠ⓜ ♂   Photo: L. Seegers

A03794-4 *Aphyosemion citrineipinnis* HUBER & RADDA, 1977
Zitronenflossen-Prachtkärpfling / Lemon-finned Killi "G 21/76"
5 km N Yéno, Mogambi, Ngounié River system, S Gabon; B; 4,5 cm
◁♫⚘♪①☺☻⊞▱➡ ⚠ⓜ ♂   Photo: S. Hellner-

A03292-4 *Aphyosemion coeleste* HUBER & RADDA, 1977
Himmelblauer Prachtkärpfling / Sky-blue Killi "G 15/76" [T.t.]
Massango, 13 km NW Moanda on road to Lastoursville, S Gabon; B; 4,5 cm
◁ ♫♩P❶☺☺☻⊞🖼➡ ⚠🖼 ♂   Photo: E. Pürzl

A03292-4 *Aphyosemion coeleste* HUBER & RADDA, 1977
Himmelblauer Prachtkärpfling / Sky-blue Killi "G 15/76" [T.t.]
Massango, 13 km NW Moanda on road to Lastoursville, S Gabon; B; 4,5 cm
◁ ♫♩P❶☺☺☻⊞🖼➡ ⚠🖼 ♀   Photo: L. Seegers

A03293-4 *Aphyosemion coeleste* HUBER & RADDA, 1977
Himmelblauer Prachtkärpfling / Sky-blue Killi "GHP 85/13"
Malinga, Süd-Gabun / Malinga, southern Gabon; W; 4,5 cm
◁ ♫♩P❶☺☺☻⊞🖼➡ ⚠🖼 ♂   Photo: E. Pürzl

A03293-4 *Aphyosemion coeleste* HUBER & RADDA, 1977
Himmelblauer Prachtkärpfling / Sky-blue Killi "GHP 85/13"
Malinga, Süd-Gabun / Malinga, southern Gabon; W; 4,5 cm
◁ ♫♩P❶☺☺☻⊞🖼➡ ⚠🖼 ♀   Photo: E. Pürzl

A03294-4 *Aphyosemion coeleste* HUBER & RADDA, 1977
Himmelblauer Prachtkärpfling / Sky-blue Killi "GHP 85/13"
Malinga, Süd-Gabun / Malinga, southern Gabon; B; 4,5 cm
◁ ♫♩P❶☺☺☻⊞🖼➡ ⚠🖼 ♂   Photo: L. Seegers

A03795-4 *Aphyosemion coeleste* HUBER & RADDA, 1977
Himmelblauer Prachtkärpfling / Sky-blue Killi "GBG 93/2"
Süd-Gabun / Southern Gabon; W; 4,5 cm
◁ ♫♩P❶☺☺☻⊞🖼➡ ⚠🖼 ♂   Photo: S. Hellner-

A03796-4 *Aphyosemion coeleste* HUBER & RADDA, 1977
Himmelblauer Prachtkärpfling / Sky-blue Killi "RPC 5"
Kongo / Congo; B; 4,5 cm
◁ ♫♩P❶☺☺☻⊞🖼➡ ⚠🖼 ♂   Photo: L. Seegers

A03797-4 *Aphyosemion coeleste* HUBER & RADDA, 1977
Himmelblauer Prachtkärpfling / Sky-blue Killi
Titi, Kongo / Titi, Congo; B; 4,5 cm
◁ ♫♩P❶☺☺☻⊞🖼➡ ⚠🖼 ♂   Photo: L. Seegers

A03295-4 *Aphyosemion cognatum* MEINKEN, 1951
Roter Prachtkärpfling / Red-spotted Killi
Brazzaville, Kongo / Brazzaville, Congo; B; 5,0 cm
Photo: E. Pürzl

A03801-4 *Aphyosemion cognatum* MEINKEN, 1951
Roter Prachtkärpfling / Red-spotted Killi
Djoue, Süd-Kongo / Djoue, southern Congo; B; 5,0 cm
Photo: S. Hellner-

A03802-4 *Aphyosemion cognatum* MEINKEN, 1951
Roter Prachtkärpfling / Red-spotted Killi, "Z 18/82"
Kenge, Zaïre; W; 5,0 cm
Photo: E. Pürzl

A03803-4 *Aphyosemion cognatum* MEINKEN, 1951
Roter Prachtkärpfling / Red-spotted Killi
Kimwenza, West-Zaïre / Kimwenza, western Zaïre; B; 5,0 cm
Photo: L. Seegers

A03804-4 *Aphyosemion cognatum* MEINKEN, 1951
Roter Prachtkärpfling / Red-spotted Killi
Kinshasa, Zaïre; W; 5,0 cm
Photo: L. Seegers

A03805-4 *Aphyosemion cognatum* MEINKEN, 1951
Roter Prachtkärpfling / Red-spotted Killi
Umgebung von Kinshasa, Zaïre / Vicinity of Kinshasa, Zaïre; W; 5,0 cm
Photo: L. Seegers

A03806-4 *Aphyosemion cognatum* MEINKEN, 1951
Roter Prachtkärpfling / Red-spotted Killi
Kwambila, West-Zaïre / Kwambila, western Zare; B; 5,0 cm
Photo: E. Pürzl

A03807-4 *Aphyosemion cognatum* MEINKEN, 1951
Roter Prachtkärpfling / Red-spotted Killi
Madimba, West-Zaïre / Madimba, western Zaïre; W; 5,0 cm
Photo: L. Seegers

A03808-4 *Aphyosemion cognatum* MEINKEN, 1951
Roter Prachtkärpfling / Red-spotted Killi, "Z 2/82"
Mbanza Ngungu, Zaïre; W; 5,0 cm
▷🏋️◑☺☻⊞🖼️🐛➡️◈⚠️🅼 ♂️   Photo: E. Pürzl

A03808-4 *Aphyosemion cognatum* MEINKEN, 1951
Roter Prachtkärpfling / Red-spotted Killi, "Z 2/82"
Mbanza Ngungu, Zaïre; W; 5,0 cm
▷🏋️◑☺☻⊞🖼️🐛➡️◈⚠️🅼 ♀️   Photo: E. Pürzl

A03809-3 *Aphyosemion cognatum* MEINKEN, 1951
Roter Prachtkärpfling / Red-spotted Killi, "Z 22/82"
Pool Malebo, Zaïre; W; 5,0 cm
▷🏋️◑☺☻⊞🖼️🐛➡️◈⚠️🅼 ♂️   Photo: E. Pürzl

A03809-3 *Aphyosemion cognatum* MEINKEN, 1951
Roter Prachtkärpfling / Red-spotted Killi, "Z 23/82"
Pool Malebo, Zaïre; W; 5,0 cm
▷🏋️◑☺☻⊞🖼️🐛➡️◈⚠️🅼 ♂️   Photo: E. Pürzl

A03810-4 *Aphyosemion cognatum* MEINKEN, 1951
Roter Prachtkärpfling / Red-spotted Killi
Aquarienstamm / Aquarium strain; B; 5,0 cm
▷🏋️◑☺☻⊞🖼️🐛➡️◈⚠️🅼 ♂️   Photo: L. Seegers

A03810-4 *Aphyosemion cognatum* MEINKEN, 1951
Roter Prachtkärpfling / Red-spotted Killi
Aquarienstamm / Aquarium strain; B; 5,0 cm
▷🏋️◑☺☻⊞🖼️🐛➡️◈⚠️🅼 ♂️   Photo: E. Pürzl

A03810-4 *Aphyosemion cognatum* MEINKEN, 1951
Roter Prachtkärpfling / Red-spotted Killi
Aquarienstamm / Aquarium strain; B; 5,0 cm
▷🏋️◑☺☻⊞🖼️🐛➡️◈⚠️🅼 ♂️   Photo: L. Seegers

A03811-4 *Aphyosemion cognatum* MEINKEN, 1951
Roter Prachtkärpfling / Red-spotted Killi
Tirbak-Stamm / Tirbak's strain; B; 5,0 cm
▷🏋️◑☺☻⊞🖼️🐛➡️◈⚠️🅼 ♂️   Photo: L. Seegers

A03296-4 *Aphyosemion congicum* (AHL, 1924)
Schwarzflossen-Prachtkärpfling / Congo Killi, Goldstein's Killi, "Z 17/82"
Takundi, Südwest-Zaïre / Takundi, southwestern Zaïre; W; 4,5 cm
▷♫◐☺☻⊞🖳➡ ◇⚠🄼♂ 　　Photo: E. Pürzl

A03296-4 *Aphyosemion congicum* (AHL, 1924)
Schwarzflossen-Prachtkärpfling / Congo Killi, Goldstein's Killi, "Z 17/82"
Takundi, Südwest-Zaïre / Takundi, southwestern Zaïre; W; 4,5 cm
▷♫◐☺☻⊞🖳➡ ◇⚠🄼♀ 　　Photo: E. Pürzl

A03297-4 *Aphyosemion congicum* (AHL, 1924)
Schwarzflossen-Prachtkärpfling / Congo Killi, Goldstein's Killi
Aquarienstamm / Aquarium strain; B; 4,5 cm
▷♫◐☺☻⊞🖳➡ ◇⚠🄼♂ 　　Photo: L. Seegers

A03298-4 *Aphyosemion congicum* (AHL, 1924)
Schwarzflossen-Prachtkärpfling / Congo Killi, Goldstein's Killi
"A. melanopterus" strain, Gamba (Gembo) River, SW Zaïre; W; 4,5 cm
▷♫◐☺☻⊞🖳➡ ◇⚠🄼♂ 　　Photo: L. Seegers

A03302-4 *Aphyosemion dargei* AMIET, 1987, yellow phenotype
Mbam-Prachtkärpfling, Darges Prachtkärpfling / Mbam Killi
NW of Bafia near ferry across M'bam River, Cameroon; W; 4,5 cm
▷♫◐☺☻⊞🖳➡ ◇⚠🄼♂ 　　Photo: E. Pürzl

A03812-4 *Aphyosemion dargei* AMIET, 1987, blue phenotype
Mbam-Prachtkärpfling, Darges Prachtkärpfling / Mbam Killi
NW of Bafia near ferry across M'bam River, Cameroon; W; 4,5 cm
▷♫◐☺☻⊞🖳➡ ◇⚠🄼♂ 　　Photo: E. Pürzl

A03813-4 *Aphyosemion dargei* AMIET, 1987
Mbam-Prachtkärpfling, Darges Prachtkärpfling / Mbam Killi
Goura I near ferry across M'bam River, Cameroon; B; 4,5 cm
▷♫◐☺☻⊞🖳➡ ◇⚠🄼♂ 　　Photo: L. Seegers

A03813-4 *Aphyosemion dargei* AMIET, 1987
Mbam-Prachtkärpfling, Darges Prachtkärpfling / Mbam Killi
Goura I near ferry across M'bam River, Cameroon; B; 4,5 cm
▷♫◐☺☻⊞🖳➡ ◇⚠🄼♂ 　　Photo: L. Seegers

A03814-3 *Aphyosemion dargei* AMIET, 1987
Mbam-Prachtkärpfling, Darges Prachtkärpfling / Mbam Killi
"C 90" (= "GKC 90/23"?), Zentral-Kamerun; W; 4,5 cm
▷ß❶◐☺☹⊞🔲➡ ◈⚠🔲 ♂   Photo: S. Hellner

A03815-4 *Aphyosemion* cf. *dargei* AMIET, 1987
Mbam-Prachtkärpfling, Darges Prachtkärpfling / Mbam Killi
Aquarienstamm / Aquarium strain; Kreuzung? / cross-breed?; 4,5 cm
▷ß❶◐☺☹⊞🔲➡ ◈⚠🔲 ♂   Photo: L. Seegers

A03816-4 ? *Aphyosemion decorsei* (PELLEGRIN, 1904)
Bangui-Prachtkärpfling / Decorse's Killi
Mobaye (?), Central African Republic; B; 4,5 cm
▷ß❶◐☺☹⊞🔲➡ ⚠🔲 ♂   Photo: E. Pürzl

A03303-4 *Aphyosemion (F.) deltaense* RADDA, 1976
Delta-Prachtkärpfling / Delta Killi
Aquarienstamm vom Nigerdelta / Aquarium strain; B; 7,0 cm
⚠ß❶◐☺☹⊞🔲➡ ⚠🔲 ♂   Photo: L. Seegers

A03303-4 *Aphyosemion (F.) deltaense* RADDA, 1976
Delta-Prachtkärpfling / Delta Killi
Aquarienstamm vom Nigerdelta / Aquarium strain; B; 7,0 cm
⚠ß❶◐☺☹⊞🔲➡ ⚠🔲 ♂   Photo: E. Pürzl

A03303-4 *Aphyosemion (F.) deltaense* RADDA, 1976
Delta-Prachtkärpfling / Delta Killi
Aquarienstamm vom Nigerdelta / Aquarium strain; B; 7,0 cm
⚠ß❶◐☺☹⊞🔲➡ ⚠🔲 ♀   Photo: L. Seegers

A03303-4 *Aphyosemion (F.) deltaense* RADDA, 1976
Delta-Prachtkärpfling / Delta Killi
Aquarienstamm vom Nigerdelta / Aquarium strain; B; 7,0 cm
⚠ß❶◐☺☹⊞🔲➡ ⚠🔲 ♂   Photo: L. Seegers

A03303-4 *Aphyosemion (F.) deltaense* RADDA, 1976
Delta-Prachtkärpfling / Delta Killi
Aquarienstamm vom Nigerdelta / Aquarium strain; B; 7,0 cm
⚠ß❶◐☺☹⊞🔲➡ ⚠🔲 ♂   Photo: L. Seegers

A03304-4 *Aphyosemion edeanum* AMIET, 1987
Edea-Prachtkärpfling / Edea Killi
18 km from Edea on road to Yaounde, western Cameroon; B; 4,5 cm
▷ 🐟 ◑ ☺ ☺ ⊞ 🖳 ➤ ◈ ⚠ 𝕞 ♂
Photo: L. Seegers

A03304-4 *Aphyosemion edeanum* AMIET, 1987
Edea-Prachtkärpfling / Edea Killi
18 km from Edea on road to Yaounde, western Cameroon; B; 4,5 cm
▷ 🐟 ◑ ☺ ☺ ⊞ 🖳 ➤ ◈ ⚠ 𝕞 ♀
Photo: L. Seegers

A03817-3 *Aphyosemion edeanum* AMIET, 1987
Edea-Prachtkärpfling / Edea Killi, "EMS 90/11"
Edea, West-Kamerun / Edea, western Cameroon; W; 4,5 cm
▷ 🐟 ◑ ☺ ☺ ⊞ 🖳 ➤ ◈ ⚠ 𝕞 ♂
Photo: S. Hellner

A03838-4 *Aphyosemion edeanum* AMIET, 1987
Edea-Prachtkärpfling / Edea Killi, "HJRK 92/1"
Edea, West-Kamerun / Edea, western Cameroon; W; 4,5 cm
▷ 🐟 ◑ ☺ ☺ ⊞ 🖳 ➤ ◈ ⚠ 𝕞 ♂
Photo: S. Hellner

A03819-4 *Aphyosemion elberti* (AHL, 1924)
Rotstreifen-Prachtkärpfling / Red barred Killi
Bamendjing, Kamerun / Bamendjing, Cameroon; W; 4,0 cm
◁ ▷ 🐟 ◑ ☺ ☹ ⊞ 🖳 ➤ ◈ ⚠ 𝕞 ♂
Photo: L. Seegers

A03819-4 *Aphyosemion elberti* (AHL, 1924)
Rotstreifen-Prachtkärpfling / Red barred Killi
Bamendjing, Kamerun / Bamendjing, Cameroon; W; 4,0 cm
◁ ▷ 🐟 ◑ ☺ ☹ ⊞ 🖳 ➤ ◈ ⚠ 𝕞 ♀
Photo: L. Seegers

A03820-4 *Aphyosemion elberti* (AHL, 1924)
Rotstreifen-Prachtkärpfling / Red barred Killi
Bamessi, Kamerun / Bamessi, Cameroon; W; 4,0 cm
◁ ▷ 🐟 ◑ ☺ ☺ ⊞ 🖳 ➤ ◈ ⚠ 𝕞 ♂
Photo: E. Pürzl

A03821-4 *Aphyosemion elberti* (AHL, 1924)
Rotstreifen-Prachtkärpfling / Red barred Killi
Diang, Kamerun / Diang, Cameroon; W; 4,0 cm
◁ ▷ 🐟 ◑ ☺ ☺ ⊞ 🖳 ➤ ◈ ⚠ 𝕞 ♂
Photo: L. Seegers

A03822-4 *Aphyosemion elberti* (Ahl, 1924)
Rotstreifen-Prachtkärpfling / Red barred Killi
Koupa Matapit, Kamerun / Koupa Matapit, Cameroon; W; 4,0 cm

Photo: E. Pürzl

A03823-4 *Aphyosemion elberti* (Ahl, 1924)
Rotstreifen-Prachtkärpfling / Red barred Killi
N'dikinimeki, Kamerun / N'dikinimeki, Cameroon; B; 4,0 cm

Photo: L. Seegers

A03824-4 *Aphyosemion elberti* (Ahl, 1924)
Rotstreifen-Prachtkärpfling / Red barred Killi
Ngoundere, Kamerun / Ngoundere, Cameroon; W; 4,0 cm

Photo: E. Pürzl

A03825-4 *Aphyosemion elberti* (Ahl, 1924)
Rotstreifen-Prachtkärpfling / Red barred Killi
Ngoundere, Kamerun / Ngoundere, Cameroon; B; 4,0 cm

Photo: L. Seegers

A03826-4 *Aphyosemion elberti* (Ahl, 1924)
Rotstreifen-Prachtkärpfling / Red barred Killi
Ndop, Kamerun / Ndop, Cameroon; W; 4,0 cm

Photo: L. Seegers

A03827-4 *Aphyosemion elberti* (Ahl, 1924)
Rotstreifen-Prachtkärpfling / Red barred Killi
Ntui, Kamerun / Ntui, Cameroon; W; 4,0 cm

Photo: L. Seegers

A03828-4 *Aphyosemion elberti* (Ahl, 1924)
Rotstreifen-Prachtkärpfling / Red barred Killi
"Roter" Aquarienstamm / "Red" Aquarium strain; B; 4,0 cm

Photo: L. Seegers

A03829-4 *Aphyosemion elberti* (Ahl, 1924)
Kekem-Rotstreifen-Prachtkärpfling / Red barred Killi from Kekem
Kekem, Kamerun / Kekem, Cameroon; B; 4,0 cm

Photo: L. Seegers

A03305-4 *Aphyosemion elegans* (Boulenger, 1899)
Eleganter Prachtkärpfling / Elegant Killi, "NSC 5"
Aquarienstamm / Aquarium strain; B; 5,0 cm

▷♟◐☺☻⊞▨🐾➡ ◈⚠ⅿ♂   Photo: L. Seegers

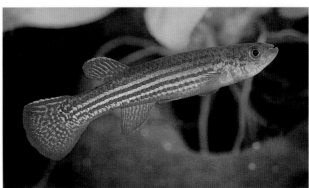

A03307-4 *Aphyosemion escherichi* (Ahl, 1924)
Escherichs Prachtkärpfling / Escherich's Killi
Cap Esterias, Gabun / Cap Esterias, Gabon; W; 5,0 cm

▷♟◐☺☻⊞▨🐾➡ ◈⚠ⅿ♂   Photo: E. Pürzl

A03308-4 *Aphyosemion escherichi* (Ahl, 1924)
Escherichs Prachtkärpfling / Escherich's Killi
Lambarene, Gabun / Lambarene, Gabon; W; 5,0 cm

▷♟◐☺☻⊞▨🐾➡ ◈⚠ⅿ♂   Photo: E. Pürzl

A03309-4 *Aphyosemion escherichi* (Ahl, 1924)
Escherichs Prachtkärpfling / Escherich's Killi
Lambarene, Gabun / Lambarene, Gabon; B; 5,0 cm

▷♟◐☺☻⊞▨🐾➡ ◈⚠ⅿ♀   Photo: E. Pürzl

A03830-4 *Aphyosemion escherichi* (Ahl, 1924)
Escherichs Prachtkärpfling / Escherich's Killi
Mayombe, Gabun / Mayombe, Gabon; W; 5,0 cm

▷♟◐☺☻⊞▨🐾➡ ◈⚠ⅿ♂   Photo: L. Seegers

A03831-4 *Aphyosemion escherichi* (Ahl, 1924)
Escherichs Prachtkärpfling / Escherich's Killi
Kristallberge, Gabun / Crystal Mountains, Gabon; B; 5,0 cm

▷♟◐☺☻⊞▨🐾➡ ◈⚠ⅿ♂   Photo: L. Seegers

A03832-4 *Aphyosemion escherichi* (Ahl, 1924)
Escherichs Prachtkärpfling / Escherich's Killi
Boko Songo, Kongo / Boko Songo, Congo; B; 5,0 cm

▷♟◐☺☻⊞▨🐾➡ ◈⚠ⅿ♂   Photo: L. Seegers

A03833-4 *Aphyosemion escherichi* (Ahl, 1924)
Escherichs Prachtkärpfling / Escherich's Killi
Moanda, Zaïre; W; 5,0 cm

▷♟◐☺☻⊞▨🐾➡ ◈⚠ⅿ♂   Photo: E. Pürzl

A03310-4 *Aphyosemion exigoideum* RADDA & HUBER, 1977
Rotpunkt-Prachtkärpfling / False Jewel Killi [T.t.]
Mandilou, West-Gabun / Mandilou, western Gabon; W; 5,0 cm
▷♫◐☺☹⊞🖵➜ ◈⚠🅜 ♂　　　Photo: E. Pürzl

A03312-4 *Aphyosemion exigoideum* RADDA & HUBER, 1977
Rotpunkt-Prachtkärpfling / False Jewel Killi
Ngoudoufala, West-Gabun / Ngoudoufala, western Gabon; B; 5,0 cm
▷♫◐☺☹⊞🖵➜ ◈⚠🅜 ♂　　　Photo: L. Seegers

A03311-4 *Aphyosemion exigoideum* RADDA & HUBER, 1977
Rotpunkt-Prachtkärpfling / False Jewel Killi
Aquarienstamm / Aquarium strain; B; 5,0 cm
▷♫◐☺☹⊞🖵➜ ◈⚠🅜 ♂　　　Photo: L. Seegers

A03311-4 *Aphyosemion exigoideum* RADDA & HUBER, 1977
Rotpunkt-Prachtkärpfling / False Jewel Killi
Aquarienstamm / Aquarium strain; B; 5,0 cm
▷♫◐☺☹⊞🖵➜ ◈⚠🅜 ♀　　　Photo: L. Seegers

A03315-4 *Aphyosemion exiguum* (BOULENGER, 1911)
Gelber Rotstreifen-Prachtkärpfling / Jewel Killi
Ndeng, Kamerun / Ndeng, Cameroon; W; 4,0 cm
◁▷♫◐☺☹⊞🖵🐾 ◈⚠🅜 ♂　　　Photo: L. Seegers

A03315-4 *Aphyosemion exiguum* (BOULENGER, 1911)
Gelber Rotstreifen-Prachtkärpfling / Jewel Killi
Ndeng, Kamerun / Ndeng, Cameroon; W; 4,0 cm
◁▷♫◐☺☹⊞🖵🐾 ◈⚠🅜 ♀　　　Photo: L. Seegers

A03316-4 *Aphyosemion exiguum* (BOULENGER, 1911)
Gelber Rotstreifen-Prachtkärpfling / Jewel Killi
Akono, Kamerun / Akono, Cameroon; W; 4,0 cm
◁▷♫◐☺☹⊞🖵🐾 ◈⚠🅜 ♂　　　Photo: E. Pürzl

A03317-3 *Aphyosemion exiguum* (BOULENGER, 1911)
Gelber Rotstreifen-Prachtkärpfling / Jewel Killi
Djoum, Kamerun / Djoum, Cameroon; W; 4,0 cm
◁▷♫◐☺☹⊞🖵🐾 ◈⚠🅜 ♂　　　Photo: E. Pürzl

A03318-4 *Aphyosemion exiguum* (BOULENGER, 1911)
Gelber Rotstreifen-Prachtkärpfling / Jewel Killi
Elom, Kamerun / Elom, Cameroon; W; 4,0 cm

◁ ▷ 🏠 ◐ ☺ 😐 ⊞ 🗷 ➡ ◈ ⚠ 🔳 ♂   Photo: L. Seegers

A03319-4 *Aphyosemion exiguum* (BOULENGER, 1911)
Gelber Rotstreifen-Prachtkärpfling / Jewel Killi
Nloup, Kamerun / Nloup, Cameroon; B; 4,0 cm

◁ ▷ 🏠 ◐ ☺ 😐 ⊞ 🗷 ➡ ◈ ⚠ 🔳 ♂   Photo: S. Hellner-

A03834-4 *Aphyosemion exiguum* (BOULENGER, 1911)
Gelber Rotstreifen-Prachtkärpfling / Jewel Killi
Sangmelima, Kamerun / Sangmelima, Cameroon; B; 4,0 cm

◁ ▷ 🏠 ◐ ☺ 😐 ⊞ 🗷 ➡ ◈ ⚠ 🔳 ♂   Photo: E. Pürzl

A03834-4 *Aphyosemion exiguum* (BOULENGER, 1911)
Gelber Rotstreifen-Prachtkärpfling / Jewel Killi
Sangmelima, Kamerun / Sangmelima, Cameroon; B; 4,0 cm

◁ ▷ 🏠 ◐ ☺ 😐 ⊞ 🗷 ➡ ◈ ⚠ 🔳 ♂   Photo: L. Seegers

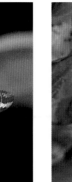

A03835-4 *Aphyosemion exiguum* (BOULENGER, 1911)
Gelber Rotstreifen-Prachtkärpfling / Jewel Killi
Zoetele, Kamerun / Zoetele, Cameroon; W; 4,0 cm

◁ ▷ 🏠 ◐ ☺ 😐 ⊞ 🗷 ➡ ◈ ⚠ 🔳 ♂   Photo: E. Pürzl

A03836-4 *Aphyosemion exiguum* (BOULENGER, 1911)
Gelber Rotstreifen-Prachtkärpfling / Jewel Killi
Süd-Kamerun / Southern Cameroon; W; 4,0 cm

◁ ▷ 🏠 ◐ ☺ 😐 ⊞ 🗷 ➡ ◈ ⚠ 🔳 ♂   Photo: S. Hellner

A03837-4 *Aphyosemion exiguum* (BOULENGER, 1911)
Gelber Rotstreifen-Prachtkärpfling / Jewel Killi
Aquarienstamm / Aquarium strain; B; 4,0 cm

◁ ▷ 🏠 ◐ ☺ 😐 ⊞ 🗷 ➡ ◈ ⚠ 🔳 ♂   Photo: L. Seegers

A03837-4 *Aphyosemion exiguum* (BOULENGER, 1911)
Gelber Rotstreifen-Prachtkärpfling / Jewel Killi
Aquarienstamm / Aquarium strain; B; 4,0 cm

◁ ▷ 🏠 ◐ ☺ 😐 ⊞ 🗷 ➡ ◈ ⚠ 🔳 ♂   Photo: R. Lütje

A03320-4 *Aphyosemion (F.) fallax* Ahl, 1935
Kribi-Prachtkärpfling / Kribi Killi
Kribi, Kamerun / Kribi, Cameroon; W; 8,0 cm
▷ᙕᛞ⓪☺☻⊞🔛➡ ⚠ⓜ ♂
Photo: L. Seegers

A03320-4 *Aphyosemion (F.) fallax* Ahl, 1935
Kribi-Prachtkärpfling / Kribi Killi
Kribi, Kamerun / Kribi, Cameroon; W; 8,0 cm
▷ᙕᛞ⓪☺☻⊞🔛➡ ⚠ⓜ ♀
Photo: L. Seegers

A03320-4 *Aphyosemion (F.) fallax* Ahl, 1935
Kribi-Prachtkärpfling / Kribi Killi
Kribi, Kamerun / Kribi, Cameroon; W; 8,0 cm
▷ᙕᛞ⓪☺☻⊞🔛➡ ⚠ⓜ ♂
Photo: E. Pürzl

A03320-4 *Aphyosemion (F.) fallax* Ahl, 1935
Kribi-Prachtkärpfling / Kribi Killi
Kribi, Kamerun / Kribi, Cameroon; W; 8,0 cm
▷ᙕᛞ⓪☺☻⊞🔛➡ ⚠ⓜ ♂
Photo: L. Seegers

A03321-4 *Aphyosemion (F.) fallax* Ahl, 1935
Kribi-Prachtkärpfling / Kribi Killi
Kribi, Kamerun / Kribi, Cameroon; B; 8,0 cm
▷ᙕᛞ⓪☺☻⊞🔛➡ ⚠ⓜ ♂
Photo: L. Seegers

A03322-4 *Aphyosemion (F.) fallax* Ahl, 1935
Kribi-Prachtkärpfling / Kribi Killi
Malende, Kamerun / Malende, Cameroon; B; 8,0 cm
▷ᙕᛞ⓪☺☻⊞🔛➡ ⚠ⓜ ♂
Photo: L. Seegers

A03323-4 *Aphyosemion (F.) fallax* Ahl, 1935
Kribi-Prachtkärpfling / Kribi Killi
Mouanko, Kamerun / Mouanko, Cameroon; B; 8,0 cm
▷ᙕᛞ⓪☺☻⊞🔛➡ ⚠ⓜ ♂
Photo: L. Seegers

A03323-4 *Aphyosemion (F.) fallax* Ahl, 1935
Kribi-Prachtkärpfling / Kribi Killi
Mouanko, Kamerun / Mouanko, Cameroon; B; 8,0 cm
▷ᙕᛞ⓪☺☻⊞🔛➡ ⚠ⓜ ♂
Photo: L. Seegers

A03325-3 *Aphyosemion (F.) filamentosum* (Meinken, 1933)
Faden-Prachtkärpfling / Blue Killi
Süd-Togo / Southern Togo; W; 5,0 cm
▷♗◐☺☹⊞🐛➨ ◈⚠ⓜ ♂   Photo: E. Pürzl

A03325-4 *Aphyosemion (F.) filamentosum* (Meinken, 1933)
Faden-Prachtkärpfling / Blue Killi
Süd-Togo / Southern Togo; W; 5,0 cm
▷♗◐☺☹⊞🐛➨ ◈⚠ⓜ ♀   Photo: E. Pürzl

A03326-4 *Aphyosemion (F.) filamentosum* (Meinken, 1933)
Faden-Prachtkärpfling / Blue Killi
Süd-Benin / Southern Benin; W; 5,0 cm
▷♗◐☺☹⊞🐛➨ ◈⚠ⓜ ♂   Photo: E. Pürzl

A03326-4 *Aphyosemion (F.) filamentosum* (Meinken, 1933)
Faden-Prachtkärpfling / Blue Killi
Süd-Benin / Southern Benin; W; 5,0 cm
▷♗◐☺☹⊞🐛➨ ◈⚠ⓜ ♂   Photo: E. Pürzl

A03327-4 *Aphyosemion (F.) filamentosum* (Meinken, 1933)
Faden-Prachtkärpfling / Blue Killi
Aquarienstamm / Aquarium strain; B; 5,0 cm
▷♗◐☺☹⊞🐛➨ ◈⚠ⓜ ♂   Photo: H.J. Mayland

A03327-4 *Aphyosemion (F.) filamentosum* (Meinken, 1933)
Faden-Prachtkärpfling / Blue Killi
Aquarienstamm / Aquarium strain; B; 5,0 cm
▷♗◐☺☹⊞🐛➨ ◈⚠ⓜ ♂   Photo: S. Hellner

A03327-4 *Aphyosemion (F.) filamentosum* (Meinken, 1933)
Faden-Prachtkärpfling / Blue Killi
Aquarienstamm / Aquarium strain; B; 5,0 cm
▷♗◐☺☹⊞🐛➨ ◈⚠ⓜ ♂   Photo: L. Seegers

A03327-4 *Aphyosemion (F.) filamentosum* (Meinken, 1933)
Faden-Prachtkärpfling / Blue Killi
Aquarienstamm / Aquarium strain; B; 5,0 cm
▷♗◐☺☹⊞🐛➨ ◈⚠ⓜ ♀   Photo: L. Seegers

A03335-4 *Aphyosemion franzwerneri* SCHEEL, 1971
Grundel-Prachtkärpfling / Goby Killi
15 km from jct. of Douala, Edea, Yabassi rd. to Yabassi, Cameroon; W; 5,0 cm
▷ ♫ ◐ ☺ ☺ ⊞ 🖥 ➡ 🛑 m ♂   Photo: E. Pürzl

A03335-4 *Aphyosemion franzwerneri* SCHEEL, 1971
Grundel-Prachtkärpfling / Goby Killi
15 km from jct. of Douala, Edea, Yabassi rd. to Yabassi, Cameroon; W; 5,0 cm
▷ ♫ ◐ ☺ ☺ ⊞ 🖥 ➡ 🛑 m ♀   Photo: E. Pürzl

A03335-4 *Aphyosemion franzwerneri* SCHEEL, 1971
Grundel-Prachtkärpfling / Goby Killi
15 km from jct. of Douala, Edea, Yabassi rd. to Yabassi, Cameroon; W; 5,0 cm
▷ ♫ ◐ ☺ ☺ ⊞ 🖥 ➡ 🛑 m ♂   Photo: L. Seegers

A03336-4 *Aphyosemion franzwerneri* SCHEEL, 1971
Grundel-Prachtkärpfling / Goby Killi
Bonepoupa, Kamerun / Bonepoupa, Cameroon; W; 5,0 cm
▷ ♫ ◐ ☺ ☺ ⊞ 🖥 ➡ 🛑 m ♂   Photo: R. Lütje

A03341-4 *Aphyosemion gabunense gabunense* RADDA, 1975
Gabun-Prachtkärpfling / Gabon Killi
30 km SE Lambarene on road RN 1 to Mouila, Gabon; W; 5,0 cm
▷ ♫ ◐ ☺ ☺ ⊞ 🖥 ➡ ◈ ⚠ m ♂   Photo: E. Pürzl

A03818-4 *Aphyosemion gabunense gabunense* RADDA, 1975
Gabun-Prachtkärpfling / Gabon Killi
30 km SE Lambarene on road RN 1 to Mouila, Gabon; B; 5,0 cm
▷ ♫ ◐ ☺ ☺ ⊞ 🖥 ➡ ◈ ⚠ m ♂ ♀   Photo: L. Seegers

A03838-4 *Aphyosemion gabunense gabunense* RADDA, 1975
Gabun-Prachtkärpfling / Gabon Killi
30 km SE Lambarene on road RN 1 to Mouila, Gabon; B; 5,0 cm
▷ ♫ ◐ ☺ ☺ ⊞ 🖥 ➡ ◈ ⚠ m ♂   Photo: L. Seegers

A03340-4 *Aphyosemion gabunense boehmi* RADDA & HUBER, 1977
Böhms Gabun-Prachtkärpfling / Boehm's Gabon Killi
Brook on road from Bigouenia to Mora, Gabon; W; 5,0 cm
▷ ♫ ◐ ☺ ☺ ⊞ 🖥 ➡ ◈ ⚠ m ♂   Photo: L. Seegers

A03453-4 Zwei Männchen von *Aphyosemion ogoense ottogartneri* im Revier- oder Rangordnungskampf.
Two males of Aphyosemion ogoense ottogartneri *fighting for a territory or the rank order.*

A03449-4 Breitseitdrohende Männchen von *Aphyosemion oeseri.*
Lateral threat behavior of two males of Aphyosemion oeseri.

A03342-4 *Aphyosemion gabunense marginatum* RADDA & HUBER, 1977
Gelbflossen-Gabunprachtkärpfling / Yellow Gabon Killi, "G 76/34"
9 km SW Bifoun on National Road No. 1, Gabon; B; 5,0 cm
▷ ♫ ◑ ☺ ☹ ⊞ 🐾 ➡ ◈ ⚠ 🔟 ♂
Photo: L. Seegers

A03342-4 *Aphyosemion gabunense marginatum* RADDA & HUBER, 1977
Gelbflossen-Gabunprachtkärpfling / Yellow Gabon Killi, "G 76/34"
9 km SW Bifoun on National Road No. 1, Gabon; B; 5,0 cm
▷ ♫ ◑ ☺ ☹ ⊞ 🐾 ➡ ◈ ⚠ 🔟 ♂
Photo: E. Pürzl

A03350-4 *Aphyosemion (F.) gardneri gardneri* (BOULENGER, 1911)
Gardners Prachtkärpfling / Gardner's Killi
Lafia, Nigeria; B; 6,0 cm
▷ ♫ ◑ ☺ ☹ ⊞ 🐾 ➡ ◈ 🔟 ♂
Photo: H.J. Mayland

A03839-4 *Aphyosemion (F.) gardneri gardneri* (BOULENGER, 1911)
Gardners Prachtkärpfling / Gardner's Killi
Nsukka, Nigeria; W; 6,0 cm
▷ ♫ ◑ ☺ ☹ ⊞ 🐾 ➡ ◈ 🔟 ♂
Photo: E. Pürzl

A03840-4 *Aphyosemion (F.) gardneri gardneri* (BOULENGER, 1911)
Gardners Prachtkärpfling / Gardner's Killi
Udi, Nigeria; B; 6,0 cm
▷ ♫ ◑ ☺ ☹ ⊞ 🐾 ➡ ◈ 🔟 ♂
Photo: E. Pürzl

A03352-4 *Aphyosemion (F.) gardneri lacustre* RADDA, 1974
Ejagham-Prachtkärpfling / Ejagham Killi [T.t.]
Lake Ejagham, West-Kamerun / Western Cameroon; W; 6,0 cm
▷ ♫ ◑ ☺ ☹ ⊞ 🐾 ➡ ◈ 🔟 ♂
Photo: E. Pürzl

A03841-4 *Aphyosemion (F.) gardneri lacustre* RADDA, 1974
Ejagham-Prachtkärpfling / Ejagham Killi
Lake Ejagham, West-Kamerun / Western Cameroon; B; 6,0 cm
▷ ♫ ◑ ☺ ☹ ⊞ 🐾 ➡ ◈ 🔟 ♂
Photo: L. Seegers

A03842-4 *Aphyosemion (F.) gardneri lacustre* RADDA, 1974
Ejagham-Prachtkärpfling / Ejagham Killi, Mutante
Lake Ejagham, West-Kamerun / Western Cameroon; B; 6,0 cm
▷ ♫ ◑ ☺ ☹ ⊞ 🐾 ➡ ◈ 🔟 ♂
Photo: L. Seegers

A03353-4 *Aphyosemion (F.) gardneri mamfense* RADDA, 1974
Mamfe-Prachtkärpfling / Mamfe Killi [T.t.]
3 km S Bachou-Akagbe towards Manyemen, West Cameroon; W; 6,0 cm
▷⊞❶◑☺☻⊞▱➤ ◈▥♂   Photo: E. Pürzl

A03843-4 *Aphyosemion (F.) gardneri mamfense* RADDA, 1974
Mamfe-Prachtkärpfling / Mamfe Killi
Besongabang, West-Kamerun / West Cameroon; B; 6,0 cm
▷⊞❶◑☺☻⊞▱➤ ◈▥♂   Photo: L. Seegers

A03844-4 *Aphyosemion (F.) gardneri mamfense* RADDA, 1974
Mamfe-Prachtkärpfling / Mamfe Killi
Ossing, West-Kamerun / West Cameroon; B; 6,0 cm
▷⊞❶◑☺☻⊞▱➤ ◈▥♂   Photo: L. Seegers

A03845-4 *Aphyosemion (F.) gardneri mamfense* RADDA, 1974
Mamfe-Prachtkärpfling / Mamfe Killi
2 km O Mamfe, West-Kamerun / 2 km E Mamfe, West Cameroon; W; 6,0 cm
▷⊞❶◑☺☻⊞▱➤ ◈▥♂   Photo: L. Seegers

A03846-4 *Aphyosemion (F.) gardneri mamfense* RADDA, 1974
Mamfe-Prachtkärpfling / Mamfe Killi
8 km after Mamfe, West Cameroon; W; 6,0 cm
▷⊞❶◑☺☻⊞▱➤ ◈▥♂   Photo: L. Seegers

A03847-4 *Aphyosemion (F.) gardneri mamfense* RADDA, 1974
Mamfe-Prachtkärpfling / Mamfe Killi
1 km before Eyomojok, West Cameroon; W; 6,0 cm
▷⊞❶◑☺☻⊞▱➤ ◈▥♂   Photo: L. Seegers

A03848-4 *Aphyosemion (F.) gardneri mamfense* RADDA, 1974
Mamfe-Prachtkärpfling / Mamfe Killi
Vicinity of Mamfe, West Cameroon; W; 6,0 cm
▷⊞❶◑☺☻⊞▱➤ ◈▥♂   Photo: L. Seegers

A03849-4 *Aphyosemion (F.) gardneri mamfense* RADDA, 1974
Mamfe-Prachtkärpfling / Mamfe Killi
Xanthoristische Form / xanthoristic form; B; 6,0 cm
▷⊞❶◑☺☻⊞▱➤ ◈▥♂   Photo: L. Seegers

A03354-4 *Aphyosemion (F.) gardneri nigerianum* CLAUSEN, 1963
Nigeria-Prachtkärpfling / Nigerian Killi
28 km NW Abakaliki, Nigeria; W; 6,0 cm
▷♬◑☺☺⊞🐟🐛➤ ◈🔟 ♂   Photo: E. Pürzl

A03850-4 *Aphyosemion (F.) gardneri nigerianum* CLAUSEN, 1963
Nigeria-Prachtkärpfling / Nigerian Killi
Akamkpa, Nigeria; W; 6,0 cm
▷♬◑☺☺⊞🐟🐛➤ ◈🔟 ♂   Photo: E. Pürzl

A03851-4 *Aphyosemion (F.) gardneri nigerianum* CLAUSEN, 1963
Nigeria-Prachtkärpfling / Nigerian Killi
Akure, Nigeria; B; 6,0 cm
▷♬◑☺☺⊞🐟🐛➤ ◈🔟 ♂   Photo: L. Seegers

A03852-4 *Aphyosemion (F.) gardneri nigerianum* CLAUSEN, 1963
Nigeria-Prachtkärpfling / Nigerian Killi
Jos Plateau, Nigeria; B; 6,0 cm
▷♬◑☺☺⊞🐟🐛➤ ◈🔟 ♂   Photo: L. Seegers

A03853-4 *Aphyosemion (F.) gardneri nigerianum* CLAUSEN, 1963
Nigeria-Prachtkärpfling / Nigerian Killi
Makurdi, Nigeria; B; 6,0 cm
▷♬◑☺☺⊞🐟🐛➤ ◈🔟 ♂   Photo: L. Seegers

A03854-3 *Aphyosemion (F.) gardneri nigerianum* CLAUSEN, 1963
Nigeria-Prachtkärpfling / Nigerian Killi
Misage, Nigeria; W; 6,0 cm
▷♬◑☺☺⊞🐟🐛➤ ◈🔟 ♂   Photo: E. Pürzl

A03855-4 *Aphyosemion (F.) gardneri nigerianum* CLAUSEN, 1963
Nigeria-Prachtkärpfling / Nigerian Killi
Misage, Nigeria; B; 6,0 cm
▷♬◑☺☺⊞🐟🐛➤ ◈🔟 ♂   Photo: L. Seegers

A03856-4 *Aphyosemion (F.) gardneri nigerianum* CLAUSEN, 1963
Nigeria-Prachtkärpfling / Nigerian Killi
Obudu, Nigeria; B; 6,0 cm
▷♬◑☺☺⊞🐟🐛➤ ◈🔟 ♂   Photo: L. Seegers

A03857-4 *Aphyosemion (F.) gardneri nigerianum* Clausen, 1963
Nigeria-Prachtkärpfling / Nigerian Killi
Osira, Nigeria; W; 6,0 cm
▷♫◑☺☺⊞🗔🐛 ◈🔲♂   Photo: E. Pürzl

A03858-3 *Aphyosemion (F.) gardneri nigerianum* Clausen, 1963
Nigeria-Prachtkärpfling / Nigerian Killi
"P 82", Nigeria; B; 6,0 cm
▷♫◑☺☺⊞🗔🐛 ◈🔲♂   Photo: L. Seegers

A03859-4 *Aphyosemion (F.) gardneri nigerianum* Clausen, 1963
Nigeria-Prachtkärpfling / Nigerian Killi
Rayfield, Nigeria; B; 6,0 cm
▷♫◑☺☺⊞🗔🐛 ◈🔲♂   Photo: E. Pürzl

A03859-4 *Aphyosemion (F.) gardneri nigerianum* Clausen, 1963
Nigeria-Prachtkärpfling / Nigerian Killi
Rayfield, Nigeria; B; 6,0 cm
▷♫◑☺☺⊞🗔🐛 ◈🔲♂   Photo: L. Seegers

A03860-4 *Aphyosemion (F.) gardneri nigerianum* Clausen, 1963
Nigeria-Prachtkärpfling / Nigerian Killi
33 km östlich Ugep / 33 km E of Ugep, Nigeria; W; 6,0 cm
▷♫◑☺☺⊞🗔🐛 ◈🔲♂   Photo: E. Pürzl

A03860-4 *Aphyosemion (F.) gardneri nigerianum* Clausen, 1963
Nigeria-Prachtkärpfling / Nigerian Killi
33 km östlich Ugep / 33 km E of Ugep, Nigeria; W; 6,0 cm
▷♫◑☺☺⊞🗔🐛 ◈🔲♂   Photo: E. Pürzl

A03861-4 *Aphyosemion (F.) gardneri nigerianum* Clausen, 1963
Nigeria-Prachtkärpfling / Nigerian Killi
Ugep, Nigeria; B; 6,0 cm
▷♫◑☺☺⊞🗔🐛 ◈🔲♂   Photo: L. Seegers

A03861-4 *Aphyosemion (F.) gardneri nigerianum* Clausen, 1963
Nigeria-Prachtkärpfling / Nigerian Killi
Ugep, Nigeria; B; 6,0 cm
▷♫◑☺☺⊞🗔🐛 ◈🔲♀   Photo: L. Seegers

A03355-4 *Aphyosemion geryi* LAMBERT, 1958
Zickzack-Prachtkärpfling, Gérys Prachtkärpfling / Géry's Killi
Abuko National Park, Gambia; B; 5,0 cm
▷⚠️🦀🌓☺️😊⊞🖼️🐛➡️ ◈🔲 ♂   Photo: L. Seegers

A03356-4 *Aphyosemion geryi* LAMBERT, 1958
Zickzack-Prachtkärpfling, Gérys Prachtkärpfling / Géry's Killi
Bwian, Gambia; W; 5,0 cm
▷🦀🌓☺️😊⊞🖼️🐛➡️ ◈🔲 ♂♀   Photo: L. Seegers

A03357-4 *Aphyosemion geryi* LAMBERT, 1958
Zickzack-Prachtkärpfling, Gérys Prachtkärpfling / Géry's Killi
Kampant, Gambia; W; 5,0 cm
▷🦀🌓☺️😊⊞🖼️🐛➡️ ◈🔲 ♂   Photo: S. Hellner

A03358-4 *Aphyosemion geryi* LAMBERT, 1958
Zickzack-Prachtkärpfling, Gérys Prachtkärpfling / Géry's Killi
Casamance, Senegal; B; 5,0 cm
▷🦀🌓☺️😊⊞🖼️🐛➡️ ◈🔲 ♂   Photo: L. Seegers

A03359-4 *Aphyosemion geryi* LAMBERT, 1958
Zickzack-Prachtkärpfling, Gérys Prachtkärpfling / Géry's Killi
Conakry, Guinea; B; 5,0 cm
▷🦀🌓☺️😊⊞🖼️🐛➡️ ◈🔲 ♂   Photo: L. Seegers

A03359-4 *Aphyosemion geryi* LAMBERT, 1958
Zickzack-Prachtkärpfling, Gérys Prachtkärpfling / Géry's Killi
Conakry, Guinea; B; 5,0 cm
▷🦀🌓☺️😊⊞🖼️🐛➡️ ◈🔲 ♀   Photo: L. Seegers

A03862-4 *Aphyosemion geryi* LAMBERT, 1958
Zickzack-Prachtkärpfling, Gérys Prachtkärpfling / Géry's Killi, "SL 89"
Mamanká, Sierra Leone; W; 5,0 cm
▷🦀🌓☺️😊⊞🖼️🐛➡️ ◈🔲 ♂   Photo: S. Hellner

A03862-4 *Aphyosemion geryi* LAMBERT, 1958
Zickzack-Prachtkärpfling, Gérys Prachtkärpfling / Géry's Killi, "SL 89"
Mamanká, Sierra Leone; W; 5,0 cm
▷🦀🌓☺️😊⊞🖼️🐛➡️ ◈🔲 ♂   Photo: S. Hellner

A03360-4 *Aphyosemion guignardi* (ROMAND, 1981)
Guignards Prachtkärpfling / Guignard's Killi
Labé, Guinea; B; 5,5 cm
▷🦌◑☺☹⊞🗺➡ ◈🅼 ♂   Photo: S. Hellner

A03361-4 *Aphyosemion guignardi* (ROMAND, 1981)
Guignards Prachtkärpfling / Guignard's Killi
Safakuré River, between Kindia and Mamou, Guinea; W; 5,5 cm
▷🦌◑☺☹⊞🗺➡ ◈🅼 ♂   Photo: L. Seegers

A03362-4 *Aphyosemion guignardi* (ROMAND, 1981)
Guignards Prachtkärpfling / Guignard's Killi
Sougueta, Guinea; W; 5,5 cm
▷🦌◑☺☹⊞🗺➡ ◈🅼 ♂   Photo: L. Seegers

A03362-4 *Aphyosemion guignardi* (ROMAND, 1981)
Guignards Prachtkärpfling / Guignard's Killi
Sougueta, Guinea; W; 5,5 cm
▷🦌◑☺☹⊞🗺➡ ◈🅼 ♂ ♀   Photo: L. Seegers

A03363-4 *Aphyosemion guignardi* (ROMAND, 1981)
Guignards Prachtkärpfling / Guignard's Killi
Bafing River, from Dalaba 18 km before Mamou, Guinea; B; 5,5 cm
▷🦌◑☺☹⊞🗺➡ ◈🅼 ♂   Photo: L. Seegers

A03363-4 *Aphyosemion guignardi* (ROMAND, 1981)
Guignards Prachtkärpfling / Guignard's Killi
Bafing River, from Dalaba 18 km before Mamou, Guinea; B; 5,5 cm
▷🦌◑☺☹⊞🗺➡ ◈🅼 ♀   Photo: L. Seegers

A03364-4 *Aphyosemion guignardi* (ROMAND, 1981)
Guignards Prachtkärpfling / Guignard's Killi
15 km N Banfora, Burkina Faso; W; 5,5 cm
▷🦌◑☺☹⊞🗺➡ ◈🅼 ♂   Photo: L. Seegers

A03364-4 *Aphyosemion guignardi* (ROMAND, 1981)
Guignards Prachtkärpfling / Guignard's Killi
15 km N Banfora, Burkina Faso; W; 5,5 cm
▷🦌◑☺☹⊞🗺➡ ◈🅼 ♀   Photo: L. Seegers

A03365-4 *Aphyosemion guineense* DAGET, 1954
Guinea-Prachtkärpfling / Guinean Killi
Nordost-Sierra Leone / Northeastern Sierra Leone; B; 6,5 cm
◁ ▷ ♉ ◐ ① ☺ ☻ ⊞ 🦐 ➽ ⚠ 🔟 ♂
Photo: L. Seegers

A03370-4 *Aphyosemion (F.) gulare* (BOULENGER, 1901)
Weißkehl-Prachtkärpfling / Gulare
Aquarium import from the delta of river Niger, SW Nigeria; W; 6,5 cm
▷ ⚠ ♉ ① ☺ ☻ ⊞ 🦐 ➽ ⚠ 🔟 ♂
Photo: L. Seegers

A03863-4 *Aphyosemion (F.) gulare* (BOULENGER, 1901)
Weißkehl-Prachtkärpfling / Gulare
Aquarienstamm / Aquarium strain; B; 6,5 cm
▷ ⚠ ♉ ◐ ☺ ☻ ⊞ 🦐 ➽ ⚠ 🔟 ♂
Photo: L. Seegers

A03863-4 *Aphyosemion (F.) gulare* (BOULENGER, 1901)
Weißkehl-Prachtkärpfling / Gulare
Aquarienstamm / Aquarium strain; B; 6,5 cm
▷ ⚠ ♉ ① ☺ ☻ ⊞ 🦐 ➽ ⚠ 🔟 ♂
Photo: L. Seegers

A03371-4 *Aphyosemion hanneloreae hanneloreae* RADDA & PÜRZL, 1985
Hannelores Prachtkärpfling / Hannelore's Killi [Holotype]
Bei Malinga, Süd-Gabun / Near Malinga, southern Gabon; W; 4,0 cm
◁ ♉ ① ☺ ☻ ⊞ 🦐 ➽ ⚠ 🔟 ♂
Photo: E. Pürzl

A03371-4 *Aphyosemion hanneloreae hanneloreae* RADDA & PÜRZL, 1985
Hannelores Prachtkärpfling / Hannelore's Killi, "GEB 94/20"
Bei Malinga, Süd-Gabun / Near Malinga, southern Gabon; W; 4,0 cm
◁ ♉ ① ☺ ☻ ⊞ 🦐 ➽ ⚠ 🔟 ♂
Photo: R. Lütje

A03864-4 *Aphyosemion hanneloreae wuendschi* RADDA & PÜRZL, 1985
Wündschs Prachtkärpfling / Wuendsch's Killi [T.t.]
50 km S Mbingou on road to Malinga, southern Gabon; W; 4,0 cm
◁ ♉ ① ☺ ☻ ⊞ 🦐 ➽ ⚠ 🔟 ♂
Photo: E. Pürzl

A03864-4 *Aphyosemion hanneloreae wuendschi* RADDA & PÜRZL, 1985
Wündschs Prachtkärpfling / Wuendsch's Killi [T.t.]
50 km S Mbingou on road to Malinga, southern Gabon; W; 4,0 cm
◁ ♉ ① ☺ ☻ ⊞ 🦐 ➽ ⚠ 🔟 ♀
Photo: E. Pürzl

A03708-4 *Aphyosemion heinemanni* BERKENKAMP, 1983
Heinemanns Prachtkärpfling / Heinemann's Killi [T.t.]
Song Mahi, Ost-Kamerun / Song Mahi, eastern Cameroon; W; 5,0 cm
▷ 🦎 ◑ ☺ ☺ ⊞ 🖼 ➡ ◈ ⚠ 🔲 ♂
Photo: L. Seegers

A03708-4 *Aphyosemion heinemanni* BERKENKAMP, 1983
Heinemanns Prachtkärpfling / Heinemann's Killi [T.t.]
Song Mahi, Ost-Kamerun / Song Mahi, eastern Cameroon; B; 5,0 cm
▷ 🦎 ◑ ☺ ☺ ⊞ 🖼 ➡ ◈ ⚠ 🔲 ♂
Photo: E. Pürzl

A03372-4 *Aphyosemion herzogi* RADDA, 1975
Herzogs Prachtkärpfling / Herzog's Killi [T.t.]
3 km N of Zomoko or 16 km N of Lalara, North Gabon; W; 4,0 cm
◁ ▷ 🦎 ◑ ☺ ☺ ⊞ 🖼 ➡ ⚠ 🔲 ♂
Photo: E. Pürzl

A03372-4 *Aphyosemion herzogi* RADDA, 1975
Herzogs Prachtkärpfling / Herzog's Killi [T.t.]
3 km N of Zomoko or 16 km N of Lalara, North Gabon; W; 4,0 cm
◁ ▷ 🦎 ◑ ☺ ☺ ⊞ 🖼 ➡ ⚠ 🔲 ♀
Photo: E. Pürzl

A03372-4 *Aphyosemion herzogi* RADDA, 1975
Herzogs Prachtkärpfling / Herzog's Killi [T.t.]
3 km N of Zomoko or 16 km N of Lalara, North Gabon; B; 4,0 cm
◁ ▷ 🦎 ◑ ☺ ☺ ⊞ 🖼 ➡ ⚠ 🔲 ♂
Photo: L. Seegers

A03865-4 *Aphyosemion herzogi* RADDA, 1975
Herzogs Prachtkärpfling / Herzog's Killi
Edoum, Nord-Gabun / Edoum, North Gabon; B; 4,0 cm
◁ ▷ 🦎 ◑ ☺ ☺ ⊞ 🖼 ➡ ⚠ 🔲 ♂
Photo: S. Hellner-

A03866-4 *Aphyosemion herzogi* RADDA, 1975
Herzogs Prachtkärpfling / Herzog's Killi
Médouneu, Nord-Gabun / Médouneu, North Gabon; W; 4,0 cm
◁ ▷ 🦎 ◑ ☺ ☺ ⊞ 🖼 ➡ ⚠ 🔲 ♂
Photo: L. Seegers

A03867-4 *Aphyosemion herzogi* RADDA, 1975
Herzogs Prachtkärpfling / Herzog's Killi, "GHG 83/2"
Nord-Gabun / North Gabon; B; 4,0 cm
◁ ▷ 🦎 ◑ ☺ ☺ ⊞ 🖼 ➡ ⚠ 🔲 ♂
Photo: S. Hellner-

A03868-4 *Aphyosemion herzogi* RADDA, 1975
Herzogs Prachtkärpfling / Herzog's Killi, "GWW 86/11"
Mintoum, Nord-Gabun / Mintoum, North Gabon; B; 4,0 cm
◁ ▷ ♫ ◑ ☺ ☻ ⊞ 🖼 ➠ ⚠ 🔲 ♂   Photo: S. Hellner

A03869-4 *Aphyosemion herzogi* RADDA, 1975
Herzogs Prachtkärpfling / Herzog's Killi
Mintoum, Nord-Gabun / Mintoum, North Gabon; B; 4,0 cm
◁ ▷ ♫ ◑ ☺ ☻ ⊞ 🖼 ➠ ⚠ 🔲 ♂   Photo: L. Seegers

A03870-4 *Aphyosemion herzogi* RADDA, 1975
Herzogs Prachtkärpfling / Herzog's Killi, "GBN 88/31"
Nord-Gabun / North Gabon; W; 4,0 cm
◁ ▷ ♫ ◑ ☺ ☻ ⊞ 🖼 ➠ ⚠ 🔲 ♂   Photo: S. Hellner-

A03871-4 *Aphyosemion herzogi* RADDA, 1975
Herzogs Prachtkärpfling / Herzog's Killi, "GBN 88/33"
Nord-Gabun / North Gabon; W; 4,0 cm
◁ ▷ ♫ ◑ ☺ ☻ ⊞ 🖼 ➠ ⚠ 🔲 ♂   Photo: S. Hellner-

A03872-4 *Aphyosemion herzogi* RADDA, 1975
Herzogs Prachtkärpfling / Herzog's Killi, "CHJR 94"
Nsessoum, Nord-Gabun / Nsessoum, North Gabon; W; 4,0 cm
◁ ▷ ♫ ◑ ☺ ☻ ⊞ 🖼 ➠ ⚠ 🔲 ♂   Photo: S. Hellner

A03873-4 *Aphyosemion herzogi* RADDA, 1975
Herzogs Prachtkärpfling / Herzog's Killi
Ovan, Nord-Gabun / Ovan, North Gabon; W; 4,0 cm
◁ ▷ ♫ ◑ ☺ ☻ ⊞ 🖼 ➠ ⚠ 🔲 ♂   Photo: E. Pürzl

A03874-4 *Aphyosemion herzogi* RADDA, 1975
Herzogs Prachtkärpfling / Herzog's Killi, "LEC 93/23"
Nord-Gabun / North Gabon; W; 4,0 cm
◁ ▷ ♫ ◑ ☺ ☻ ⊞ 🖼 ➠ ⚠ 🔲 ♂   Photo: R. Lütje

A03875-4 *Aphyosemion herzogi* RADDA, 1975
Herzogs Prachtkärpfling / Herzog's Killi
"bochtleri-Form", Nord-Gabun / North Gabon; W; 4,0 cm
◁ ▷ ♫ ◑ ☺ ☻ ⊞ 🖼 ➠ ⚠ 🔲 ♀   Photo: S. Hellner-

A03373-4 *Aphyosemion hofmanni* RADDA, 1980, Holotype
Hofmanns Prachtkärpfling / Hofmann's Killi [T.t.]
Imeno Mbila, 55 km from Mimongo to Mbigou, Gabon; W; 4,0 cm
◁ ♉ ◑ ☺ ☺ ⊞ 🖼 ➤ ⚠ 🔲 ♂
Photo: E. Pürzl

A03876-3 *Aphyosemion hofmanni* RADDA, 1980
Hofmanns Prachtkärpfling / Hofmann's Killi, "GEB 94/17"
Gabun / Gabon; W; 4,0 cm
◁ ♉ ◑ ☺ ☺ ⊞ 🖼 ➤ ⚠ 🔲 ♂
Photo: R. Lütje

A03877-3 *Aphyosemion hofmanni* RADDA, 1980
Hofmanns Prachtkärpfling / Hofmann's Killi, "GBG 93/17"
Gabun / Gabon; W; 4,0 cm
▷ ♉ ◑ ☺ ☺ ⊞ 🖼 ➤ ⚠ 🔲 ♂
Photo: S. Hellner-

A03878-4 *Aphyosemion jeanpoli* (BERKENKAMP & ETZEL, 1979)
Jeanpols Prachtkärpfling / Jeanpol's Killi [T.t.]
Voinjama, Nord-Liberia / Voinjama, northern Liberia; B; 5,5 cm
▷ ♉ ◑ ☺ ☺ ⊞ 🖼 ➤ ⚠ 🔲 ♂
Photo: E. Pürzl

A03878-4 *Aphyosemion jeanpoli* (BERKENKAMP & ETZEL, 1979)
Jeanpols Prachtkärpfling / Jeanpol's Killi [T.t.]
Voinjama, Nord-Liberia / Voinjama, northern Liberia; B; 5,5 cm
▷ ♉ ◑ ☺ ☺ ⊞ 🖼 ➤ ⚠ 🔲 ♂
Photo: L. Seegers

A03878-4 *Aphyosemion jeanpoli* (BERKENKAMP & ETZEL, 1979)
Jeanpols Prachtkärpfling / Jeanpol's Killi
Voinjama, Nord-Liberia / Voinjama, northern Liberia; B; 5,5 cm
▷ ♉ ◑ ☺ ☺ ⊞ 🖼 ➤ ⚠ 🔲 ♂
Photo: L. Seegers

A03879-4 *Aphyosemion jeanpoli* (BERKENKAMP & ETZEL, 1979)
Jeanpols Prachtkärpfling / Jeanpol's Killi
Macenta (= Maesenta ?), Ost-Guinea / Eastern Guinea; B; 5,5 cm
▷ ♉ ◑ ☺ ☺ ⊞ 🖼 ➤ ⚠ 🔲 ♂
Photo: L. Seegers

A03879-4 *Aphyosemion jeanpoli* (BERKENKAMP & ETZEL, 1979)
Jeanpols Prachtkärpfling / Jeanpol's Killi
Macenta (= Maesenta ?), Ost-Guinea / Eastern Guinea; B; 5,5 cm
▷ ♉ ◑ ☺ ☺ ⊞ 🖼 ➤ ⚠ 🔲 ♀
Photo: L. Seegers

A03374-3 *Aphyosemion joergenscheeli* HUBER & RADDA, 1977
Joergen Scheels Prachtkärpfling / Joergen Scheel's Killi
Mimongo, Gabun / Mimongo, Gabon; W; 4,5 cm
◁ ♫ ❶ ☺ ☻ ⊞ 🖳 ➡ ⚠ m ♂   Photo: E. Pürzl

A03374-4 *Aphyosemion joergenscheeli* HUBER & RADDA, 1977
Joergen Scheels Prachtkärpfling / Joergen Scheel's Killi
Mimongo, Gabun / Mimongo, Gabon; W; 4,5 cm
◁ ♫ ❶ ☺ ☻ ⊞ 🖳 ➡ ⚠ m ♀   Photo: E. Pürzl

A03880-4 *Aphyosemion joergenscheeli* HUBER & RADDA, 1977
Joergen Scheels Prachtkärpfling / Joergen Scheel's Killi, "GBG 93/21"
Gabun / Gabon; B; 4,5 cm
◁ ♫ ❶ ☺ ☻ ⊞ 🖳 ➡ ⚠ m ♂   Photo: L. Seegers

A03881-4 *Aphyosemion joergenscheeli* HUBER & RADDA, 1977
Joergen Scheels Prachtkärpfling / Joergen Scheel's Killi, "PEG 93/4"
Gabun / Gabon; W; 4,5 cm
◁ ♫ ❶ ☺ ☻ ⊞ 🖳 ➡ ⚠ m ♂   Photo: R. Lütje

A03882-3 *Aphyosemion joergenscheeli* HUBER & RADDA, 1977
Joergen Scheels Prachtkärpfling / Joergen Scheel's Killi, "GBN 88/20"
Gabun / Gabon; W; 4,5 cm
◁ ♫ ❶ ☺ ☻ ⊞ 🖳 ➡ ⚠ m ♂   Photo: S. Hellner-

A03883-4 *Aphyosemion joergenscheeli* HUBER & RADDA, 1977
Joergen Scheels Prachtkärpfling / Joergen Scheel's Killi, "GBN 88/29"
Gabun / Gabon; W; 4,5 cm
◁ ♫ ❶ ☺ ☻ ⊞ 🖳 ➡ ⚠ m ♂   Photo: S. Hellner-

A03380-4 *Aphyosemion labarrei* POLL, 1951
Labarres Prachtkärpfling / Labarre's Killi
Aquarienstamm von Zaïre / Aquarium strain from Zaïre; B; 5,5 cm
▷ ♫ ❶ ☺ ☻ ⊞ 🖳 ➡ ⚠ m ♂   Photo: E. Pürzl

A03380-4 *Aphyosemion labarrei* POLL, 1951
Labarres Prachtkärpfling / Labarre's Killi
Aquarienstamm von Zaïre / Aquarium strain from Zaïre; B; 5,5 cm
▷ ♫ ❶ ☺ ☻ ⊞ 🖳 ➡ ⚠ m ♀   Photo: E. Pürzl

A03380-4 *Aphyosemion labarrei* Poll, 1951
Labarres Prachtkärpfling / Labarre's Killi
Aquarienstamm von Zaïre / Aquarium strain from Zaïre; B; 5,5 cm
▷♌◑☺☻⊞🖼➡ ⚠🔲♂   Photo: E. Pürzl

A03885-4 *Aphyosemion labarrei* Poll, 1951
Labarres Prachtkärpfling / Labarre's Killi, "blauer" Stamm / "blue" strain
Aquarienstamm von Zaïre / Aquarium strain from Zaïre; B; 5,5 cm
▷♌◑☺☻⊞🖼➡ ⚠🔲♂   Photo: H.J. Mayland

A03884-4 *Aphyosemion labarrei* Poll, 1951
Labarres Prachtkärpfling / Labarre's Killi, "roter" Stamm / "red" strain
Aquarienstamm von Zaïre / Aquarium strain from Zaïre; B; 5,5 cm
▷♌◑☺☻⊞🖼➡ ⚠🔲♂   Photo: L. Seegers

A03884-4 *Aphyosemion labarrei* Poll, 1951
Labarres Prachtkärpfling / Labarre's Killi, "roter" Stamm / "red" strain
Aquarienstamm von Zaïre / Aquarium strain from Zaïre; B; 5,5 cm
▷♌◑☺☻⊞🖼➡ ⚠🔲♂   Photo: L. Seegers

A03383-4 *Aphyosemion lamberti* Radda & Huber, 1977
Lamberts Prachtkärpfling / Lambert's Killi, "GHP 80/5"
34 km NW Moanda, Gabun / Gabon; W; 4,5 cm
▷♌◑☺☻⊞🖼➡ ◇⚠🔲♂   Photo: E. Pürzl

A03886-4 *Aphyosemion lamberti* Radda & Huber, 1977
Lamberts Prachtkärpfling / Lambert's Killi, "G 76/10"
Région des Abeilles, 146 km NW Lastoursville, Gabon; B; 4,5 cm
▷♌◑☺☻⊞🖼➡ ◇⚠🔲♂   Photo: L. Seegers

A03887-4 *Aphyosemion lefiniense* Woeltjes, 1984
Lefini-Prachtkärpfling / Lefini Killi
Aquarienstamm / Aquarium strain from Brazzaville, Kongo; B; 4,5 cm
▷♌◑☺☻⊞🖼➡ ◇⚠🔲♂   Photo: S. Hellner-

A03888-4 *Aphyosemion lefiniense* Woeltjes, 1984
Lefini-Prachtkärpfling / Lefini Killi
La Lefini on Lefini River, 200 km N Brazzaville, Kongo; B; 4,5 cm
▷♌◑☺☻⊞🖼➡ ◇⚠🔲♂   Photo: L. Seegers

A03385-4 *Aphyosemion liberiense liberiense* (Boulenger, 1908)
Liberia-Prachtkärpfling / Liberian Killi
Monrovia, Liberia; W; 4,5 cm
▷🐟◑☺☻⊞🖼➡ ◈⚠ⓜ♂   Photo: L. Seegers

A03385-4 *Aphyosemion liberiense liberiense* (Boulenger, 1908)
Liberia-Prachtkärpfling / Liberian Killi
Monrovia, Liberia; W; 4,5 cm
▷🐟◑☺☻⊞🖼➡ ◈⚠ⓜ♂   Photo: L. Seegers

A03386-4 *Aphyosemion liberiense liberiense* (Boulenger, 1908)
Liberia-Prachtkärpfling / Liberian Killi
"mülleri"-Stamm / "muelleri"-strain; B; 4,5 cm
▷🐟◑☺☻⊞🖼➡ ◈⚠ⓜ♂   Photo: L. Seegers

A03387-4 *Aphyosemion liberiense liberiense* (Boulenger, 1908)
Liberia-Prachtkärpfling / Liberian Killi
"mülleri 3"-Stamm / "muelleri 3"-strain; B; 4,5 cm
▷🐟◑☺☻⊞🖼➡ ◈⚠ⓜ♂   Photo: L. Seegers

A03388-4 *Aphyosemion liberiense liberiense* (Boulenger, 1908)
Liberia-Prachtkärpfling / Liberian Killi
"CalDal"-Stamm / "CalDal"-strain; B; 4,5 cm
▷🐟◑☺☻⊞🖼➡ ◈⚠ⓜ♂   Photo: L. Seegers

A03889-4 *Aphyosemion liberiense liberiense* (Boulenger, 1908)
Liberia-Prachtkärpfling / Liberian Killi
Aquarium strain from Firestone Plantation, Liberia; B; 4,5 cm
▷🐟◑☺☻⊞🖼➡ ◈⚠ⓜ♂   Photo: L. Seegers

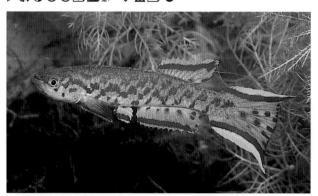

A03890-4 *Aphyosemion liberiense liberiense* (Boulenger, 1908)
Liberia-Prachtkärpfling / Liberian Killi
From Bomi 20 km before Robertsport, Liberia; W; 4,5 cm
▷🐟◑☺☻⊞🖼➡ ◈⚠ⓜ♂   Photo: L. Seegers

A03891-4 *Aphyosemion liberiense liberiense* (Boulenger, 1908)
Liberia-Prachtkärpfling / Liberian Killi
"calabarica"-Aquarienstamm / "calabarica" aquarium strain; B; 4,5 cm
▷🐟◑☺☻⊞🖼➡ ◈⚠ⓜ♂   Photo: L. Seegers

A03892-4 *Aphyosemion liberiense liberiense* (BOULENGER, 1908)
Liberia-Prachtkärpfling / Liberian Killi
Aquarienstamm / Aquarium strain; B; 4,5 cm
▷♁❶◐☺☻⊞🏞➤ ◈⚠🅼 ♂
Photo: L. Seegers

A03893-4 *Aphyosemion liberiense liberiense* (BOULENGER, 1908)
Liberia-Prachtkärpfling / Liberian Killi, "RL 20"
200 m after Bango-Town, NW Liberia; W; 4,5 cm
▷♁❶◐☺☻⊞🏞➤ ◈⚠🅼 ♂
Photo: L. Seegers

A03894-4 *Aphyosemion liberiense liberiense* (BOULENGER, 1908)
Liberia-Prachtkärpfling / Liberian Killi, "RL 29"
Monrovia - Robertsport road, 500 m after Bomi jct., Liberia; W; 4,5 cm
▷♁❶◐☺☻⊞🏞➤ ◈⚠🅼 ♂
Photo: L. Seegers

A03895-4 *Aphyosemion liberiense liberiense* (BOULENGER, 1908)
Liberia-Prachtkärpfling / Liberian Killi, "RL 40"
5 km south of Bama, NW Liberia; W; 4,5 cm
▷♁❶◐☺☻⊞🏞➤ ◈⚠🅼 ♂
Photo: L. Seegers

A03896-4 *Aphyosemion liberiense liberiense* (BOULENGER, 1908)
Liberia-Prachtkärpfling / Liberian Killi, "RL 77a"
Konala, north of Monrovia, 7 km after Soja Town, Liberia; W; 4,5 cm
▷♁❶◐☺☻⊞🏞➤ ◈⚠🅼 ♂
Photo: L. Seegers

A03897-4 *Aphyosemion liberiense liberiense* (BOULENGER, 1908)
Liberia-Prachtkärpfling / Liberian Killi, "RL 78"
Senja-Town, north of Monrovia, Liberia; W; 4,5 cm
▷♁❶◐☺☻⊞🏞➤ ◈⚠🅼 ♂
Photo: L. Seegers

A03898-4 *Aphyosemion liberiense liberiense* (BOULENGER, 1908)
Liberia-Prachtkärpfling / Liberian Killi, "RL 80"
5 km after Suehn, Liberia; W; 4,5 cm
▷♁❶◐☺☻⊞🏞➤ ◈⚠🅼 ♂
Photo: L. Seegers

A03899-4 *Aphyosemion liberiense schmitti* (ROMAND, 1979)
Schmitts Liberia-Prachtkärpfling / Schmitt's Liberian Killi
Juarzon, Liberia; B; 5,0 cm
▷♁❶◐☺☻⊞🏞➤ ◈⚠🅼 ♂
Photo: L. Seegers

A03390-4 *Aphyosemion loennbergii* (BOULENGER, 1903)
Lönnbergs Prachtkärpfling / Loennberg's Killi
Kribi, Kamerun / Kribi, Cameroon; W; 5,0 cm
▷ ♫ ◑ ☺ ☻ ⊞ ⛟ ➤ ◈ 🔲 ♂
Photo: E. Pürzl

A03390-4 *Aphyosemion loennbergii* (BOULENGER, 1903)
Lönnbergs Prachtkärpfling / Loennberg's Killi
Kribi, Kamerun / Kribi, Cameroon; W; 5,0 cm
▷ ♫ ◑ ☺ ☻ ⊞ ⛟ ➤ ◈ 🔲 ♀
Photo: E. Pürzl

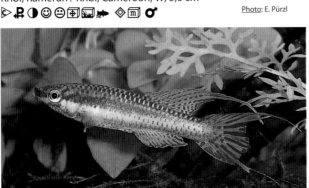

A03391-4 *Aphyosemion loennbergii* (BOULENGER, 1903)
Lönnbergs Prachtkärpfling / Loennberg's Killi, CCMP 85/12"
Soca Palm, Kamerun / Soca Palm, Cameroon; B; 5,0 cm
▷ ♫ ◑ ☺ ☻ ⊞ ⛟ ➤ ◈ 🔲 ♂
Photo: L. Seegers

A03392-4 *Aphyosemion loennbergii* (BOULENGER, 1903)
Lönnbergs Prachtkärpfling / Loennberg's Killi
Pouma, Kamerun / Pouma, Cameroon; W; 5,0 cm
▷ ♫ ◑ ☺ ☻ ⊞ ⛟ ➤ ◈ 🔲 ♂
Photo: E. Pürzl

A03393-4 *Aphyosemion loennbergii* (BOULENGER, 1903)
Lönnbergs Prachtkärpfling / Loennberg's Killi
Aquarienstamm / Aquarium strain; B; 5,0 cm
▷ ♫ ◑ ☺ ☻ ⊞ ⛟ ➤ ◈ 🔲 ♂
Photo: L. Seegers

A03394-4 *Aphyosemion loennbergii* (BOULENGER, 1903)
Lönnbergs Prachtkärpfling / Loennberg's Killi, "HJRK 92/?"
Kamerun / Cameroon; W; 5,0 cm
▷ ♫ ◑ ☺ ☻ ⊞ ⛟ ➤ ◈ 🔲 ♂
Photo: S. Hellner

A03901-4 *Aphyosemion loennbergii* (BOULENGER, 1903)
Lönnbergs Prachtkärpfling / Loennberg's Killi, "HJRK 92/20"
Mbébé, PK 50 on road Edéa-Kribi, Cameroon; B; 5,0 cm
▷ ♫ ◑ ☺ ☻ ⊞ ⛟ ➤ ◈ 🔲 ♂
Photo: W. Eigelshofen

A03902-4 *Aphyosemion loennbergii* (BOULENGER, 1903)
Lönnbergs Prachtkärpfling / Loennberg's Killi, "C 89/21"
Song Bibai, Kamerun / Song Bibai, Cameroon; B; 5,0 cm
▷ ♫ ◑ ☺ ☻ ⊞ ⛟ ➤ ◈ 🔲 ♂
Photo: R. Lütje

A03395-4 *Aphyosemion louessense* (PELLEGRIN, 1931)
Louessé-Prachtkärpfling / Louessé Killi, "RPC 31/78"
Tongo River on road Sibiti-Zanaga, Congo; W; 5,0 cm
◁ ♬ ◑ ☺ ☻ ⊞ 🐟 🐛 ◈ ⚠ 🔟 ♂   Photo: L. Seegers

A03396-4 *Aphyosemion louessense* (PELLEGRIN, 1931)
Louessé-Prachtkärpfling / Louessé Killi, "RPC 33/78"
Kingouama, Kongo / Kingouama, Congo; W; 5,0 cm
◁ ♬ ◑ ☺ ☻ ⊞ 🐟 🐛 ◈ ⚠ 🔟 ♂ ♀ (top)   Photo: L. Seegers

A03396-4 *Aphyosemion louessense* (PELLEGRIN, 1931)
Louessé-Prachtkärpfling / Louessé Killi, "RPC 33/78"
Kingouama, Kongo / Kingouama, Congo; W; 5,0 cm
◁ ♬ ◑ ☺ ☻ ⊞ 🐟 🐛 ◈ ⚠ 🔟 ♂   Photo: L. Seegers

A03397-4 *Aphyosemion louessense* (PELLEGRIN, 1931)
Louessé-Prachtkärpfling / Louessé Killi, "RPC 24/78"
1 km from Lekoli Magogo, Congo; B; 5,0 cm
◁ ♬ ◑ ☺ ☻ ⊞ 🐟 🐛 ◈ ⚠ 🔟 ♂   Photo: L. Seegers

A03398-4 *Aphyosemion lugens* AMIET, 1991
Trauer-Prachtkärpfling / Mourning Killi
Afan Essokié, Kamerun / Afan Essokié, Cameroon; F1; 5,0 cm
▷ ♬ ◑ ☺ ☻ ⊞ 🐟 🐛 ⚠ 🔟 ♂   Photo: M. Chauche

A03398-4 *Aphyosemion lugens* AMIET, 1991
Trauer-Prachtkärpfling / Mourning Killi
Afan Essokié, Kamerun / Afan Essokié, Cameroon; F1; 5,0 cm
▷ ♬ ◑ ☺ ☻ ⊞ 🐟 🐛 ⚠ 🔟 ♀   Photo: M. Chauche

A03400-4 ? *Aphyosemion lujae* (BOULENGER, 1911) [*A. cognatum?*]
Luja-Prachtkärpfling / Luja Killi
Lake Fwa, Kasai-province, Zaïre; W; 4,5 cm
▷ ♬ ◑ ☺ ☻ ⊞ 🐟 🐛 ◈ 🔟 ♂   Photo: L. Seegers

A03400-4 ? *Aphyosemion lujae* (BOULENGER, 1911) [*A. cognatum?*]
Luja-Prachtkärpfling / Luja Killi
Lake Fwa, Kasai-province, Zaïre; W; 4,5 cm
▷ ♬ ◑ ☺ ☻ ⊞ 🐟 🐛 ◈ 🔟 ♀   Photo: L. Seegers

A03402-4 *Aphyosemion maculatum* RADDA & PÜRZL, 1977
Gefleckter Prachtkärpfling / Speckled Killi, "G 75/36" [T.t.]
33 km E Koumameyong on RN 4, northern Gabon; W; 4,5 cm
◁ ▷ ♫ ◖ ☺ ☹ ⊞ 🖼 🐾 ◈ ⚠ 🔲 ♂   Photo: E. Pürzl

A03402-4 *Aphyosemion maculatum* RADDA & PÜRZL, 1977
Gefleckter Prachtkärpfling / Speckled Killi, "G 75/36" [T.t.]
33 km E Koumameyong on RN 4, northern Gabon; W; 4,5 cm
◁ ▷ ♫ ◖ ☺ ☹ ⊞ 🖼 🐾 ◈ ⚠ 🔲 ♀   Photo: E. Pürzl

A03402-3 *Aphyosemion maculatum* RADDA & PÜRZL, 1977
Gefleckter Prachtkärpfling / Speckled Killi, "G 75/36" [T.t.]
33 km E Koumameyong on RN 4, northern Gabon; W; 4,5 cm
◁ ▷ ♫ ◖ ☺ ☹ ⊞ 🖼 🐾 ◈ ⚠ 🔲 ♂   Photo: L. Seegers

A03403-4 *Aphyosemion maculatum* RADDA & PÜRZL, 1977
Gefleckter Prachtkärpfling / Speckled Killi
Koumameyong, Nord-Gabun / Northern Gabon; B; 4,5 cm
◁ ▷ ♫ ◖ ☺ ☹ ⊞ 🖼 🐾 ◈ ⚠ 🔲 ♂   Photo: L. Seegers

A03903-4 *Aphyosemion maculatum* RADDA & PÜRZL, 1977
Gefleckter Prachtkärpfling / Speckled Killi, "GAB 90/19"
33 km E Koumameyong on RN 4, northern Gabon; B; 4,5 cm
◁ ▷ ♫ ◖ ☺ ☹ ⊞ 🖼 🐾 ◈ ⚠ 🔲 ♂   Photo: R. Lütje

A03904-4 *Aphyosemion maculatum* RADDA & PÜRZL, 1977
Gefleckter Prachtkärpfling / Speckled Killi, "LEC 93/4"
Ebé, 12 km from Ovan on road to Koumameyong, N Gabon; W; 4,5 cm
◁ ▷ ♫ ◖ ☺ ☹ ⊞ 🖼 🐾 ◈ ⚠ 🔲 ♂   Photo: R. Lütje

A03905-4 *Aphyosemion maculatum* RADDA & PÜRZL, 1977
Gefleckter Prachtkärpfling / Speckled Killi, "PEG 93/14"
Matora, 18 km W of crossing in Koumameyong, N Gabon; W; 4,5 cm
◁ ▷ ♫ ◖ ☺ ☹ ⊞ 🖼 🐾 ◈ ⚠ 🔲 ♂   Photo: R. Lütje

A03906-4 *Aphyosemion maculatum* RADDA & PÜRZL, 1977
Gefleckter Prachtkärpfling / Speckled Killi, "PEG 94/17"
Lolo I, NW Koumameyong, Nord-Gabun / N Gabon; W; 4,5 cm
◁ ▷ ♫ ◖ ☺ ☹ ⊞ 🖼 🐾 ◈ ⚠ 🔲 ♂   Photo: R. Lütje

A03907-4 *Aphyosemion maeseni* POLL, 1941
Maesens Prachtkärpfling / Maesen's Killi
Beple, Nordost-Liberia / Beple, northeastern Liberia; B; 5,5 cm
◁ ₿ ◑ ☺ ☻ ⊞ 🖼 ➤ ◈ ⚠ 🎞 ♂   Photo: S. Hellner

A03908-4 *Aphyosemion maeseni* POLL, 1941
Maesens Prachtkärpfling / Maesen's Killi
Gouessesso, W-Elfenbeinküste / Western Ivory Coast; B; 5,5 cm
◁ ₿ ◑ ☺ ☻ ⊞ 🖼 ➤ ◈ ⚠ 🎞 ♂   Photo: L. Seegers

A03909-4 *Aphyosemion maeseni* POLL, 1941
Maesens Prachtkärpfling / Maesen's Killi
Lema, Liberia; B; 5,5 cm
◁ ₿ ◑ ☺ ☻ ⊞ 🖼 ➤ ◈ ⚠ 🎞 ♂   Photo: L. Seegers

A03909-4 *Aphyosemion maeseni* POLL, 1941
Maesens Prachtkärpfling / Maesen's Killi
Lema, Liberia; B; 5,5 cm
◁ ₿ ◑ ☺ ☻ ⊞ 🖼 ➤ ◈ ⚠ 🎞 ♀   Photo: L. Seegers

A03910-4 *Aphyosemion maeseni* POLL, 1941
Maesens Prachtkärpfling / Maesen's Killi
Liberia; B; 5,5 cm
◁ ₿ ◑ ☺ ☻ ⊞ 🖼 ➤ ◈ ⚠ 🎞 ♂   Photo: E. Pürzl

A03406-4 *Aphyosemion marmoratum* RADDA, 1973
Marmorierter Prachtkärpfling / Marbled Killi
6 km after Meme River on road to Funge, W Cameroon; W; 5,0 cm
▷ ₿ ◑ ☺ ☻ ⊞ 🖼 ➤ ◈ 🎞 ♂   Photo: L. Seegers

A03405-4 *Aphyosemion marmoratum* RADDA, 1973
Marmorierter Prachtkärpfling / Marbled Killi [T.t.]
16 km NE Mbonge on road to Kumba, western Cameroon; W; 5,0 cm
▷ ₿ ◑ ☺ ☻ ⊞ 🖼 ➤ ◈ 🎞 ♂   Photo: E. Pürzl

A03405-4 *Aphyosemion marmoratum* RADDA, 1973
Marmorierter Prachtkärpfling / Marbled Killi [T.t.]
16 km NE Mbonge on road to Kumba, western Cameroon; W; 5,0 cm
▷ ₿ ◑ ☺ ☻ ⊞ 🖼 ➤ ◈ 🎞 ♀   Photo: E. Pürzl

A03410-4 *Aphyosemion mimbon* HUBER, 1977
Mimbon-Prachtkärpfling / Mimbon Killi
Edoum, Nord-Gabun / Edoum, northern Gabon; B; 4,5 cm
◁ ♫ ◑ ☺ ☺ 🎛 🗺➡ ◈ ⚠ 🔲 ♂   Photo: S. Hellner-

A03411-4 *Aphyosemion mimbon* HUBER, 1977
Mimbon-Prachtkärpfling / Mimbon Killi, "LEC 93/18"
16 km W Médouneu on road to Libreville, northern Gabon; B; 4,5 cm
◁ ♫ ◑ ☺ ☺ 🎛 🗺➡ ◈ ⚠ 🔲 ♂   Photo: R. Lütje

A03412-4 *Aphyosemion mimbon* HUBER, 1977
Mimbon-Prachtkärpfling / Mimbon Killi, "GEB 94/25"
Oyab River, 1 km N Edoum, northern Gabon; B; 4,5 cm
◁ ♫ ◑ ☺ ☺ 🎛 🗺➡ ◈ ⚠ 🔲 ♂   Photo: R. Lütje

A03413-4 *Aphyosemion mimbon* HUBER, 1977
Mimbon-Prachtkärpfling / Mimbon Killi, "PEG 94/45"
Avang, 18 km SW Edoum, northern Gabon; B; 4,5 cm
◁ ♫ ◑ ☺ ☺ 🎛 🗺➡ ◈ ⚠ 🔲 ♂   Photo: R. Lütje

A03414-4 *Aphyosemion (F.) mirabile mirabile* RADDA, 1970
Wunderkärpfling / Miracle Killi
Mbio, on road to Kumba, western Cameroon; B; 6,0 cm
▷ ♫ ◑ ☺ ☺ 🎛 🗺🐛➡ ◈ 🔲 ♂   Photo: L. Seegers

A03415-3 *Aphyosemion (F.) mirabile mirabile* RADDA, 1970
Wunderkärpfling / Miracle Killi
Bakebe-area, western Cameroon; W; 6,0 cm
▷ ♫ ◑ ☺ ☺ 🎛 🗺➡ ◈ 🔲 ♂   Photo: L. Seegers

A03415-4 *Aphyosemion (F.) mirabile intermittens* RADDA, 1974
Wunderkärpfling / Miracle Killi [T.t.]
Bakebe, West-Kamerun / Bakebe, western Cameroon; W; 6,0 cm
▷ ♫ ◑ ☺ ☺ 🎛 🗺➡ ◈ 🔲 ♂   Photo: E. Pürzl

A03416-4 *Aphyosemion (F.) mirabile intermittens* RADDA, 1974
Wunderkärpfling / Miracle Killi
Tinto, West-Kamerun / Tinto, western Cameroon; W; 6,0 cm
▷ ♫ ◑ ☺ ☺ 🎛 🗺➡ ◈ 🔲 ♂   Photo: L. Seegers

A03419-4 *Aphyosemion (F.) mirabile moense* RADDA, 1970
Wunderkärpfling / Miracle Killi [T.t.]
Between Kendem and Noumba, western Cameroon; W; 6,0 cm
▷♨◐☺☹⊞🖼➤ ◈🅜 ♂   Photo: E. Pürzl

A03420-4 *Aphyosemion (F.) mirabile traudeae* RADDA, 1971
Wunderkärpfling / Miracle Killi [T.t.]
Manyemen, West-Kamerun / Western Cameroon; B; 6,0 cm
▷♨◐☺☹⊞🖼➤ ◈🅜 ♂   Photo: L. Seegers

A03421-4 *Aphyosemion (F.) mirabile traudeae* RADDA, 1971
Wunderkärpfling / Miracle Killi
West-Kamerun / Western Cameroon; W; 6,0 cm
▷♨◐☺☹⊞🖼➤ ◈🅜 ♂   Photo: L. Seegers

A03422-4 *Aphyosemion (F.) mirabile traudeae* RADDA, 1971
Wunderkärpfling / Miracle Killi
Aquarienstamm / Aquarium strain; B; 6,0 cm
▷♨◐☺☹⊞🖼➤ ◈🅜 ♂   Photo: L. Seegers

A03423-4 *Aphyosemion (F.) mirabile traudeae* RADDA, 1971
Wunderkärpfling / Miracle Killi
8 km from crossing Bakebe-Bingwa-Nguti to Nguti, Cameroon; W; 6,0 cm
▷♨◐☺☹⊞🖼➤ ◈🅜 ♂   Photo: L. Seegers

A03424-4 *Aphyosemion (F.) sp. aff. mirabile* RADDA, 1970
Wunderkärpfling / Miracle Killi
Takwai, West-Kamerun / Western Cameroon; B; 6,0 cm
▷♨◐☺☹⊞🖼➤ ◈🅜 ♂   Photo: E. Pürzl

A03425-4 *Aphyosemion (F.) sp. aff. mirabile* RADDA, 1970
Wunderkärpfling / Miracle Killi
Takwai, West-Kamerun / Western Cameroon; W; 6,0 cm
▷♨◐☺☹⊞🖼➤ ◈🅜 ♂   Photo: L. Seegers

A03425-4 *Aphyosemion (F.) sp. aff. mirabile* RADDA, 1970
Wunderkärpfling / Miracle Killi
Takwai, West-Kamerun / Western Cameroon; W; 6,0 cm
▷♨◐☺☹⊞🖼➤ ◈🅜 ♀   Photo: L. Seegers

A03427-4 *Aphyosemion monroviae* Roloff & Ladiges, 1972
Monrovia-Prachtkärpfling / Monrovia Killi [T.t.], roter Phänotypus
25 Meilen von Monrovia / 25 miles from Monrovia, Liberia; B; 7,0 cm
▷⚠♗◑☺☹⊞▣➤ ◈⚠⊞ ♂   Photo: L. Seegers

A03428-4 *Aphyosemion monroviae* Roloff & Ladiges, 1972
Monrovia-Prachtkärpfling / Monrovia Killi [T.t.], blauer Phänotypus
25 Meilen von Monrovia / 25 miles from Monrovia, Liberia; B; 7,0 cm
▷⚠♗◑☺☹⊞▣➤ ◈⚠⊞ ♂   Photo: L. Seegers

A03429-4 *Aphyosemion monroviae* Roloff & Ladiges, 1972
Monrovia-Prachtkärpfling / Monrovia Killi
Aquarienstamm / Aquarium strain; B; 7,0 cm
▷⚠♗◑☺☹⊞▣➤ ◈⚠⊞ ♂   Photo: H.J. Mayland

A03429-4 *Aphyosemion monroviae* Roloff & Ladiges, 1972
Monrovia-Prachtkärpfling / Monrovia Killi
Aquarienstamm / Aquarium strain; B; 7,0 cm
▷⚠♗◑☺☹⊞▣➤ ◈⚠⊞ ♂   Photo: E. Pürzl

A03426-4 *Aphyosemion monroviae* Roloff & Ladiges, 1972
Monrovia-Prachtkärpfling / Monrovia Killi
Harbel, Liberia; B; 7,0 cm
▷⚠♗◑☺☹⊞▣➤ ◈⚠⊞ ♂   Photo: L. Seegers

A03430-4 *Aphyosemion (F.) ndianum* Scheel, 1968
Ndian-Prachtkärpfling / Ndian Killi
Aquarienstamm / Aquarium strain; B; 7,0 cm
▷♗◑☺☹⊞▣➤ ◈⚠⊞ ♂   Photo: L. Seegers

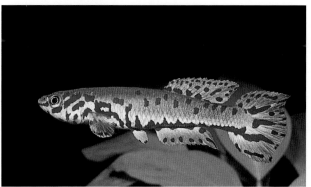

A03431-4 *Aphyosemion (F.) ndianum* Scheel, 1968
Ndian-Prachtkärpfling / Ndian Killi
Südost-Nigeria / Southeastern Nigeria; B; 7,0 cm
▷♗◑☺☹⊞▣➤ ◈⚠⊞ ♂   Photo: E. Pürzl

A03431-4 *Aphyosemion (F.) ndianum* Scheel, 1968
Ndian-Prachtkärpfling / Ndian Killi
Südost-Nigeria / Southeastern Nigeria; B; 7,0 cm
▷♗◑☺☹⊞▣➤ ◈⚠⊞ ♀   Photo: E. Pürzl

A03445-4 *Aphyosemion occidentale occidentale* CLAUSEN, 1966
Goldfasan-Prachtkärpfling / Golden Pheasant
Largo, Sierra Leone, "roter" Phänotyp / "red" phenotype; B; 8,0 cm
▷⚠️🅱️◑☺☹⊞🔜➡ ◈⚠️🔲 ♂ Photo: E. Pürzl

A03446-4 *Aphyosemion occidentale occidentale* CLAUSEN, 1966
Goldfasan-Prachtkärpfling / Golden Pheasant
Largo, Sierra Leone, "blauer" Phänotyp / "blue" phenotype; B; 8,0 cm
▷⚠️🅱️◑☺☹⊞🔜➡ ◈⚠️🔲 ♂ Photo: E. Pürzl

A03911-4 *Aphyosemion occidentale occidentale* CLAUSEN, 1966
Goldfasan-Prachtkärpfling / Golden Pheasant, "*A. huwaldi*-Stamm"
Near Ngabu, 20 km from Moyamba, Sierra Leone; F₁; 8,0 cm
▷⚠️🅱️◑☺☹⊞🔜➡ ◈⚠️🔲 ♂ Photo: L. Seegers

A03911-4 *Aphyosemion occidentale occidentale* CLAUSEN, 1966
Goldfasan-Prachtkärpfling / Golden Pheasant, "*A. huwaldi*-Stamm"
Near Ngabu, 20 km from Moyamba, Sierra Leone; F₁; 8,0 cm
▷⚠️🅱️◑☺☹⊞🔜➡ ◈⚠️ ♀ Photo: L. Seegers

A03912-4 *Aphyosemion occidentale occidentale* CLAUSEN, 1966
Goldfasan-Prachtkärpfling / Golden Pheasant
Moyamba, Sierra Leone; B; 8,0 cm
▷⚠️🅱️◑☺☹⊞🔜➡ ◈⚠️🔲 ♂ Photo: E. Pürzl

A03913-4 *Aphyosemion occidentale occidentale* CLAUSEN, 1966
Goldfasan-Prachtkärpfling / Golden Pheasant
Bahama, Sierra Leone; B; 8,0 cm
▷⚠️🅱️◑☺☹⊞🔜➡ ◈⚠️🔲 ♂ Photo: L. Seegers

A03914-4 *Aphyosemion occidentale occidentale* CLAUSEN, 1966
Goldfasan-Prachtkärpfling / Golden Pheasant
Magbenta, Sierra Leone; F₁; 8,0 cm
▷⚠️🅱️◑☺☹⊞🔜➡ ◈⚠️🔲 ♂ Photo: S. Hellner

A03915-4 *Aphyosemion occidentale occidentale* CLAUSEN, 1966
Goldfasan-Prachtkärpfling / Golden Pheasant, "SL 89"
Fallaba, Sierra Leone; W; 8,0 cm
▷⚠️🅱️◑☺☹⊞🔜➡ ◈⚠️🔲 ♂ Photo: S. Hellner

A03916-4 *Aphyosemion occidentale occidentale* CLAUSEN, 1966
Goldfasan-Prachtkärpfling / Golden Pheasant, "SL 89"
Teme Yellah, Sierra Leone; B; 8,0 cm
▷⚠🅱🌓◐☺☹⊞🖼🐛 ◈⚠ⓜ ♂   Photo: S. Hellner

A03917-4 *Aphyosemion occidentale occidentale* CLAUSEN, 1966
Goldfasan-Prachtkärpfling / Golden Pheasant, "SL 89"
Wanja River, Sierra Leone; B; 8,0 cm
▷⚠🅱🌓◐☺☹⊞🖼🐛➤ ◈⚠ⓜ ♂   Photo: S. Hellner

A03918-4 *Aphyosemion occidentale occidentale* CLAUSEN, 1966
Goldfasan-Prachtkärpfling / Golden Pheasant, "SL 89"
Romeni, Sierra Leone; W; 8,0 cm
▷⚠🅱◐☺☹⊞🖼🐛➤ ◈⚠ⓜ ♂   Photo: S. Hellner

A03918-4 *Aphyosemion occidentale occidentale* CLAUSEN, 1966
Goldfasan-Prachtkärpfling / Golden Pheasant, "SL 89"
Romeni, Sierra Leone; B; 8,0 cm
▷⚠🅱🌓◐☺☹⊞🖼🐛➤ ◈⚠ⓜ ♂   Photo: E. Pürzl

A03550-4 *Aphyosemion occidentale toddi* CLAUSEN, 1966
Blauer Goldfasan-Prachtkärpfling / Blue Golden Pheasant
Aquarienstamm von Barmoi, Sierra Leone; B; 8,0 cm
▷⚠🅱🌓◐☺☹⊞🖼🐛➤ ◈⚠ⓜ ♂   Photo: L. Seegers

A03550-4 *Aphyosemion occidentale toddi* CLAUSEN, 1966
Blauer Goldfasan-Prachtkärpfling / Blue Golden Pheasant
Aquarienstamm von Barmoi, Sierra Leone; B; 8,0 cm
▷⚠🅱🌓◐☺☹⊞🖼🐛➤ ◈⚠ⓜ ♂   Photo: S. Hellner

A03447-4 *Aphyosemion ocellatum* HUBER & RADDA, 1977
Schulterfleck-Prachtkärpfling / Ocellated Killi, "G 20/76" [T.t.]
6 km W Mimongo on road to Lebamba, Ngounié, Gabon; W; 4,5 cm
◁ 🅱🅿🌓◐☺☹⊞🖼🐛➤ ◈⚠ⓜ ♂   Photo: E. Pürzl

A03447-4 *Aphyosemion ocellatum* HUBER & RADDA, 1977
Schulterfleck-Prachtkärpfling / Ocellated Killi, "G 20/76" [T.t.]
6 km W Mimongo on road to Lebamba, Ngounié, Gabon; W; 4,5 cm
◁ 🅱🅿🌓◐☺☹⊞🖼🐛➤ ◈⚠ⓜ ♀   Photo: E. Pürzl

A03447-4 *Aphyosemion ocellatum* HUBER & RADDA, 1977
Schulterfleck-Prachtkärpfling / Ocellated Killi, "G 20/76" [T.t.]
6 km W Mimongo on road to Lebamba, Ngounié, Gabon; W; 4,5 cm
◁ ♬♩℘ ◑☺☻⊞🐟➡ ◈⚠ⓜ ♂   Photo: E. Pürzl

A03919-4 *Aphyosemion ocellatum* HUBER & RADDA, 1977
Schulterfleck-Prachtkärpfling / Ocellated Killi, "G 80/6"
2 km NW Mbigou, Gabon; B; 4,5 cm
◁ ♬♩℘ ◑☺☻⊞🐟➡ ◈⚠ⓜ ♂   Photo: L. Seegers

A03920-4 *Aphyosemion ocellatum* HUBER & RADDA, 1977
Schulterfleck-Prachtkärpfling / Ocellated Killi
Bolapessa, Gabun / Bolapessa, Gabon; W; 4,5 cm
◁ ♬♩℘ ◑☺☻⊞🐟➡ ◈⚠ⓜ ♂   Photo: E. Pürzl

A03921-3 *Aphyosemion ocellatum* HUBER & RADDA, 1977
Schulterfleck-Prachtkärpfling / Ocellated Killi
Zenzele, Gabun / Zenzele, Gabon; B; 4,5 cm
◁ ♬♩℘ ◑☺☻⊞🐟➡ ◈⚠ⓜ ♂   Photo: R. Lütje

A03922-4 *Aphyosemion ocellatum* HUBER & RADDA, 1977
Schulterfleck-Prachtkärpfling / Ocellated Killi, "PEG 93/9"
Gabun / Gabon; W; 4,5 cm
◁ ♬♩℘ ◑☺☻⊞🐟➡ ◈⚠ⓜ ♂   Photo: R. Lütje

A03923-4 *Aphyosemion ocellatum* HUBER & RADDA, 1977
Schulterfleck-Prachtkärpfling / Ocellated Killi, "PEG 96/22"
Gabun / Gabon; W; 4,5 cm
◁ ♬♩℘ ◑☺☻⊞🐟➡ ◈⚠ⓜ ♂   Photo: R. Lütje

A03449-4 *Aphyosemion oeseri* (SCHMIDT, 1928)
Fernando Poo-Prachtkärpfling, Ösers Prachtkärpfling / Oeser's Killi
Fernando Poo (= Bioko), Äquatorialguinea / Equatorial Guinea; B; 6,0 cm
▷♬ ◑☺☻⊞🐟➡ ◈ⓜ ♂   Photo: L. Seegers

A03449-4 *Aphyosemion oeseri* (SCHMIDT, 1928)
Fernando Poo-Prachtkärpfling, Ösers Prachtkärpfling / Oeser's Killi
Fernando Poo (= Bioko), Äquatorialguinea / Equatorial Guinea; B; 6,0 cm
▷♬ ◑☺☻⊞🐟➡ ◈ⓜ ♂   Photo: H.J. Mayland

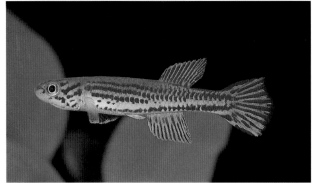

A03450-4 *Aphyosemion ogoense ogoense* (PELLEGRIN, 1930)
Ogowe-Prachtkärpfling / Ogowe Killi, "RPC 207"
Bambama, Kongo / Bambama, Congo; W; 5,5 cm
◁ ♫♪✿ ◑ ☺ ☻ ⊞ 🖭 ➤ ◈ ⚠ 🔲 ♂   Photo: E. Pürzl

A03450-4 *Aphyosemion ogoense ogoense* (PELLEGRIN, 1930)
Ogowe-Prachtkärpfling / Ogowe Killi, "RPC 207"
Bambama, Kongo / Bambama, Congo; W; 5,5 cm
◁ ♫♪✿ ◑ ☺ ☻ ⊞ 🖭 ➤ ◈ ⚠ 🔲 ♂   Photo: L. Seegers

A03451-4 *Aphyosemion ogoense ogoense* (PELLEGRIN, 1930)
Ogowe-Prachtkärpfling / Ogowe Killi, "GHP 24/80"
Mongouango, 61 km S Franceville, Gabon; W; 5,5 cm
◁ ♫♪✿ ◑ ☺ ☻ ⊞ 🖭 ➤ ◈ ⚠ 🔲 ♂   Photo: E. Pürzl

A03453-4 *Aphyosemion ogoense ottogartneri* RADDA, 1980
Ogowe-Prachtkärpfling / Ogowe Killi, "NSC 4"
Lutete, Nord-Kongo / Lutete, northern Congo; B; 5,5 cm
▷ ♫♪✿ ◑ ☺ ☻ ⊞ 🖭 ➤ ◈ ⚠ 🔲 ♂   Photo: L. Seegers

A03453-4 *Aphyosemion ogoense ottogartneri* RADDA, 1980
Ogowe-Prachtkärpfling / Ogowe Killi, "NSC 4"
Lutete, Nord-Kongo / Lutete, northern Congo; B; 5,5 cm
▷ ♫♪✿ ◑ ☺ ☻ ⊞ 🖭 ➤ ◈ ⚠ 🔲 ♂   Photo: L. Seegers

A03454-4 *Aphyosemion ogoense ottogartneri* RADDA, 1980
Ogowe-Prachtkärpfling / Ogowe Killi
Gabun / Gabon; W; 5,5 cm
▷ ♫♪✿ ◑ ☺ ☻ ⊞ 🖭 ➤ ◈ ⚠ 🔲 ♂   Photo: E. Pürzl

A03456-4 *Aphyosemion ogoense ottogartneri* RADDA, 1980
Ogowe-Prachtkärpfling / Ogowe Killi, "RPC 170"
Kindamba, Kongo / Kindamba, Congo; B; 5,5 cm
▷ ♫♪✿ ◑ ☺ ☻ ⊞ 🖭 ➤ ◈ ⚠ 🔲 ♂   Photo: E. Pürzl

A03456-4 *Aphyosemion ogoense ottogartneri* RADDA, 1980
Ogowe-Prachtkärpfling / Ogowe Killi, "RPC 170"
Kindamba, Kongo / Kindamba, Congo; B; 5,5 cm
▷ ♫♪✿ ◑ ☺ ☻ ⊞ 🖭 ➤ ◈ ⚠ 🔲 ♂   Photo: L. Seegers

A03924-4 *Aphyosemion ogoense ottogartneri* RADDA, 1980
Ogowe-Prachtkärpfling / Ogowe Killi, "G 212"
30 km W Malinga, Gabun / Gabon; B; 5,5 cm
▷ 🐟💲🅟 ◑ ☺ ☺ ⊞ 🖼 ➡ ◈ ⚠ 🔟 ♂   Photo: L. Seegers

A03452-4 *Aphyosemion ogoense pyrophore* RADDA, 1980
Flammenschwanz-Prachtkärpfling / Flame-tailed Killi, "GHP 1/80"
2 km E Mvengue, W Franceville, Gabun / Gabon; W; 5,5 cm
◁ 🐟💲🅟 ◑ ☺ ☺ ⊞ 🖼 ➡ ◈ ⚠ 🔟 ♂   Photo: E. Pürzl

A03925-4 *Aphyosemion ogoense pyrophore* RADDA, 1980
Flammenschwanz-Prachtkärpfling / Flame-tailed Killi, "GHP 1/80"
2 km E Mvengue, W Franceville, Gabun / Gabon; B; 5,5 cm
◁ 🐟💲🅟 ◑ ☺ ☺ ⊞ 🖼 ➡ ◈ ⚠ 🔟 ♂   Photo: L. Seegers

A03926-4 *Aphyosemion ogoense pyrophore* RADDA, 1980
Flammenschwanz-Prachtkärpfling / Flame-tailed Killi, "GHP 23/80"
Mopia, 30 km S Franceville, Gabun / Gabon; B; 5,5 cm
◁ 🐟💲🅟 ◑ ☺ ☺ ⊞ 🖼 ➡ ◈ ⚠ 🔟 ♂   Photo: L. Seegers

A03927-4 *Aphyosemion ogoense pyrophore* RADDA, 1980
Flammenschwanz-Prachtkärpfling / Flame-tailed Killi, "GHP 23/80"
Mopia, 30 km S Franceville, Gabun / Gabon; W; 5,5 cm
◁ 🐟💲🅟 ◑ ☺ ☺ ⊞ 🖼 ➡ ◈ ⚠ 🔟 ♂   Photo: E. Pürzl

A03927-4 *Aphyosemion ogoense pyrophore* RADDA, 1980
Flammenschwanz-Prachtkärpfling / Flame-tailed Killi, "GHP 23/80"
Mopia, 30 km S Franceville, Gabun / Gabon; W; 5,5 cm
◁ 🐟💲🅟 ◑ ☺ ☺ ⊞ 🖼 ➡ ◈ ⚠ 🔟 ♀   Photo: E. Pürzl

A03928-4 *Aphyosemion ogoense pyrophore* RADDA, 1980
Flammenschwanz-Prachtkärpfling / Flame-tailed Killi
Komono, Kongo / Komono, Congo; B; 5,5 cm
◁ 🐟💲🅟 ◑ ☺ ☺ ⊞ 🖼 ➡ ◈ ⚠ 🔟 ♂   Photo: E. Pürzl

A03928-4 *Aphyosemion ogoense pyrophore* RADDA, 1980
Flammenschwanz-Prachtkärpfling / Flame-tailed Killi
Komono, Kongo / Komono, Congo; B; 5,5 cm
◁ 🐟💲🅟 ◑ ☺ ☺ ⊞ 🖼 ➡ ◈ ⚠ 🔟 ♀   Photo: E. Pürzl

A03929-4 *Aphyosemion ogoense pyrophore* Radda, 1980
Flammenschwanz-Prachtkärpfling / Flame-tailed Killi, "CMBB 89/14"
Mbila, Kongo / Mbila, Congo; B; 5,5 cm
◁ ♫ℙ ◑ ☺ ☻ ⊞ 🖼 ➹ ◈ ⚠ 🔲 ♂
Photo: H.J. Mayland

A03930-4 *Aphyosemion ogoense pyrophore* Radda, 1980
Flammenschwanz-Prachtkärpfling / Flame-tailed Killi, "RPC 78/18"
Road Mossendjo-Komono, 5 km after Mpoukou River, Congo; W; 5,5 cm
◁ ♫ℙ ◑ ☺ ☻ ⊞ 🖼 ➹ ◈ ⚠ 🔲 ♂ ♀
Photo: L. Seegers

A03457-4 *Aphyosemion pascheni* (Ahl, 1928)
Grauer Prachtkärpfling / Paschen's Killi
20 km after Kribi on road to Bipindi, Cameroon; W; 5,0 cm
▷ ♫ℙ ◑ ☺ ☻ ⊞ 🖼 ➹ ◈ ⚠ 🔲 ♂
Photo: E. Pürzl

A03458-4 *Aphyosemion pascheni* (Ahl, 1928)
Grauer Prachtkärpfling / Paschen's Killi
Aquarienstamm, Kamerun / Aquarium strain, Cameroon; B; 5,0 cm
▷ ♫ℙ ◑ ☺ ☻ ⊞ 🖼 ➹ ◈ ⚠ 🔲 ♀
Photo: L. Seegers

A03458-4 *Aphyosemion pascheni* (Ahl, 1928)
Grauer Prachtkärpfling / Paschen's Killi
Aquarienstamm, Kamerun / Aquarium strain, Cameroon; B; 5,0 cm
▷ ♫ℙ ◑ ☺ ☻ ⊞ 🖼 ➹ ◈ ⚠ 🔲 ♂
Photo: S. Hellner

A03458-4 *Aphyosemion pascheni* (Ahl, 1928)
Grauer Prachtkärpfling / Paschen's Killi
Aquarienstamm, Kamerun / Aquarium strain, Cameroon; B; 5,0 cm
▷ ♫ℙ ◑ ☺ ☻ ⊞ 🖼 ➹ ◈ ⚠ 🔲 ♂
Photo: L. Seegers

A03931-4 *Aphyosemion passaroi* Huber, 1994
Passaros Prachtkärpfling / Passaro's Killi, "PEG 93/10"
Gabun / Gabon; W; 4,5 cm
◁ ▷ ♫ℙ ◑ ☺ ☻ ⊞ 🖼 ➹ ◈ ⚠ 🔲 ♂
Photo: R. Lütje

A03931-4 *Aphyosemion passaroi* Huber, 1994
Passaros Prachtkärpfling / Passaro's Killi, "GBN 88/24"
Gabun / Gabon; B; 4,5 cm
◁ ▷ ♫ℙ ◑ ☺ ☻ ⊞ 🖼 ➹ ◈ ⚠ 🔲 ♀
Photo: S. Hellner-

A03460-4 *Aphyosemion petersi* (Sauvage, 1882)
Peters' Prachtkärpfling / Peters' Killi
Banco NP, Abidjan, Südost-Elfenbeinküste / SE Ivory Coast; B; 4,5 cm
▷△♫❶◐☺☻⊞◫➨ ◈⚠▥ ♂
Photo: L. Seegers

A03460-4 *Aphyosemion petersi* (Sauvage, 1882)
Peters' Prachtkärpfling / Peters' Killi
Banco NP, Abidjan, Südost-Elfenbeinküste / SE Ivory Coast; B; 4,5 cm
▷△♫❶◐☺☻⊞◫➨ ◈⚠▥ ♀
Photo: L. Seegers

A03932-4 *Aphyosemion petersi* (Sauvage, 1882)
Peters' Prachtkärpfling / Peters' Killi
Bonoua, Südost-Elfenbeinküste / SE Ivory Coast; W; 4,5 cm
▷△♫❶◐☺☻⊞◫➨ ◈⚠▥ ♂
Photo: E. Pürzl

A03933-4 *Aphyosemion petersi* (Sauvage, 1882)
Peters' Prachtkärpfling / Peters' Killi, "CI 54"
Südost-Elfenbeinküste / SE Ivory Coast; B; 4,5 cm
▷△♫❶◐☺☻⊞◫➨ ◈⚠▥ ♂
Photo: L. Seegers

A03934-4 *Aphyosemion petersi* (Sauvage, 1882)
Peters' Prachtkärpfling / Peters' Killi
Toupa Falls, Südost-Elfenbeinküste / SE Ivory Coast; B; 4,5 cm
▷△♫❶◐☺☻⊞◫➨ ◈⚠▥ ♂
Photo: L. Seegers

A03935-4 *Aphyosemion petersi* (Sauvage, 1882)
Peters' Prachtkärpfling / Peters' Killi
Awaso, Ghana; W; 4,5 cm
▷△♫❶◐☺☻⊞◫➨ ◈⚠▥ ♂
Photo: E. Pürzl

A03462-4 *Aphyosemion poliaki* Amiet, 1991
Mt. Kamerun-Prachtkärpfling / Mt. Kamerun-Killi, "C 94/3"
33 km from Limbe on Limbe-Kumba road, Cameroon; B; 5,5 cm
◁ ♫❶◐☺☻⊞◫➨ ◈⚠▥ ♂
Photo: W. Eigelshofen

A03463-4 *Aphyosemion poliaki* Amiet, 1991
Mt. Kamerun-Prachtkärpfling / Mt. Kamerun-Killi
"Mile 29", slopes of Mt. Cameroon, Cameroon; B; 5,5 cm
◁ ♫❶◐☺☻⊞◫➨ ◈⚠▥ ♂
Photo: W. Eigelshofen

A03465-4 *Aphyosemion primigenium* RADDA & HUBER, 1977
Douano-Prachtkärpfling / Douano Killi, "G 27/76" [T.t.]
Douano-system near Banyanga, Mayumbe Mountains, Gabon; W; 4,5 cm
◁ ▷ ₿ ◑ ☺ ☻ ⊞ 🐛 ➠ ◈ ⚠ 🔲 ♂   Photo: E. Pürzl

A03466-4 *Aphyosemion primigenium* RADDA & HUBER, 1977
Douano-Prachtkärpfling / Douano Killi, "G 24/76"
Lebamba, Gabun / Lebamba, Gabon; W; 4,5 cm
◁ ▷ ₿ ◑ ☺ ☻ ⊞ 🐛 ➠ ◈ ⚠ 🔲 ♂   Photo: E. Pürzl

A03467-4 *Aphyosemion primigenium* RADDA & HUBER, 1977
Douano-Prachtkärpfling / Douano Killi, "G 23/76"
Douano-system, Mayumbe Mountains, Gabon; B; 4,5 cm
◁ ▷ ₿ ◑ ☺ ☻ ⊞ 🐛 ➠ ◈ ⚠ 🔲 ♂   Photo: L. Seegers

A03468-4 *Aphyosemion primigenium* RADDA & HUBER, 1977
Douano-Prachtkärpfling / Douano Killi
Mutante, Aquarienstamm / Aquarium strain; B; 4,5 cm
◁ ▷ ₿ ◑ ☺ ☻ ⊞ 🐛 ➠ ◈ ⚠ 🔲 ♂   Photo: L. Seegers

A03470-4 *Aphyosemion (F.) puerzli* RADDA & SCHEEL, 1974
Pürzls Prachtkärpfling / Puerzl's Killi [T.t.]
27 km NE crossing Douala-Edea-Yabassi to Yabassi, Cameroon; W; 7,0 cm
▷ ⚠ ₿ ◑ ☺ ☻ ⊞ 🐛 ➠ ◈ 🔲 ♂   Photo: E. Pürzl

A03470-4 *Aphyosemion (F.) puerzli* RADDA & SCHEEL, 1974
Pürzls Prachtkärpfling / Puerzl's Killi [T.t.]
27 km NE crossing Douala-Edea-Yabassi to Yabassi, Cameroon; W; 7,0 cm
▷ ⚠ ₿ ◑ ☺ ☻ ⊞ 🐛 ➠ ◈ 🔲 ♀   Photo: E. Pürzl

A03471-4 *Aphyosemion (F.) puerzli* RADDA & SCHEEL, 1974
Pürzls Prachtkärpfling / Puerzl's Killi
Aquarienstamm / Aquarium strain; B; 7,0 cm
▷ ⚠ ₿ ◑ ☺ ☻ ⊞ 🐛 ➠ ◈ 🔲 ♂   Photo: L. Seegers

A03936-4 *Aphyosemion (F.) puerzli* RADDA & SCHEEL, 1974
Pürzls Prachtkärpfling / Puerzl's Killi, "EMS ?"
Ndokama, Kamerun / Ndokama Cameroon; B; 7,0 cm
▷ ⚠ ₿ ◑ ☺ ☻ ⊞ 🐛 ➠ ◈ 🔲 ♂   Photo: S. Hellner

A03472-4 *Aphyosemion punctatum* RADDA & PÜRZL, 1977
Punktierter Prachtkärpfling / Dotted Killi
Ovan, Gabun / Ovan, Gabon; W; 4,5 cm
◁ ▷ ♉ ◐ ☺ ☻ 田 🔧 ➤ ⚠ 🔟 ♂   Photo: E. Pürzl

A03937-4 *Aphyosemion punctatum* RADDA & PÜRZL, 1977
Punktierter Prachtkärpfling / Dotted Killi
Zoolende, Gabun / Zoolende, Gabon; W; 4,5 cm
◁ ▷ ♉ ◐ ☺ ☻ 田 🔧 ➤ ⚠ 🔟 ♂   Photo: E. Pürzl

A03938-4 *Aphyosemion punctatum* RADDA & PÜRZL, 1977
Punktierter Prachtkärpfling / Dotted Killi, "LEC 93/7"
49 km W Makokou on RN 4, Gabon; W; 4,5 cm
◁ ▷ ♉ ◐ ☺ ☻ 田 🔧 ➤ ⚠ 🔟 ♂   Photo: R. Lütje

A03939-4 *Aphyosemion punctatum* RADDA & PÜRZL, 1977
Punktierter Prachtkärpfling / Dotted Killi
Mekambo, Gabun / Mekambo, Gabon; B; 4,5 cm
◁ ▷ ♉ ◐ ☺ ☻ 田 🔧 ➤ ⚠ 🔟 ♂   Photo: S. Hellner-

A03473-4 *Aphyosemion raddai* SCHEEL, 1975
Raddas Prachtkärpfling / Radda's Killi
From Pouma 25 km before Yaounde, Cameroon; W; 4,5 cm
▷ ⚠ ♉ ◐ ☺ ☻ 田 🔧 ➤ ⚠ 🔟 ♂   Photo: L. Seegers

A3474-4 *Aphyosemion raddai* SCHEEL, 1975
Raddas Prachtkärpfling / Radda's Killi
Modé, Kamerun / Modé, Cameroon; B; 4,5 cm
▷ ⚠ ♉ ◐ ☺ ☻ 田 🔧 ➤ ⚠ 🔟 ♂   Photo: L. Seegers

A03475-4 *Aphyosemion rectogoense* RADDA & HUBER, 1977
Léconi-Prachtkärpfling / Léconi Killi, "G 11/76" [T.t.]
6 km W Léconi town on Franceville-Bongoville road, Gabon; W; 4,5 cm
▷ ♉ ◐ ☺ ☻ 田 🔧 ➤ ◇ ⚠ 🔟 ♂   Photo: E. Pürzl

A03476-4 *Aphyosemion rectogoense* RADDA & HUBER, 1977
Léconi-Prachtkärpfling / Léconi Killi, "G 11/76" [T.t.]
6 km W Léconi town on Franceville-Bongoville road, Gabon; B; 4,5 cm
▷ ♉ ◐ ☺ ☻ 田 🔧 ➤ ◇ ⚠ 🔟 ♂   Photo: L. Seegers

A03477-4 *Aphyosemion rectogoense* RADDA & HUBER, 1977
Léconi-Prachtkärpfling / Léconi Killi
Aquarienstamm / Aquarium strain; B; 4,5 cm
▷♫❶☺☹⊞🖼️➼ ◈⚠️🔲 ♂
Photo: H.J. Mayland

A03480-4 *Aphyosemion riggenbachi* (AHL, 1924)
Riggenbachs Prachtkärpfling / Riggenbach's Killi
Aquarienstamm / Aquarium strain; B; 4,5 cm
▷⚠️♫❶☺☹⊞🖼️➼ ◈⚠️🔲 ♂
Photo: H.J. Mayland

A03480-4 *Aphyosemion riggenbachi* (AHL, 1924)
Riggenbachs Prachtkärpfling / Riggenbach's Killi
Aquarienstamm / Aquarium strain; B; 7,0 cm
▷⚠️♫❶☺☹⊞🖼️➼ ◈⚠️🔲 ♂
Photo: L. Seegers

A03481-3 *Aphyosemion riggenbachi* (AHL, 1924)
Riggenbachs Prachtkärpfling / Riggenbach's Killi
Somakak, Kamerun / Somakak, Cameroon; B; 7,0 cm
▷⚠️♫❶☺☹⊞🖼️➼ ◈⚠️🔲 ♂
Photo: E. Pürzl

A03482-4 *Aphyosemion riggenbachi* (AHL, 1924)
Riggenbachs Prachtkärpfling / Riggenbach's Killi
Yabassi, Kamerun / Yabassi, Cameroon; W; 7,0 cm
▷⚠️♫❶☺☹⊞🖼️➼ ◈⚠️🔲 ♂
Photo: E. Pürzl

A03483-4 *Aphyosemion riggenbachi* (AHL, 1924)
Riggenbachs Prachtkärpfling / Riggenbach's Killi
Süd-Kamerun / Southern Cameroon; W; 7,0 cm
▷⚠️♫❶☺☹⊞🖼️➼ ◈⚠️🔲 ♂
Photo: L. Seegers

A03487-4 *Aphyosemion (F.) robertsoni* RADDA & SCHEEL, 1974
Robertsons Prachtkärpfling / Robertson's Killi [T.t.]
CDC Rubber Plant. Ekona, 1 km N Bolifamba, Cameroon; W; 5,0 cm
▷⚠️♫❶☺☹⊞🖼️➼ ⚠️🔲 ♂
Photo: E. Pürzl

A03488-4 *Aphyosemion (F.) robertsoni* RADDA & SCHEEL, 1974
Robertsons Prachtkärpfling / Robertson's Killi [T.t.]
CDC Rubber Plant. Ekona, 1 km N Bolifamba, Cameroon; B; 5,0 cm
▷⚠️♫❶☺☹⊞🖼️➼ ⚠️🔲 ♂
Photo: L. Seegers

A03490-4 *Aphyosemion roloffi* ROLOFF, 1936
Roloffs Prachtkärpfling / Roloff's Killi
"Roloffia etzeli"-strain, Kirma, Sierra Leone; B; 5,0 cm
▷⚠️♉◑☺☺⊞🖼️🐾➡️ ◈⚠️🅜 ♂
Photo: L. Seegers

A03490-4 *Aphyosemion roloffi* ROLOFF, 1936
Roloffs Prachtkärpfling / Roloff's Killi
"Roloffia etzeli"-strain, Kirma, Sierra Leone; B; 5,0 cm
▷⚠️♉◑☺☺⊞🖼️🐾➡️ ◈⚠️🅜 ♀
Photo: L. Seegers

A03492-4 *Aphyosemion* cf. *roloffi* ROLOFF, 1936
Roloffs Prachtkärpfling / Roloff's Killi, "SL 89"
Brama Town, Sierra Leone; W; 5,0 cm
▷⚠️♉◑☺☺⊞🖼️🐾➡️ ◈⚠️🅜 ♂
Photo: S. Hellner

A03491-4 *Aphyosemion* cf. *roloffi* ROLOFF, 1936
Roloffs Prachtkärpfling / Roloff's Killi, "SL 89"
Brama Junction, Sierra Leone; W; 5,0 cm
▷⚠️♉◑☺☺⊞🖼️🐾➡️ ◈⚠️🅜 ♂
Photo: S. Hellner

A03493-4 *Aphyosemion* cf. *roloffi* ROLOFF, 1936
Roloffs Prachtkärpfling / Roloff's Killi, "RL 30"
Road Monrovia - Robertsport, 1500 m after Bomi jct., Liberia; W; 5,0 cm
▷⚠️♉◑☺☺⊞🖼️🐾➡️ ◈⚠️🅜 ♂
Photo: L. Seegers

A03494-4 *Aphyosemion* cf. *roloffi* ROLOFF, 1936
Roloffs Prachtkärpfling / Roloff's Killi, "SL 32"
Sierra Leone; W; 5,0 cm
▷⚠️♉◑☺☺⊞🖼️🐾➡️ ◈⚠️🅜 ♂
Photo: L. Seegers

A03940-4 *Aphyosemion* cf. *roloffi* ROLOFF, 1936
Roloffs Prachtkärpfling / Roloff's Killi
Matanga, Sierra Leone; W; 5,0 cm
▷⚠️♉◑☺☺⊞🖼️🐾➡️ ◈⚠️🅜 ♂ ♀
Photo: S. Hellner

A03941-4 *Aphyosemion* cf. *roloffi* ROLOFF, 1936
Roloffs Prachtkärpfling / Roloff's Killi
Kasawe Hills, Sierra Leone; B; 5,0 cm
▷⚠️♉◑☺☺⊞🖼️🐾➡️ ◈⚠️🅜 ♂
Photo: E. Pürzl

A03500-4 *Aphyosemion (F.) rubrolabiale* Radda, 1973
Rotlippen-Prachtkärpfling / Redlipped Killi [T.t.]
19 km NW Mbonge, West-Kamerun / Western Cameroon; W; 5,0 cm
🔺🩸◑☺☹⊞🔫➡ ⚠🔲 ♂ Photo: E. Pürzl

A03500-4 *Aphyosemion (F.) rubrolabiale* Radda, 1973
Rotlippen-Prachtkärpfling / Redlipped Killi [T.t.]
19 km NW Mbonge, West-Kamerun / Western Cameroon; W; 5,0 cm
🔺🩸◑☺☹⊞🔫➡ ⚠🔲 ♀ Photo: E. Pürzl

A03501-4 *Aphyosemion (F.) rubrolabiale* Radda, 1973
Rotlippen-Prachtkärpfling / Redlipped Killi
West-Kamerun / Western Cameroon; W; 5,0 cm
🔺🩸◑☺☹⊞🔫➡ ⚠🔲 ♂ Photo: L. Seegers

A03501-4 *Aphyosemion (F.) rubrolabiale* Radda, 1973
Rotlippen-Prachtkärpfling / Redlipped Killi
West-Kamerun / Western Cameroon; W; 5,0 cm
🔺🩸◑☺☹⊞🔫➡ ⚠🔲 ♀ Photo: L. Seegers

A03502-4 *Aphyosemion (F.) rubrolabiale* Radda, 1973
Rotlippen-Prachtkärpfling / Redlipped Killi
Malende, West-Kamerun / Malende, western Cameroon; W; 5,0 cm
🔺🩸◑☺☹⊞🔫➡ ⚠🔲 ♂ Photo: S. Hellner

A03503-4 *Aphyosemion (F.) rubrolabiale* Radda, 1973
Rotlippen-Prachtkärpfling / Redlipped Killi
Aquarienstamm / Aquarium strain; B; 5,0 cm
🔺🩸◑☺☹⊞🔫➡ ⚠🔲 ♂ Photo: L. Seegers

A03505-4 *Aphyosemion scheeli* Radda, 1970
Scheels Prachtkärpfling / Scheel's Killi
Aquarienstamm / Aquarium strain; B; 6,0 cm
▷🔺🩸◑☺☹⊞🔫➡ ◈🔲 ♂ Photo: L. Seegers

A03505-4 *Aphyosemion scheeli* Radda, 1970
Scheels Prachtkärpfling / Scheel's Killi
Aquarienstamm / Aquarium strain; B; 6,0 cm
▷🔺🩸◑☺☹⊞🔫➡ ◈🔲 ♂ Photo: E. Pürzl

A03505-4 *Aphyosemion scheeli* RADDA, 1970
Scheels Prachtkärpfling / Scheel's Killi
Aquarienstamm / Aquarium strain; B; 6,0 cm
▷△₿❶☺☺❶⊞▨➸ ◈▥♂   Photo: L. Seegers

A03506-4 *Aphyosemion scheeli* RADDA, 1970
Scheels Prachtkärpfling / Scheel's Killi
20 km NW Akamkpa, Nigeria; W; 6,0 cm
▷△₿❶☺☺❶⊞▨➸ ◈▥♂   Photo: E. Pürzl

A03510-4 *Aphyosemion schioetzi* HUBER & SCHEEL, 1981
Schioetz' Prachtkärpfling / Schioetz's Killi
Equateur, Zaïre; W; 5,0 cm
△₿❶☺☺❶⊞▨➸ ◈△▥♂   Photo: L. Seegers

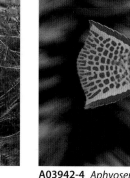

A03942-4 *Aphyosemion schioetzi* HUBER & SCHEEL, 1981
Schioetz' Prachtkärpfling / Schioetz's Killi
Mindouli, Kongo /Mindouli, Congo; W; 5,0 cm
△₿❶☺☺❶⊞▨➸ ◈△▥♂   Photo: E. Pürzl

A03943-4 *Aphyosemion schioetzi* HUBER & SCHEEL, 1981
Schioetz' Prachtkärpfling / Schioetz's Killi
Aquarienstamm von Zaïre / Aquarium strain from Zaïre; B; 5,0 cm
△₿❶☺☺❶⊞▨➸ ◈△▥♂   Photo: L. Seegers

A03944-4 *Aphyosemion schioetzi* HUBER & SCHEEL, 1981
Schioetz' Prachtkärpfling / Schioetz's Killi, "RPC 78/253" [T.t.]
Taba, Kongo / Taba, Congo; B; 5,0 cm
△₿❶☺☺❶⊞▨➸ ◈△▥♂   Photo: L. Seegers

A03512-4 *Aphyosemion schluppi* HUBER & SCHEEL, 1981
Schlupps Prachtkärpfling / Schlupp's Killi
Brook on road from Zanaga to Ogowe River, Congo; W; 4,5 cm
◁ ₿⍦❶☺☺❶⊞▨➸ △▥♂   Photo: E. Pürzl

A03513-3 *Aphyosemion schluppi* HUBER & SCHEEL, 1981
Schlupps Prachtkärpfling / Schlupp's Killi, "RPC 28"
Ékouma River, between Zanaga and Voula II, Congo; W; 4,5 cm
◁ ₿⍦❶☺☺❶⊞▨➸ △▥♂   Photo: L. Seegers

A03520-4 *Aphyosemion (F.) sjoestedti* (LÖNNBERG, 1895)
Sjöstedts Prachtkärpfling / Blue Gularis
Aquarienstamm / Aquarium strain; B; 12 cm
▷🎣◑☺☺⊞🖳➟ ◈🔲♂♀   Photo: L. Seegers

A03520-4 *Aphyosemion (F.) sjoestedti* (LÖNNBERG, 1895)
Sjöstedts Prachtkärpfling / Blue Gularis
Aquarienstamm / Aquarium strain; B; 12 cm
▷🎣◑☺☺⊞🖳➟ ◈🔲♀   Photo: L. Seegers

A03520-4 *Aphyosemion (F.) sjoestedti* (LÖNNBERG, 1895)
Sjöstedts Prachtkärpfling / Blue Gularis
Aquarienstamm / Aquarium strain; B; 12 cm
▷🎣◑☺☺⊞🖳➟ ◈🔲♂   Photo: L. Seegers

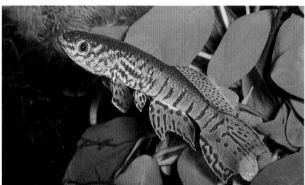

A03521-4 *Aphyosemion (F.) sjoestedti* (LÖNNBERG, 1895)
Sjöstedts Prachtkärpfling / Blue Gularis
Ndian River, Kamerun / Cameroon; W; 12 cm
▷🎣◑☺☺⊞🖳➟ ◈🔲♂   Photo: L. Seegers

A03521-4 *Aphyosemion (F.) sjoestedti* (LÖNNBERG, 1895)
Sjöstedts Prachtkärpfling / Blue Gularis
Ndian River, Kamerun / Cameroon; W; 12 cm
▷🎣◑☺☺⊞🖳➟ ◈🔲♂   Photo: L. Seegers

A03523-4 *Aphyosemion (F.) sjoestedti* (LÖNNBERG, 1895)
Sjöstedts Prachtkärpfling / Blue Gularis
"USA"-Aquarienstamm / "USA" strain; B; 12 cm
▷🎣◑☺☺⊞🖳➟ ◈🔲♂   Photo: L. Seegers

A03524-4 *Aphyosemion (F.) sjoestedti* (LÖNNBERG, 1895)
Sjöstedts Prachtkärpfling / Blue Gularis
Loé, Kamerun / Loé, Cameroon; W; 12 cm
▷🎣◑☺☺⊞🖳➟ ◈🔲♂   Photo: E. Pürzl

A03522-4 *Aphyosemion (F.) sjoestedti* (LÖNNBERG, 1895)
Sjöstedts Prachtkärpfling / Blue Gularis
"Roter" Aquarienstamm / "red" strain; B; 12 cm
▷🎣◑☺☺⊞🖳➟ ◈🔲♂   Photo: L. Seegers

A03530-4 *Aphyosemion splendopleure* (Brüning, 1929)
Grüner Glanzprachtkärpfling / Splendid Killi
Oron, SW Nigeria; W; 5,5 cm

▷♫◑☺☹⊞🐛➤ ◈🔟♂
Photo: E. Pürzl

A03942-4 *Aphyosemion splendopleure* (Brüning, 1929)
Grüner Glanzprachtkärpfling / Splendid Killi
Bolifamba, West-Kamerun / Bolifamba, western Cameroon; B; 5,5 cm

▷♫◑☺☹⊞🐛➤ ◈🔟♂
Photo: L. Seegers

A03943-4 *Aphyosemion splendopleure* (Brüning, 1929)
Grüner Glanzprachtkärpfling / Splendid Killi, "C 89/33"
Dizangue, West-Kamerun / Dizangue, western Cameroon; B; 5,5 cm

▷♫◑☺☹⊞🐛➤ ◈🔟♂
Photo: L. Seegers

A03944-4 *Aphyosemion splendopleure* (Brüning, 1929)
Grüner Glanzprachtkärpfling / Splendid Killi
Douala, West-Kamerun / Douala, western Cameroon; W; 5,5 cm

▷♫◑☺☹⊞🐛➤ ◈🔟♂
Photo: E. Pürzl

A03945-4 *Aphyosemion splendopleure* (Brüning, 1929)
Grüner Glanzprachtkärpfling / Splendid Killi
Ekondo Titi, West-Kamerun / Western Cameroon; W; 5,5 cm

▷♫◑☺☹⊞🐛➤ ◈🔟♂
Photo: E. Pürzl

A03946-4 *Aphyosemion splendopleure* (Brüning, 1929)
Grüner Glanzprachtkärpfling / Splendid Killi
Kumba, West-Kamerun / Kumba, western Cameroon; W; 5,5 cm

▷♫◑☺☹⊞🐛➤ ◈🔟♂
Photo: E. Pürzl

A03947-4 *Aphyosemion splendopleure* (Brüning, 1929)
Grüner Glanzprachtkärpfling / Splendid Killi
Mambanda, West-Kamerun / Western Cameroon; B; 5,5 cm

▷♫◑☺☹⊞🐛➤ ◈🔟♂
Photo: L. Seegers

A03947-4 *Aphyosemion splendopleure* (Brüning, 1929)
Grüner Glanzprachtkärpfling / Splendid Killi
Mambanda, West-Kamerun / Western Cameroon; F1; 5,5 cm

▷♫◑☺☹⊞🐛➤ ◈🔟♂
Photo: L. Seegers

A03948-4 *Aphyosemion splendopleure* (Brüning, 1929)
Grüner Glanzprachtkärpfling / Splendid Killi
Meme River, West-Kamerun / Western Cameroon; W; 5,5 cm
▷♨◑☺☹⊞🔦🐾 ◈⊡ ♂   Photo: L. Seegers

A03948-4 *Aphyosemion splendopleure* (Brüning, 1929)
Grüner Glanzprachtkärpfling / Splendid Killi
Meme River, West-Kamerun / Western Cameroon; W; 5,5 cm
▷♨◑☺☹⊞🔦🐾 ◈⊡ ♀   Photo: L. Seegers

A03949-4 *Aphyosemion splendopleure* (Brüning, 1929)
Grüner Glanzprachtkärpfling / Splendid Killi
Tiko, West-Kamerun / Tiko, western Cameroon; B; 5,5 cm
▷♨◑☺☹⊞🔦🐾 ◈⊡ ♂   Photo: S. Hellner

A03950-4 *Aphyosemion splendopleure* (Brüning, 1929)
Grüner Glanzprachtkärpfling / Splendid Killi
Yoko, West-Kamerun / Yoko, western Cameroon; B; 5,5 cm
▷♨◑☺☹⊞🔦🐾 ◈⊡ ♂   Photo: L. Seegers

A03951-4 *Aphyosemion splendopleure* (Brüning, 1929)
Grüner Glanzprachtkärpfling / Splendid Killi, "HJRK 92/16"
Bibabivotou, Südwest-Kamerun / SW Cameroon; B; 5,5 cm
▷♨◑☺☹⊞🔦🐾 ◈⊡ ♂   Photo: S. Hellner

A03952-3 *Aphyosemion splendopleure* (Brüning, 1929)
Grüner Glanzprachtkärpfling / Splendid Killi
Cap Esterias, NW Gabun / Cap Esterias, NW Gabon; W; 5,5 cm
▷♨◑☺☹⊞🔦🐾 ◈⊡ ♂   Photo: S. Hellner-

A03532-4 *Aphyosemion (F.) spoorenbergi* Berkenkamp, 1976
Spoorenbergs Prachtkärpfling / Spoorenberg's Killi
Aquarienpopulation / Aquarium strain; B; 7,0 cm
▷♨◑☺☹⊞🔦🐾 ◈⊡ ♂   Photo: L. Seegers

A03532-4 *Aphyosemion (F.) spoorenbergi* Berkenkamp, 1976
Spoorenbergs Prachtkärpfling / Spoorenberg's Killi
Aquarienpopulation / Aquarium strain; B; 7,0 cm
▷♨◑☺☹⊞🔦🐾 ◈⊡ ♀   Photo: E. Pürzl

A03540-4 *Aphyosemion striatum* (BOULENGER, 1911)
Streifen-Prachtkärpfling / Red Striped Killi
Cocobeach, NW Gabun / Cocobeach, northwest Gabon; W; 5,0 cm
▷ ♬ ◑ ☺ ☻ ⊞ 🖳➡ ◈ ⚠ 𝕞 ♂   Photo: E. Pürzl

A03953-4 *Aphyosemion striatum* (BOULENGER, 1911)
Streifen-Prachtkärpfling / Red Striped Killi
Cap Esterias, NW Gabun / Cap Esterias, NW Gabon; W; 5,0 cm
▷ ♬ ◑ ☺ ☻ ⊞ 🖳➡ ◈ ⚠ 𝕞 ♂   Photo: E. Pürzl

A03954-4 *Aphyosemion striatum* (BOULENGER, 1911)
Streifen-Prachtkärpfling / Red Striped Killi
Lambarene, NW Gabun / Lambarene, northwest Gabon; B; 5,0 cm
▷ ♬ ◑ ☺ ☻ ⊞ 🖳➡ ◈ ⚠ 𝕞 ♂   Photo: L. Seegers

A03954-4 *Aphyosemion striatum* (BOULENGER, 1911)
Streifen-Prachtkärpfling / Red Striped Killi
Lambarene, NW Gabun / Lambarene, northwest Gabon; W; 5,0 cm
▷ ♬ ◑ ☺ ☻ ⊞ 🖳➡ ◈ ⚠ 𝕞 ♂   Photo: E. Pürzl

A03955-3 *Aphyosemion striatum* (BOULENGER, 1911)
Streifen-Prachtkärpfling / Red Striped Killi
Kristallberge, NW Gabun / Crystal Mountains, NW Gabon; W; 5,0 cm
▷ ♬ ◑ ☺ ☻ ⊞ 🖳➡ ◈ ⚠ 𝕞 ♂   Photo: L. Seegers

A03956-4 *Aphyosemion striatum* (BOULENGER, 1911)
Streifen-Prachtkärpfling / Red Striped Killi
Macoura, NW Gabun / Macoura, NW Gabon; B; 5,0 cm
▷ ♬ ◑ ☺ ☻ ⊞ 🖳➡ ◈ ⚠ 𝕞 ♂   Photo: W. Eigelshofen

A03542-4 *Aphyosemion thysi* RADDA & HUBER, 1978
Thys' Prachtkärpfling / Thys' Killi
Loumbamba River, 3 km from Ngala, Congo; W; 5,0 cm
◁ ♬ ◑ ☺ ☻ ⊞ 🖳➡ ◈ ⚠ 𝕞 ♂   Photo: E. Pürzl

A03543-4 *Aphyosemion thysi* RADDA & HUBER, 1978
Thys' Prachtkärpfling / Thys' Killi, "RPC 78/9"
Birabélé River, Kongo / Congo; B; 5,0 cm
◁ ♬ ◑ ☺ ☻ ⊞ 🖳➡ ◈ ⚠ 𝕞 ♂   Photo: L. Seegers

A03544-4 *Aphyosemion thysi* RADDA & HUBER, 1978
Thys' Prachtkärpfling / Thys' Killi, "RPC 78/20"
1,5 km nach Gnimi, Kongo / 1.5 km after Gnimi, Congo; W; 5,0 cm
◁ ♬ ◐ ☺ ☻ ⊞ ⊡ ⇻ ◇ ⚠ 🔲 ♂   Photo: L. Seegers

A03957-4 *Aphyosemion viride* (LADIGES & ROLOFF, 1973)
Grüner Prachtkärpfling / Green Killi
Salayea, Nordwest-Liberia / Salayea, northwestern Liberia; B; 5,0 cm
◁ ▷ ♬ ◐ ☺ ☻ ⊞ ⊡ ⇻ ◇ ⚠ 🔲 ♂   Photo: L. Seegers

A03558-4 *Aphyosemion wachtersi wachtersi* RADDA & HUBER, 1978
Wachters' Prachtkärpfling / Wachters' Killi, "RPC 78/30" [T.t.]
Spring in Voula II, 9 km NE Zanaga on road to Ogowe River; W; 5,0 cm
◁ ♬ ◐ ☺ ☻ ⊞ ⊡ ⇻ ⚠ 🔲 ♂   Photo: E. Pürzl

A03558-4 *Aphyosemion wachtersi wachtersi* RADDA & HUBER, 1978
Wachters' Prachtkärpfling / Wachters' Killi, "RPC 78/30" [T.t.]
Spring in Voula II, 9 km NE Zanaga on road to Ogowe River; W; 5,0 cm
◁ ♬ ◐ ☺ ☻ ⊞ ⊡ ⇻ ⚠ 🔲 ♀   Photo: L. Seegers

A03559-4 *Aphyosemion wachtersi wachtersi* RADDA & HUBER, 1978
Wachters' Prachtkärpfling / Wachters' Killi, "RPC 78/30" [T.t.]
Spring in Voula II, 9 km NE Zanaga on road to Ogowe River; B; 5,0 cm
◁ ♬ ◐ ☺ ☻ ⊞ ⊡ ⇻ ⚠ 🔲 ♂   Photo: L. Seegers

A03958-4 *Aphyosemion wachtersi mikeae* RADDA, 1980
Mikes Prachtkärpfling / Mike's Killi, "RPC 78/19" [T.t.]
Mpoutoulou River bei Gnimi-Quartier Mbaya, S Congo; W; 4,5 cm
◁ ♬ ◐ ☺ ☻ ⊞ ⊡ ⇻ ⚠ 🔲 ♂   Photo: J. Tomas

A03958-4 *Aphyosemion wachtersi mikeae* RADDA, 1980
Mikes Prachtkärpfling / Mike's Killi, "RPC 78/19" [T.t.]
Mpoutoulou River bei Gnimi-Quartier Mbaya, S Congo; W; 4,5 cm
◁ ♬ ◐ ☺ ☻ ⊞ ⊡ ⇻ ⚠ 🔲 ♂   Photo: E. Pürzl

A03958-4 *Aphyosemion wachtersi mikeae* RADDA, 1980
Mikes Prachtkärpfling / Mike's Killi, "RPC 78/19" [T.t.]
Mpoutoulou River bei Gnimi-Quartier Mbaya, S Congo; W; 4,5 cm
◁ ♬ ◐ ☺ ☻ ⊞ ⊡ ⇻ ⚠ 🔲 ♂   Photo: L. Seegers

A03560-4 *Aphyosemion (F.) walkeri* (Boulenger, 1911)
Walkers Prachtkärpfling / Walker's Killi
Abidjan, Elfenbeinküste / Abidjan, Ivory Coast; B; 6,0 cm
▷⚑❂☺☻⊞⬇🗔➠ ◈🔲 ♂
Photo: L. Seegers

A03560-4 *Aphyosemion (F.) walkeri* (Boulenger, 1911)
Walkers Prachtkärpfling / Walker's Killi
Abidjan, Elfenbeinküste / Abidjan, Ivory Coast; B; 6,0 cm
▷⚑❂☺☻⊞⬇🗔➠ ◈🔲 ♀
Photo: L. Seegers

A03561-4 *Aphyosemion (F.) walkeri* (Boulenger, 1911)
Walkers Prachtkärpfling / Walker's Killi, "GH 2/74, spurrelli-Form"
Kutunse, Ghana; W; 6,0 cm
▷⚑❂☺☻⊞⬇🗔➠ ◈🔲 ♂
Photo: L. Seegers

A03561-4 *Aphyosemion (F.) walkeri* (Boulenger, 1911)
Walkers Prachtkärpfling / Walker's Killi, "GH 2/74, spurrelli-Form"
Kutunse, Ghana; W; 6,0 cm
▷⚑❂☺☻⊞⬇🗔➠ ◈🔲 ♀
Photo: L. Seegers

A03562-4 *Aphyosemion (F.) walkeri* (Boulenger, 1911)
Walkers Prachtkärpfling / Walker's Killi, "GH 2/74, spurrelli-Form"
Kutunse, Ghana; B; 6,0 cm
▷⚑❂☺☻⊞⬇🗔➠ ◈🔲 ♂
Photo: L. Seegers

A03563-4 *Aphyosemion (F.) walkeri* (Boulenger, 1911)
Walkers Prachtkärpfling / Walker's Killi
Aquarienpopulation / Aquarium strain; B; 6,0 cm
▷⚑❂☺☻⊞⬇🗔➠ ◈🔲 ♂
Photo: L. Seegers

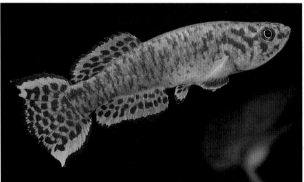

A03959-4 *Aphyosemion (F.) walkeri* (Boulenger, 1911)
Walkers Prachtkärpfling / Walker's Killi
Agboville, Elfenbeinküste / Agboville, Ivory Coast; W; 6,0 cm
▷⚑❂☺☻⊞⬇🗔➠ ◈🔲 ♂
Photo: E. Pürzl

A03960-4 *Aphyosemion (F.) walkeri* (Boulenger, 1911)
Walkers Prachtkärpfling / Walker's Killi
Eri Mobaje, Elfenbeinküste / Eri Mobaje, Ivory Coast; W; 6,0 cm
▷⚑❂☺☻⊞⬇🗔➠ ◈🔲 ♂
Photo: E. Pürzl

A03961-3 *Aphyosemion (F.) walkeri* (Boulenger, 1911)
Walkers Prachtkärpfling / Walker's Killi
Elfenbeinküste / Ivory Coast; W; 6,0 cm
▷♫◐☺☹⊞⬇🐌🐟 ◈🅜 ♂
Photo: E. Pürzl

A03961-4 *Aphyosemion (F.) walkeri* (Boulenger, 1911)
Walkers Prachtkärpfling / Walker's Killi
Elfenbeinküste / Ivory Coast; W; 6,0 cm
▷♫◐☺☹⊞⬇🐌🐟➡ ◈🅜 ♂
Photo: E. Pürzl

A03565-4 *Aphyosemion wildekampi* Berkenkamp, 1973
Wildekamps Prachtkärpfling / Wildekamp's Killi
Diang, Kamerun / Diang, Cameroon; B; 4,5 cm
◁▷♫◐☺☹⊞🐌➡ ⚠🅜 ♂
Photo: L. Seegers

A03565-4 *Aphyosemion wildekampi* Berkenkamp, 1973
Wildekamps Prachtkärpfling / Wildekamp's Killi
Diang, Kamerun / Diang, Cameroon; B; 4,5 cm
◁▷♫◐☺☹⊞🐌➡ ⚠🅜 ♂
Photo: E. Pürzl

A03566-4 *Aphyosemion wildekampi* Berkenkamp, 1973
Wildekamps Prachtkärpfling / Wildekamp's Killi, "GKCAR 90/7"
Between Ndola, Central Afr. Rep., and Yokadouma, Cameroon; B; 4,5 cm
◁▷♫◐☺☹⊞🐌➡ ⚠🅜 ♂
Photo: L. Seegers

A03575-4 *Aphyosemion zygaima* Huber, 1981
Mindouli-Prachtkärpfling / Mindouli Killi
Mindouli, Kongo / Mindouli, Congo; B; 4,5 cm
▷♫◐☺☹⊞🐌➡ ⚠🅜 ♂
Photo: E. Pürzl

A03576-4 *Aphyosemion zygaima* Huber, 1981
Mindouli-Prachtkärpfling / Mindouli Killi, "CHP 82/4"
Kongo / Congo; B; 4,5 cm
▷♫◐☺☹⊞🐌➡ ⚠🅜 ♂
Photo: L. Seegers

A03580-4 *Aphyosemion* spec.
"GEB 94/17"
Gabun / Gabon; W; 4,5 cm
◁♫◐☺☹⊞🐌➡ ⚠🅜 ♂
Photo: R. Lütje

A03581-4 *Aphyosemion* spec. "GS 2"
Gabun / Gabon; B; 5,0 cm

▷ ₿ ⫪P ◑ ☺ ☺ ⊞ 🖼 ➽ ⚠ ⊡ ♂

A03288-4 *Aphyosemion* spec. "Oyo" = *Aphyosemion* cf. *christyi* (BOULENGER, 1915)
Oyo, Kongo / Oyo, Congo; B; 5,0 cm

▷ ₿ ⫪P ◑ ☺ ☺ ⊞ 🖼 ➽ ◈ ⚠ ⊡ ♂

A03962-4 *Aphyosemion amieti*
X *Aphyosemion scheeli*
Kreuzung / Cross breeding; B; 5,0 cm

▷♣◑☺☻⊞▱➔ 🛑 m ♂
Photo: L. Seegers

A03963-4 *Aphyosemion gardneri nigerianum*
X *Aphyosemion walkeri*
Kreuzung / Cross breeding; B; 6,0 cm

▷♣◑☺☻⊞▱➔ 🛑 m ♂
Photo: L. Seegers

A03964-3 *Aphyosemion gardneri nigerianum*
X *Aphyosemion amieti*
Kreuzung / Cross breeding; B; 6,0 cm

▷♣◑☺☻⊞▱➔ 🛑 m ♂
Photo: L. Seegers

A03965-4 *Aphyosemion gardneri nigerianum*
X *Aphyosemion walkeri*
Kreuzung / Cross breeding; B; 6,0 cm

▷♣◑☺☻⊞▱➔ 🛑 m ♂
Photo: L. Seegers

A03966-4 *Aphyosemion walkeri* "Abidjan"
X *Aphyosemion walkeri* "Kutunse", GH 2/74
Kreuzung / Cross breeding; B; 6,0 cm

▷♣◑☺☻⊞▱➔ 🛑 m ♂
Photo: L. Seegers

A03967-4 *Aphyosemion pascheni*
X *Aphyosemion gardneri nigerianum*
Kreuzung / Cross breeding; B; 7,0 cm

▷♣◑☺☻⊞▱➔ 🛑 m ♂
Photo: L. Seegers

A03968-4 *Aphyosemion fallax*
X *Aphyosemion sjoestedti*
Kreuzung / Cross breeding; B; 10 cm

▷♣◑☺☻⊞▱➔ 🛑 m ♂
Photo: L. Seegers

A03969-3 *Aphyosemion ogoense* "GHR 1/88"
X *Aphyosemion exigoideum*
Kreuzung / Cross breeding; B; 7,0 cm

▷♣◑☺☻⊞▱➔ 🛑 m ♂
Photo: E. Pürzl

A03424-4 *Aphyosemion* sp. aff. *mirabile* RADDA, 1970
Photo: L. Seegers
Wunderkärpfling / Miracle Killi
Diese Form aus der *Aphyosemion mirabile*-Gruppe ist vorzugsweise ein Bodenlaicher.
This form is a member of the Aphyosemion mirabile *species group and prefers to spawn as a soil spawner.*

A03424-4 *Aphyosemion* sp. aff. *mirabile* RADDA, 1970
Photo: L. Seegers
Wunderkärpfling / Miracle Killi
Das ablaichende Paar drückt sich fest gegen den Bodengrund um Eier und Spermien abzugeben.
The spawning pair is pressed firmly against the soil to release eggs and sperm.

A3853-4 *Aphyosemion (F.) gardneri nigerianum* CLAUSEN, 1963
Nigeria-Prachtkärpfling / Nigerian Killi
Makurdi, Nigeria; B; 6,0 cm

▷♨◑☺☹⊞🖻➔ ◈🔳 ♂

Aphyosemion gardneri ist in Süd-Nigeria und West-Kamerun weit verbreitet. Es existieren zahlreiche Farbformen, von denen einige als Unterarten betrachtet werden. Bezüglich ihres Ablaichverhaltens sind die *A. gardneri*-Formen wenig wählerisch, sie laichen

Aphyosemion gardneri is widespread in southern Nigeria and western Cameroon. A lot of color forms are known of which some basic phenotypes are considered as subspecies. As to their spawning habits A. gardneri forms are not restricted to a certain medium, they

sowohl an feinfiedrigen Pflanzen oder Wurzeln als auch auf dem Bodengrund ab. Bei der Zucht kann man als Ablaichsubstrat Torffasern oder einen Mop aus Kunstfasern verwenden, der mit Hilfe eines Korkens an der Wasseroberfläche schwimmt.

may spawn as soil spawners but as plant spawners as well. This group sometimes was called "switch spawners". For this type of killifish peat or spawning mops made from yarn are useful as spawning media. The latter may float at the water surface held by a cork.

A03356-4 *Aphyosemion geryi* LAMBERT, 1958
Zickzack-Prachtkärpfling, Gérys Prachtkärpfling / Géry's Killi
Bwian, Gambia

A03356-4 *Aphyosemion geryi* ist der nordwestlichste Vertreter der Gattung, er wurde früher zur Gruppe der "kleinen
Roloffia-Arten" gezählt. Die Fische laichen an Pflanzen, aber auch am Bodengrund ab.

*Aphyosemion geryi is the most northwesterly member of the genus. Formerly the species was included in the
group of small* Roloffia *species. The fish spawn between plants but as soil spawners too.*

A03475-4 *Aphyosemion rectogoense* RADDA & HUBER, 1977
Léconi-Prachtkärpfling / Léconi Killi, "G 11/76" [T.t.]
6 km W Léconi town on Franceville-Bongoville road, Gabon; W; 4,5 cm

Das typische Ablaichverhalten aller *Aphyosemion*-Arten beginnt damit, daß das Männchen über das Weibchen schwimmt und der Partnerin in engem Kontakt zu einem Ablaichort folgt. Dort hält das Weibchen an und das Männchen schwimmt an seine Seite.

Usually the spawning habit of Aphyosemion *species starts in that the male approaches the female and swims over the partner. It is the female which looks for a suitable spawning locality followed by the male which keeps close contact. Then the female stops and the male*

Dieses versucht dann das Weibchen mit der Rückenflosse zu umgreifen, und beide Tiere drücken sich gegen den Bodengrund. Das Weibchen gibt ein Ei ab, das vom Männchen befruchtet wird, und beide Tiere trennen sich mit einem Ruck voneinander.

swims alongside trying to "embrace" the partner with fins overlapped. The body is firmly pressed against the spawning medium. The fish quickly jerk their bodies expelling a single egg into the plants or peat.

A03506-4 *Aphyosemion scheeli* RADDA, 1970
Scheels Prachtkärpfling / Scheel's Killi
20 km NW Akamkpa, Nigeria; W; 6,0 cm
▷🜂🜍◑☺☻⊞🖼️➽ ◈🔟 ♂♀

5 Photos: W. Eigelshofen

Die ersten *Aphyosemion scheeli* wurden als Aquaristik-Importe aus Nigeria nach Deutschland importiert und zunächst mit dem ungültigen Phantasienamen "Aphyosemion Burundi" verbreitet. Der genaue Fundort war unbekannt. RADDA beschrieb die Fische

The first specimens of Aphyosemion scheeli were imported as ornamental fish from Nigeria to Germany and spread with the invalid name "Aphyosemion Burundi". The exact collecting locality then was unknown. RADDA described the species in honour of J. J. SCHEEL.

zu Ehren von J. J. SCHEEL. Erst später wurde durch Aufsammlungen von RADDA die Vermutung bestätigt, daß diese Art in Südost-Nigeria beheimatet ist. Die Fische gehören in die *A. gardneri*-Gruppe und laichen wie diese Art als Boden- oder Pflanzenlaicher ab.

Only later on it was confirmed by collections of RADDA that this species indeed occurs in southeastern Nigeria. The fish are belonging to the A. gardneri species group and as most or all members of this group they use to spawn both as soil spawners or as plant spawners.

A03946-4 *Aphyosemion splendopleure* (BRÜNING, 1929)
Grüner Glanzprachtkärpfling / Splendid Killi
Kumba, West-Kamerun (= ex *volcanum*) / Kumba, western Cameroon (= ex *volcanum*); W; 5,5 cm

▷🕭◐☺☹⊞🖼➤ ◈ⅿ♂

Aphyosemion splendopleure weist eine weite Verbreitung entlang des kamerunischen Küsteneinzugs auf. Hier ist die als *A. volcanum* beschriebene Form aus Kumba zu sehen. Alle Arten der Untergattung *Chromaphyosemion*, zu der *A. splendopleure* gehört, laichen

Aphyosemion splendopleure has a wide distribution along the coastal drainage of mainly Cameroon. Here the phenotype is shown which was described as A. volcanum *from Kumba. All members of the subgenus* Chromaphyosemion *to which* A. splen-

sowohl als Haftlaicher an Pflanzen und Wurzeln ab, als auch als Bodenlaicher. Die Zucht ist deshalb mit Torf wie bei Saisonfischen möglich, aber die Eier können auch von Pflanzen oder einem Ablaichmop abgelesen und in Wasser zur Entwicklung gebracht werden.

dopleure belongs are able to spawn as plant spawners as well as soil spawners. It is possible, therefore, to breed this species like a seasonal fish by using peat, but it is also possible to use plants and to move the eggs to containers for development.

A03560-4 *Aphyosemion (F.) walkeri* (BOULENGER, 1911)
Walkers Prachtkärpfling / Walker's Killi
Abidjan, Elfenbeinküste / Abidjan, Ivory Coast; B; 6,0 cm
▷🔥◑☺☻⊞⬇🐟➤ ◈🔲 ♂ ♀

A03560-4 *Aphyosemion walkeri* ist in der Gattung *Aphyosemion* ein typischer Bodenlaicher. Beim Ablaichen drückt sich das Paar tief in den Bodengrund, um die Eier in der Trockenzeit vor dem Austrocknen zu schützen.

Within the genus Aphyosemion, A. walkeri *is a typical soil spawner. When spawning the pair presses its body deeply into the soft soil to protect the eggs against desiccation during the dry season.*

Ergänzungen/*Stickups*
hier einkleben

erhältlich zusammen mit Ihrer
Aqualognews
der ersten internationalen Zeitung
für den Aquarianer

Aqualog *Bücher & Zeitung*
jetzt auch im Net:

http:// www. aqualog. de
mit Informationen zu den Ergänzungen
und Neuerscheinungen

Supplements/stickups
Please attach here

Stickups are available in
Aqualognews
the international newspaper for aquarists

Aqualog *books & news*
now in the Internet

http:// www. aqualog. de
the latest information on supplements
and new publications

Ergänzungen/*Stickups*
hier einkleben

erhältlich zusammen mit Ihrer
Aqualognews
der ersten internationalen Zeitung
für den Aquarianer

Aqualog *Bücher & Zeitung*
jetzt auch im Net:

http:// www. aqualog. de
mit Informationen zu den Ergänzungen
und Neuerscheinungen

Supplements/stickups
Please attach here

Stickups are available in
Aqualognews
the international newspaper for aquarists

Aqualog *books & news*
now in the Internet

http:// www. aqualog. de
the latest information on supplements
and new publications

Ergänzungen/*Stickups*
hier einkleben

erhältlich zusammen mit Ihrer
Aqualognews
der ersten internationalen Zeitung
für den Aquarianer

Aqualog *Bücher & Zeitung*
jetzt auch im Net:

http:// www. aqualog. de
mit Informationen zu den Ergänzungen
und Neuerscheinungen

Supplements/stickups
Please attach here

Stickups are available in
Aqualognews
the international newspaper for aquarists

Aqualog *books & news*
now in the Internet

http:// www. aqualog. de
the latest information on supplements
and new publications

Ergänzungen/*Stickups*
hier einkleben

erhältlich zusammen mit Ihrer
Aqualog*news*
der ersten internationalen Zeitung
für den Aquarianer

Aqualog *Bücher & Zeitung*
jetzt auch im Net:

http:// www. aqualog. de
mit Informationen zu den Ergänzungen
und Neuerscheinungen

Supplements/stickups
Please attach here

Stickups are available in
Aqualog*news*
the international newspaper for aquarists

Aqualog *books & news*
now in the Internet

http:// www. aqualog. de
the latest information on supplements
and new publications

Code-Nr.	Genus	Species	Population	Common name	Page
A00075	Adamas	formosus	Aquarian strain	Starhead Killi	49
A00076	Adamas	formosus	Pool Malebo	Starhead Killi	49
A00077	Adamas	formosus	Tchicapika	Starhead Killi	49
A02505	Aphyoplatys	duboisi	Oyo	Dubois´Panchax	49
A02506	Aphyoplatys	duboisi	Aquarian strain	Dubois´Panchax	49
A03110	Aphyosemion	amieti, bred	Somakak	Ahl´s Lyretail	51
A03112	Aphyosemion	amieti, bred	Somakak	Ahl´s Lyretail "HJRK 92/18"	51
A03117	Aphyosemion	amoenum	Dibang	Red-Finned Killi, "CGE 91/13"	52
A03122	Aphyosemion	aureum, bred	Mouila	Golden Killi "GHP 80/7"	54
A03146	Aphyosemion	bivittatum	Funge	Two-banded Killi, partly xanthoristic	61
A03205	Aphyosemion	ahli	Bipade	Ahl´s Lyretail	50
A03206	Aphyosemion	ahli	Edea	Ahl´s Lyretail	50
A03207	Aphyosemion	ahli	Kribi	Ahl´s Lyretail	50
A03208	Aphyosemion	ahli	Mayukka	Ahl´s Lyretail	50
A03209	Aphyosemion	ahli	Lobe	Ahl´s Lyretail	50
A03210	Aphyosemion	amieti	Somakak	Ahl´s Lyretail	51
A03211	Aphyosemion	ahli	Londji	Ahl´s Lyretail	50
A03212	Aphyosemion	ahli	SW Cameroon	Ahl´s Lyretail	50
A03213	Aphyosemion	amoenum	Cameroon	Red-Finned Killi, "EMS 90/9"	52
A03214	Aphyosemion	amoenum	San Mayo	Red-Finned Killi, "EMS 90/8"	52
A03215	Aphyosemion	amoenum	Ndoupe	Red-Finned Killi	51
A03216	Aphyosemion	amoenum	Ndoupe near Sonbo	Red-Finned Killi, "EMS 90/10"	52
A03217	Aphyosemion	amoenum	Dibang	Red-Finned Killi	52
A03218	Aphyosemion	amoenum	NKonga	Red-Finned Killi, "C89/22"	52
A03219	Aphyosemion	amoenum	Pouma	Red-Finned Killi	52
A03220	Aphyosemion	arnoldi	SW Nigeria	Arnold´s Killi	53
A03221	Aphyosemion	arnoldi	Sapele	Arnold´s Killi	53
A03222	Aphyosemion	aureum	Mouila	Golden Killi "GHP 80/7"	54
A03223	Aphyosemion	arnoldi	Warri	Arnold´s Killi	53
A03224	Aphyosemion	arnoldi	Aquarium strain	Arnold´s Killi	53
A03225	Aphyosemion	australe	Cap Esterias	Chocolate Lyretail	54
A03226	Aphyosemion	australe	Mayumba	Chocolate Lyretail	54
A03227	Aphyosemion	australe	Aquarian strain	Chocolate Lyretail	55
A03228	Aphyosemion	bamilekorum	9km NW Bafoussam	Bamileke Killi "GPE 90/4"	55
A03229	Aphyosemion	bamilekorum	Bafoussam	Bamileke Killi	55
A03230	Aphyosemion	australe	Aquarian strain	Golden Lyretail	55
A03231	Aphyosemion	australe, mutant	Aquarian strain	Golden Lyretail	55
A03232	Aphyosemion	bamilekorum	Mbouda	Bamileke Killi	55
A03234	Aphyosemion	batesii	Ayos	Bates´Killi	56
A03235	Aphyosemion	bertholdi	Liberia	Berthold´s Killi	59
A03240	Aphyosemion	bitaeniatum	Benin	Two-striped Aphyosemion	59
A03241	Aphyosemion	bitaeniatum	Togo	Two-striped Aphyosemion	59
A03242	Aphyosemion	bitaeniatum	Ikpenle	Two-striped Aphyosemion	59
A03243	Aphyosemion	bitaeniatum	Igolo	Two-striped Aphyosemion	59
A03244	Aphyosemion	bitaeniatum	Takou	Two-striped Aphyosemion	59
A03245	Aphyosemion	bivittatum	Biafra	Two-banded Killi	61
A03246	Aphyosemion	bivittatum, bred	Funge	Two-banded Killi	61
A03250	Aphyosemion	brueningi	Liberia	Bruening´s Killi	62
A03251	Aphyosemion	brueningi	Giema	Bruening´s Killi	62
A03258	Aphyosemion	buytaerti	Ekouma river	Buytaert´s Killi	62
A03261	Aphyosemion	calliurum	Nigerdelta	Banner Lyretail	62
A03262	Aphyosemion	calliurum	Funge	Banner Lyretail	62
A03263	Aphyosemion	calliurum	Monea	Banner Lyretail	62
A03264	Aphyosemion	calliurum	Campo	Banner Lyretail	62
A03265	Aphyosemion	cameronense cameronense	Bengbis	Cameroon Killi	63
A03266	Aphyosemion	cameronense haasi	27 km NW Zomoko	Haas´Cameroon Killi	67
A03267	Aphyosemion	caudofasciatum	Ekouma near Ogouee	Caudal-stripe Killi	69
A03268	Aphyosemion	cauveti	Kindia	Kindia Killi	69
A03270	Aphyosemion	celiae celiae	Badouma	Celia´s Aphyosemion	69
A03271	Aphyosemion	celiae celiae	Eboni	Celia´s Aphyosemion	69
A03272	Aphyosemion	celiae celiae	Western Cameroon	Celia´s Aphyosemion	69
A03273	Aphyosemion	celiae winifredae	New Butu	Winifred´s Aphyosemion	69
A03274	Aphyosemion	celiae winifredae	Aquarien strain	Winifred´s Aphyosemion	69
A03275	Aphyosemion	chaytori	Ngabu	Chaytor´s Aphyosemion	70
A03280	Aphyosemion	christyi	North of Kisangani	Christy´s Lyretail	70
A03281	Aphyosemion	christyi	Vicinity of Kisangani	Christy´s Lyretail	70
A03282	Aphyosemion	christyi, bred	Central African Republic	Christy´s Lyretail	71
A03283	Aphyosemion	christyi	Equateur	Christy´s Lyretail	71
A03284	Aphyosemion	christyi	Bangui	Christy´s Lyretail	71
A03285	Aphyosemion	christyi	Central african Republik	Christy´s Lyretail	71
A03286	Aphyosemion	christyi	5 km north of N´jili	Christy´s Lyretail	71
A03287	Aphyosemion	christyi	Nothern Zaire	Christy´s Lyretail	71
A03288	Aphyosemion	christyi, cf.	Oyo	Christy´s Lyretail	70,128
A03290	Aphyosemion	cinnamomeum	S Manyemen	Cinnamon Killi	72
A03291	Aphyosemion	citrineipinnis	Yeno	Lemon-finned Killi	72
A03292	Aphyosemion	coeleste	Massango	Sky-Blue Killi	73
A03293	Aphyosemion	coeleste	Malinga	Sky-Blue Killi	73
A03294	Aphyosemion	coeleste, bred	Malinga	Sky-Blue Killi	73
A03295	Aphyosemion	cognatum	Brazzaville	Red-Spotted Killi	74
A03296	Aphyosemion	congicum	Takundi	Goldstein´s Killi	76
A03297	Aphyosemion	congicum	Aquarian strain	Goldstein´s Killi	76
A03298	Aphyosemion	congicum	Gamba	Goldstein´s Killi	76
A03302	Aphyosemion	dargei, yellow phenotype	NW of Bafia	Mbam Killi	76
A03303	Aphyosemion	deltaense	Aquarian strain	Delta Killi	77
A03304	Aphyosemion	edeanum	Western Cameroon	Edea Killi	78
A03305	Aphyosemion	elegans	Aquarian strain	Elegant Killi "NSC 5"	80
A03307	Aphyosemion	escherichi	Cap Esterias	Escheich´s Killi	80
A03308	Aphyosemion	escherichi	Lambarene	Escheich´s Killi	80
A03309	Aphyosemion	escherichi, bred	Lambarene	Escheich´s Killi	80

A03310	Aphyosemion	exigoideum	Mandilou	False Jewel Killi	81
A03311	Aphyosemion	exigoideum	Aquarian strain	False Jewel Killi	81
A03312	Aphyosemion	exigoideum	Ngoudoufala	False Jewel Killi	81
A03315	Aphyosemion	exiguum	Ndeng	Jewel Killi	81
A03316	Aphyosemion	exiguum	Akono	Jewel Killi	81
A03317	Aphyosemion	exiguum	Djoum	Jewel Killi	81
A03318	Aphyosemion	exiguum	Elom	Jewel Killi	82
A03319	Aphyosemion	exiguum	Nloup	Jewel Killi	82
A03320	Aphyosemion	fallax	Kribi	Kribi Killi	83
A03321	Aphyosemion	fallax, bred	Kribi	Kribi Killi	83
A03322	Aphyosemion	fallax	Malende	Kribi Killi	83
A03323	Aphyosemion	fallax	Mouanko	Kribi Killi	83
A03325	Aphyosemion	filamentosum	Southern Togo	Blue Killi	84
A03326	Aphyosemion	filamentosum	Southern Benin	Blue Killi	84
A03327	Aphyosemion	filamentosum	Aquarian strain	Blue Killi	84
A03335	Aphyosemion	franzwerneri	15 km. from jct of Douala	Goby Killi	85
A03336	Aphyosemion	franzwerneri	Bonepoupa	Goby Killi	85
A03340	Aphyosemion	gabunense boehmi	Gabon	Boehm´s Gabon Killi	85
A03341	Aphyosemion	gabunense gabunense	30 km. SE Lambarene	Gabon Killi	85
A03342	Aphyosemion	gabunense marginatum	9 km. SW Bifoun	Yellow Gabon Killi	87
A03350	Aphyosemion	gardneri gardneri	Lafia	Gardner´s Killi	87
A03352	Aphyosemion	gardneri lacustre	Lake Ejagham	Ejagham Killi	87
A03353	Aphyosemion	gardneri mamfense	3 km. S Bachou-Akagbe	Mamfe Killi	88
A03354	Aphyosemion	gardneri nigerianum	28 km. NW Abakaliki	Nigerian Killi	89
A03355	Aphyosemion	geryi	Abuko National Park	Gery´s Killi	91
A03356	Aphyosemion	geryi	Bwian	Gery´s Killi	91,132
A03357	Aphyosemion	geryi	Kampant	Gery´s Killi	91
A03358	Aphyosemion	geryi	Casamance	Gery´s Killi	91
A03359	Aphyosemion	geryi	Conakry	Gery´s Killi	91
A03360	Aphyosemion	guignardi	Labe	Guignard´s Killi	92
A03361	Aphyosemion	guignardi	Safakure River	Guignard´s Killi	92
A03362	Aphyosemion	guignardi	Sougueta	Guignard´s Killi	92
A03363	Aphyosemion	guignardi	Bafing River	Guignard´s Killi	92
A03364	Aphyosemion	guignardi	15 km. N Banfora	Guignard´s Killi	92
A03365	Aphyosemion	guineense	Northeastern Sierra Leone	Guinean Killi	93
A03370	Aphyosemion	gulare	SW Nigeria	Gulare	93
A03371	Aphyosemion	hanneloreae hanneloreae	Near Malinga	Hannelore´s Killi "GEB 94/20"	93
A03372	Aphyosemion	herzogi	3 km. N of Zomoko	Herzog´s Killi [T.t.]	94
A03373	Aphyosemion	hofmanni	Imeno Mbila	Hofmann´s Killi [T.t.]	96
A03374	Aphyosemion	joergenscheeli	Mimongo	Joergen Scheel´s Killi	97
A03380	Aphyosemion	labarrei	Aquarian strain	Labarre´s Killi	97,98
A03383	Aphyosemion	lamberti	34 km. NW Moanda	Lambert´s Killi	98
A03385	Aphyosemion	liberiense	Monrovia	Liberian Killi	99
A03386	Aphyosemion	liberiense liberiense	"mülleri"-strain	Liberian Killi	99
A03387	Aphyosemion	liberiense liberiense	"mülleri 3"-strain	Liberian Killi	99
A03388	Aphyosemion	liberiense liberiense	"calDal"-strain	Liberian Killi	99
A03390	Aphyosemion	loennbergii	Kribi	Loennberg´s Killi	101
A03391	Aphyosemion	loennbergii	Soca Palm	Loennberg´s Killi	101
A03392	Aphyosemion	loennbergii	Pouma	Loennberg´s Killi	101
A03393	Aphyosemion	loennbergii	Aquarian strain	Loennberg´s Killi	101
A03394	Aphyosemion	loennbergii	Cameroon	Loennberg´s Killi	101
A03395	Aphyosemion	louessense	Tongo River	Louesse Killi	102
A03396	Aphyosemion	louessense	Kingouama	Louesse Killi	102
A03397	Aphyosemion	louessense	1 km. from Lekoli Magogo	Louesse Killi	102
A03398	Aphyosemion	lugens	Afan Essokie	Mourning Killi	102
A03400	Aphyosemion	lujae	Lake Fwa	Luja Killi	102
A03402	Aphyosemion	maculatum	33 km. E Koumameyong	Speckled Killi, "G 75/36" [T.t.]	103
A03403	Aphyosemion	maculatum, bred	Koumameyong	Speckled Killi	103
A03405	Aphyosemion	marmoratum	16 km. NE Mbonge	Marbled Killi	104
A03406	Aphyosemion	marmoratum	6 km. after Meme River	Marbled Killi	104
A03410	Aphyosemion	mimbon	Edoum	Mimbon Killi	105
A03411	Aphyosemion	mimbon	16 km. W Medouneu	Mimbon Killi	105
A03412	Aphyosemion	mimbon	Oyab River	Mimbon Killi	105
A03413	Aphyosemion	mimbon	Avang	Mimbon Killi	105
A03414	Aphyosemion	mirabile mirabile	Mbio	Miracle Killi	105
A03415	Aphyosemion	mirabile mirabile	Bakebe	Miracle Killi	105
A03416	Aphyosemion	mirabile intermittens	Tinto	Miracle Killi	105
A03417	Aphyosemion	mirabile intermittens	Bakebe	Miracle Killi [T.t.]	105
A03419	Aphyosemion	mirabile moense	Between Kendem and Noumba	Miracle Killi [T.t.]	106
A03420	Aphyosemion	mirabile traudeae	Manyemen	Miracle Killi [T.t.]	106
A03421	Aphyosemion	mirabile traudeae	Western Cameroon	Miracle Killi	106
A03422	Aphyosemion	mirabile traudeae	Aquarian strain	Miracle Killi	106
A03423	Aphyosemion	mirabile traudeae	Cameroon	Miracle Killi	106
A03424	Aphyosemion	mirabile sp. aff., bred	Western Cameroon	Miracle Killi	106,130
A03425	Aphyosemion	mirabile sp. aff.	Western Cameroon	Miracle Killi	106
A03426	Aphyosemion	monrovia	Harbel	Monrovia Killi	107
A03427	Aphyosemion	monrovia	25 miles from Monrovia	Monrovia Killi [T.t.], red Phänotypus	107
A03428	Aphyosemion	monrovia	25 miles from Monrovia	Monrovia Killi [T.t.], blue Phänotypus	107
A03429	Aphyosemion	monrovia	Aquarian strain	Monrovia Killi	107
A03430	Aphyosemion	ndianum	Aquarian strain	Ndian Killi	107
A03431	Aphyosemion	ndianum	Southeastern Nigeria	Ndian Killi	107
A03445	Aphyosemion	occidentale occidentale	Largo	Golden Pheasant, "red" phenotype	108
A03446	Aphyosemion	occidentale occidentale	Largo	Golden Pheasant, "blue" phenotype	108
A03447	Aphyosemion	ocellatum	Gabon	Ocellated Killi, "G 20/76" [T.t.]	109,110
A03449	Aphyosemion	oeseri	Equatorial Guinea	Oeser´s Killi	110
A03450	Aphyosemion	ogoense ogoense	Bambama	Ogowe Killi	111
A03451	Aphyosemion	ogoense ogoense	Mongouango	Ogowe Killi	111
A03452	Aphyosemion	ogoense pyrophore	2 km. E Mvengue	Flame-Tailed Killi	112
A03453	Aphyosemion	ogoense ottogartneri	Lutete	Ogowe Killi	111
A03454	Aphyosemion	ogoense ottogartneri	Gabon	Ogowe Killi	111
A03456	Aphyosemion	ogoense ottogartneri	Kindamba	Ogowe Killi	111
A03457	Aphyosemion	pascheni	Cameroon	Pascen´s Killi	113

A03458	Aphyosemion	pascheni	Aquarian strain	Pascen´s Killi	113
A03460	Aphyosemion	petersi	Banco NP	Peters´Killi	114
A03462	Aphyosemion	poliaki	33 km. from Limbe	Mt. Kamerun-Killi	114
A03463	Aphyosemion	poliaki	"Mile 29" slopes of Mt. Cameroon	Mt. Kamerun-Killi	114
A03465	Aphyosemion	primigenium	Douano-system near Banyanga	Douano Killi	115
A03466	Aphyosemion	primigenium	Lebamba	Douano Killi	115
A03467	Aphyosemion	primigenium, bred	Douano-system	Douano Killi	115
A03468	Aphyosemion	primigenium, Mutante	Aquarian strain	Douano Killi	115
A03470	Aphyosemion	puerzli	Cameroon	Puerzl´s Killi	115
A03471	Aphyosemion	puerzli	Aquarian strain	Puerzl´s Killi	115
A03472	Aphyosemion	punctatum	Ovan	Dotted Killi	116
A03473	Aphyosemion	raddai	Cameroon	Radda´s Killi	116
A03474	Aphyosemion	raddai	Mode, Cameroon	Radda´s Killi	116
A03475	Aphyosemion	rectogoense	Gabon	Leconi Killi	116,133
A03476	Aphyosemion	rectogoense, bred	Gabon	Leconi Killi	116
A03477	Aphyosemion	rectogoense	Aquarian strain	Leconi Killi	117
A03480	Aphyosemion	riggenbachi	Aquarian strain	Riggenbach´s Killi	117
A03481	Aphyosemion	riggenbachi	Somakak	Riggenbach´s Killi	117
A03482	Aphyosemion	riggenbachi	Yabassi	Riggenbach´s Killi	117
A03483	Aphyosemion	riggenbachi	Southern Cameroon	Riggenbach´s Killi	117
A03487	Aphyosemion	robertsoni	Cameroon	Robertson´s Killi	117
A03488	Aphyosemion	robertsoni, bred	Cameroon	Robertson´s Killi	117
A03490	Aphyosemion	roloffi	"Roloffia etzeli"-strain	Roloff´s Killi	118
A03491	Aphyosemion	roloffi, cf.	Brama Junction	Roloff´s Killi	118
A03492	Aphyosemion	roloffi, cf.	Brama Town	Roloff´s Killi	118
A03493	Aphyosemion	roloffi, cf.	Road Monrovia - Robertsport	Roloff´s Killi	118
A03494	Aphyosemion	roloffi, cf.	Sierra Leone	Roloff´s Killi	118
A03500	Aphyosemion	rubrolabiale	19 km. NW Mbonge	Redlipped Killi [T.t.]	119
A03501	Aphyosemion	rubrolabiale	Western Cameroon	Redlipped Killi	119
A03502	Aphyosemion	rubrolabiale	Malende	Redlipped Killi	119
A03503	Aphyosemion	rubrolabiale	Aquarian strain	Redlipped Killi	119
A03505	Aphyosemion	scheeli	Aquarian strain	Scheel´s Killi	119,120
A03506	Aphyosemion	scheeli	20 km. NW Akamkpa	Scheel´s Killi	120,134
A03510	Aphyosemion	schioetzi	Equateur	Schioetz´s Killi	120
A03512	Aphyosemion	schluppi	Congo	Schlupp´s Killi	120
A03513	Aphyosemion	schluppi	Ekouma River, Congo	Schlupp´s Killi	120
A03520	Aphyosemion	sjoestedti	Aquarian strain	Blue Gularis	121
A03521	Aphyosemion	sjoestedti	Ndian River	Blue Gularis	121
A03522	Aphyosemion	sjoestedti	"red" Aquarian strain	Blue Gularis	121
A03523	Aphyosemion	sjoestedti	"USA"-Aquarian strain	Blue Gularis	121
A03524	Aphyosemion	sjoestedti	Loe, Cameroon	Blue Gularis	121
A03530	Aphyosemion	splendopleure	Oron, SW Nigeria	Splendid Killi	122
A03532	Aphyosemion	spoorenbergi	Aquarian strain	Spoorenberg´s Killi	123
A03540	Aphyosemion	striatum	Cocobeach, Gabon	Red Striped Killi	124
A03542	Aphyosemion	thysi	Loumbamba River	Thys´Killi	124
A03543	Aphyosemion	thysi	Birabele River	Thys´Killi	124
A03544	Aphyosemion	thysi	1,5 km. after Gnimi, Congo	Thys´Killi	125
A03550	Aphyosemion	occidentale toddi	Aquarian strain from Barmoi	Blue Golden Pheasant	109
A03558	Aphyosemion	wachtersi wachtersi	Spring in Voula II	Wachter´s Killi	125
A03559	Aphyosemion	wachtersi wachtersi, bred	Spring In Voula II	Wachter´s Killi	125
A03560	Aphyosemion	walkeri	Abidjan, Ivory Coast	Walker´s Killi	126,136
A03561	Aphyosemion	walkeri	Kutunse	Walker´s Killi	126
A03562	Aphyosemion	walkeri, bred	Kutunse	Walker´s Killi	126
A03563	Aphyosemion	walkeri	Aquarian strain	Walker´s Killi	126
A03565	Aphyosemion	wildekampi	Diang, Cameroon	Wildekamp´s Killi	127
A03566	Aphyosemion	wildekampi	Between Ndola, Cameroon	Wildekamp´s Killi	127
A03575	Aphyosemion	zygaima	Mindouli, Congo	Mindouli Killi	127
A03576	Aphyosemion	zygaima	Congo	Mindouli Killi, "CHP 82/4"	127
A03580	Aphyosemion	spec.	Gabon	"GEB 94/17"	127
A03581	Aphyosemion	spec.	Gabon	"GS2"	128
A03705	Aphyosemion	cameronense halleri	southern Cameroon	Haller´s Cameroon Killi	68
A03706	Aphyosemion	cameronense obscurum	Matomb	Spotted Cameroon Killi	68
A03707	Aphyosemion	chauchei	Equateur	Chauche´sAphyosemion	70
A03708	Aphyosemion	cameronense halleri	Bikong	Haller´s Cameroon Killi	68
A03709	Aphyosemion	cameronense halleri	Billi	Haller´s Cameroon Killi	68
A03710	Aphyosemion	cameronense halleri, bred	southern Cameroon	Haller´s Cameroon Killi	68
A03735	Aphyosemion	batesii	Djoum	Bates´Killi	56
A03736	Aphyosemion	batesii	M´bandjok	Bates´Killi	56
A03737	Aphyosemion	batesii	Sangmelima	Bates´Killi	56
A03738	Aphyosemion	batesii	30 km westlich Sangmelima	Bates´Killi	56,57
A03739	Aphyosemion	batesii	Gabun	Bates´Killi "PEG 94/20"	56
A03740	Aphyosemion	batesii	Koumameyong	Bates´Killi	56
A03741	Aphyosemion	batesii	North of Oyem	Bates´Killi	57
A03742	Aphyosemion	batesii	Makokou	Bates´Killi	58
A03743	Aphyosemion	batesii	Ehombitio	Bates´Killi	58
A03744	Aphyosemion	batesii	Gabon	Bates´Killi "GBG 93/13"	58
A03745	Aphyosemion	batesii	Aquarian strain	Bates´Killi	58
A03746	Aphyosemion	batesii	Equateur	Bates´Killi	58
A03747	Aphyosemion	bitaeniatum	Zienvie	Two-striped Aphyosemion	60
A03748	Aphyosemion	bitaeniatum	Ijebu	Two-striped Aphyosemion	60
A03749	Aphyosemion	bitaeniatum	Iwere	Two-striped Aphyosemion	60
A03750	Aphyosemion	bitaeniatum	Lagos	Two-striped Aphyosemion	60
A03751	Aphyosemion	bitaeniatum	Aquarian strain	Two-striped Aphyosemion	60
A03752	Aphyosemion	bitaeniatum	Umudike	Two-striped Aphyosemion	61
A03753	Aphyosemion	cameronense cameronense	Djoum	Cameroon Killi	63
A03754	Aphyosemion	cameronense cameronense	Sangmelima	Cameroon Killi	63
A03755	Aphyosemion	cameronense cameronense	Mfoumou	Cameroon Killi "HJRK 92/7"	63
A03756	Aphyosemion	cameronense cameronense	82 km W Ebolowa	Cameroon Killi "HJRK 92/7"	63
A03757	Aphyosemion	cameronense cameronense	Meuban	Cameroon Killi "CGE 91/8"	63
A03758	Aphyosemion	cameronense cameronense	Mebassa	Cameroon Killi "CGE 91/9"	63
A03759	Aphyosemion	cameronense cameronense	Rio Ecucu	Cameroon Killi	64
A03760	Aphyosemion	cameronense cameronense	Ovan	Cameroon Killi	64

Code	Genus	Species	Locality	Common name	Page
A03761	Aphyosemion	cameronense cameronense	Abelaissi	Cameroon Killi	64
A03762	Aphyosemion	cameronense cameronense	Melen	Cameroon Killi	64
A03763	Aphyosemion	cameronense cameronense	Latta	Cameroon Killi "GWW 86/2"	64
A03764	Aphyosemion	cameronense cameronense	Mebandi	Cameroon Killi "EMS 90/3"	64
A03765	Aphyosemion	cameronense cameronense	39 km S Mitzic	Cameroon Killi "GAB 10/90"	64
A03766	Aphyosemion	cameronense cameronense	Nguem	Cameroon Killi "CGE 91/11"	64
A03767	Aphyosemion	cameronense cameronense	N Ebe	Cameroon Killi "LEC 93/3"	65
A03768	Aphyosemion	cameronense cameronense	Ayol	Cameroon Killi "LEC 93/11"	65
A03769	Aphyosemion	cameronense cameronense	48 km W Mitzic	Cameroon Killi "LEC 93/15"	65
A03770	Aphyosemion	cameronense cameronense	Sam	Cameroon Killi "LEC 93/16"	65
A03771	Aphyosemion	cameronense cameronense	NW Zomoko	Cameroon Killi "PEG 93/16"	65
A03772	Aphyosemion	cameronense cameronense	Mbomo	Cameroon Killi "PEG 94/36"	65
A03773	Aphyosemion	cameronense cameronense	nothern Gabon	Cameroon Killi "PEG 94/37"	65
A03774	Aphyosemion	cameronense cameronense	Adzap	Cameroon Killi "PEG 94/37"	65
A03780	Aphyosemion	cameronense, sp. aff. Pop. 1	Mvile	Cameroon Killi "CGE 91/12"	66
A03781	Aphyosemion	cameronense, sp. aff. Pop. 2	N Ambam	Cameroon Killi "HJRK 92/10"	66
A03782	Aphyosemion	cameronense, sp. aff. Pop. 3	Efoulan	Cameroon Killi "CGE 91/6"	66
A03783	Aphyosemion	cameronense, sp. aff. Pop. 4	Belinga	Cameroon Killi	66
A03784	Aphyosemion	cameronense, sp. aff. Pop. 5	Beleme	Cameroon Killi "GJP 80/14"	66
A03786	Aphyosemion	cameronense, sp. aff. Pop. 6	Assok	Cameroon Killi "LEC 93/21"	66,67
A03787	Aphyosemion	cameronense, sp. aff. Pop. 7	W Ebegna	Cameroon Killi "LEC 93/7"	67
A03788	Aphyosemion	cameronense, sp. aff. Pop. 8	PK 14 west of Mitzic	Cameroon Killi "LEC 93/14"	67
A03789	Aphyosemion	cameronense, sp. aff. Pop. 9	Ngoyang	Cameroon Killi "EMS 90/2"	67
A03790	Aphyosemion	cameronense haasi, cf.	southern Cameroon	Haas´Cameroon Killi	67
A03791	Aphyosemion	cinnamomeum	Western-Cameroon	Cinnamon Killi	72
A03792	Aphyosemion	cinnamomeum	Kumba	Cinnamon Killi	72
A03793	Aphyosemion	citrineipinnis, bred	Yeno	Lemon-finned Killi	72
A03794	Aphyosemion	citrineipinnis, bred	5 km. N Yeno	Lemon-finned Killi	72
A03795	Aphyosemion	coeleste	Southern-Gabun	Sky-Blue Killi	73
A03796	Aphyosemion	coeleste	Kongo	Sky-Blue Killi	73
A03797	Aphyosemion	coeleste	Titi	Sky-Blue Killi	73
A03801	Aphyosemion	cognatum	Djoue	Red-Spotted Killi	74
A03802	Aphyosemion	cognatum	Kenge	Red-Spotted Killi	74
A03803	Aphyosemion	cognatum	Kimwenza	Red-Spotted Killi	74
A03804	Aphyosemion	cognatum	Kinshasa	Red-Spotted Killi	74
A03805	Aphyosemion	cognatum	Vincinity of Kinshasa	Red-Spotted Killi	74
A03806	Aphyosemion	cognatum	Kwambila	Red-Spotted Killi	74
A03807	Aphyosemion	cognatum	Madimba	Red-Spotted Killi	74
A03808	Aphyosemion	cognatum	Mbanza	Red-Spotted Killi	75
A03809	Aphyosemion	cognatum	Pool Malebo	Red-Spotted Killi	75
A03810	Aphyosemion	cognatum	Aquarian strain	Red-Spotted Killi	75
A03811	Aphyosemion	cognatum	Tribak´s strain	Red-Spotted Killi	75
A03812	Aphyosemion	dargei, blue phenotype	NW of Bafia	Mbam Killi	76
A03813	Aphyosemion	dargei	Goura	Mbam Killi	76
A03814	Aphyosemion	dargei	Central Cameroon	Mbam Killi	77
A03815	Aphyosemion	dargei, cf.	Aquarian strain	Mbam Killi	77
A03816	Aphyosemion	decorsei	Mobaye	Decorse´s Killi	77
A03817	Aphyosemion	edeanum	Western Cameroon	Edea Killi "EMS 90/11"	78
A03818	Aphyosemion	gabunense gabunense, bred	30 km. SE Lambarene	Gabon Killi	85
A03819	Aphyosemion	elberti	Bamendijing	Red barred Killi	78
A03820	Aphyosemion	elberti	Bamessi	Red barred Killi	78
A03821	Aphyosemion	elberti	Diang	Red barred Killi	78
A03822	Aphyosemion	elberti	Koupa Matapit	Red barred Killi	79
A03823	Aphyosemion	elberti	N´dikinimeki	Red barred Killi	79
A03824	Aphyosemion	elberti	Ngoundere	Red barred Killi	79
A03825	Aphyosemion	elberti, bred	Ngoundere	Red barred Killi	79
A03826	Aphyosemion	elberti	Ndop	Red barred Killi	79
A03827	Aphyosemion	elberti	Ntui	Red barred Killi	79
A03828	Aphyosemion	elberti	"Red" Aquarian strain	Red barred Killi	79
A03829	Aphyosemion	elberti	Kekem	Red barred Killi	79
A03830	Aphyosemion	escherichi	Mayombe	Escheich´s Killi	80
A03831	Aphyosemion	escherichi	Crystal Mountains	Escheich´s Killi	80
A03832	Aphyosemion	escherichi	Boko Songo	Escheich´s Killi	80
A03833	Aphyosemion	escherichi	Moanda	Escheich´s Killi	80
A03834	Aphyosemion	exiguum	Sangmelima	Jewel Killi	82
A03835	Aphyosemion	exiguum	Zoetele	Jewel Killi	82
A03836	Aphyosemion	exiguum	Southern Cameroon	Jewel Killi	82
A03837	Aphyosemion	exiguum	Aquarian strain	Jewel Killi	82
A03838	Aphyosemion	edeanum	Western Cameroon	Edea Killi "HJRK 92/1"	78
A03839	Aphyosemion	gardneri gardneri	Nsukka	Gardner´s Killi	87
A03840	Aphyosemion	gardneri gardneri	Udi	Gardner´s Killi	87
A03841	Aphyosemion	gardneri lacustre, bred	Lake Ejagham	Ejagham Killi	87
A03842	Aphyosemion	gardneri lacustre, Mutante	Lake Ejagham	Ejagham Killi	87
A03843	Aphyosemion	gardneri mamfense	Besongabang	Mamfe Killi	88
A03844	Aphyosemion	gardneri mamfense	Ossing	Mamfe Killi	88
A03845	Aphyosemion	gardneri mamfense	2 km. O Mamfe	Mamfe Killi	88
A03846	Aphyosemion	gardneri mamfense	8 km. after Mamfe	Mamfe Killi	88
A03847	Aphyosemion	gardneri mamfense	1 km. before Eyomojok	Mamfe Killi	88
A03848	Aphyosemion	gardneri mamfense	Vicinity of Mamfe	Mamfe Killi	88
A03849	Aphyosemion	gardneri mamfense	xanthoristic form	Mamfe Killi	88
A03850	Aphyosemion	gardneri nigerianum	Akamkpa	Nigerian Killi	89
A03851	Aphyosemion	gardneri nigerianum	Akure	Nigerian Killi	89
A03852	Aphyosemion	gardneri nigerianum	Jos Plateau	Nigerian Killi	89
A03853	Aphyosemion	gardneri nigerianum	Markurdi	Nigerian Killi	89,131
A03854	Aphyosemion	gardneri nigerianum	Misage	Nigerian Killi	89
A03855	Aphyosemion	gardneri nigerianum, bred	Misage	Nigerian Killi	89
A03856	Aphyosemion	gardneri nigerianum	Obudu	Nigerian Killi	89
A03857	Aphyosemion	gardneri nigerianum	Osira	Nigerian Killi	90
A03858	Aphyosemion	gardneri nigerianum	"P 82" Nigeria	Nigerian Killi	90
A03859	Aphyosemion	gardneri nigerianum	Rayfield	Nigerian Killi	90
A03860	Aphyosemion	gardneri nigerianum	33 km. O Ugep	Nigerian Killi	90
A03861	Aphyosemion	gardneri nigerianum	Ugep	Nigerian Killi	90

A03862	Aphyosemion	geryi	Mamanka	Gery´s Killi	91
A03863	Aphyosemion	gulare	Aquarian strain	Gulare	93
A03864	Aphyosemion	hanneloreae wuendschi	50 km. S Mbingou	Wuendsch´s Killi [T.t.]	93
A03865	Aphyosemion	herzogi	Edoum	Herzog´s Killi	94
A03866	Aphyosemion	herzogi	Medouneu	Herzog´s Killi	94
A03867	Aphyosemion	herzogi, bred	North Gabon	Herzog´s Killi	94
A03868	Aphyosemion	herzogi	Mintoum	Herzog´s Killi, "GWW 86/11"	95
A03869	Aphyosemion	herzogi	Mintoum	Herzog´s Killi	95
A03870	Aphyosemion	herzogi	North Gabon	Herzog´s Killi, "GBN 88/31"	95
A03871	Aphyosemion	herzogi	North Gabon	Herzog´s Killi, "GBN 88/33"	95
A03872	Aphyosemion	herzogi	Nsessoum	Herzog´s Killi	95
A03873	Aphyosemion	herzogi	Ovan	Herzog´s Killi	95
A03874	Aphyosemion	herzogi	North Gabon	Herzog´s Killi, "LEC 93/23"	95
A03875	Aphyosemion	herzogi, "bochtleri-Form"	North Gabon	Herzog´s Killi	95
A03876	Aphyosemion	hofmanni	Gabon	Hofmann´s Killi, "GEB 94/17"	96
A03877	Aphyosemion	hofmanni	Gabon	Hofmann´s Killi, "GBG 93/17"	96
A03878	Aphyosemion	jeanpoli	Nothern Liberia	Jeanopol´s Killi	96
A03879	Aphyosemion	jeanpoli	Eastern Guinea	Jeanopol´s Killi	96
A03880	Aphyosemion	joergenscheeli	Gabon	Joergen Scheel´s Killi, "GBG 93/21"	97
A03881	Aphyosemion	joergenscheeli	Gabon	Joergen Scheel´s Killi, "PEG 93/4"	97
A03882	Aphyosemion	joergenscheeli	Gabon	Joergen Scheel´s Killi, "GBN 88/20"	97
A03883	Aphyosemion	joergenscheeli	Gabon	Joergen Scheel´s Killi, "GBN 88/29"	97
A03884	Aphyosemion	labarrei	Aquarian strain	Labarre´s Killi, "red" strain	98
A03885	Aphyosemion	labarrei	Aquarian strain	Labarre´s Killi, "blue" strain	98
A03886	Aphyosemion	lamberti	Region des Abeilles	Lambert´s Killi	98
A03887	Aphyosemion	lefiniense	Aquarian strain	Lefini Killi	98
A03888	Aphyosemion	lefiniense	Kongo	Lefini Killi	98
A03889	Aphyosemion	liberiense lieberiense	Aquarian strain	Liberian Killi	99
A03890	Aphyosemion	liberiense lieberiense	Bomi	Liberian Killi	99
A03891	Aphyosemion	liberiense lieberiense	"calabarica"-Aquarian strain	Liberian Killi	99
A03892	Aphyosemion	liberiense lieberiense	Aquarian strain	Liberian Killi	100
A03893	Aphyosemion	liberiense lieberiense	NW Liberia	Liberian Killi, "RL 20"	100
A03894	Aphyosemion	liberiense lieberiense	Monrovia - Robertsport road	Liberian Killi, "RL 29"	100
A03895	Aphyosemion	liberiense lieberiense	5 km. south of Bama	Liberian Killi, "RL 40"	100
A03896	Aphyosemion	liberiense lieberiense	Konala	Liberian Killi, "RL 77a"	100
A03897	Aphyosemion	liberiense lieberiense	Senja-Town	Liberian Killi, "RL 78"	100
A03898	Aphyosemion	liberiense lieberiense	5 km. after Suehn	Liberian Killi, "RL 80"	100
A03899	Aphyosemion	liberiense schmitti	Juarzon	Schmitt´s Liberian Killi	100
A03901	Aphyosemion	loennbergii	Mbebe	Loennberg´s Killi	101
A03902	Aphyosemion	loennbergii	Song Bibai	Loennberg´s Killi	101
A03903	Aphyosemion	maculatum, bred	33 km. E Koumameyong	Speckled Killi	103
A03904	Aphyosemion	maculatum	Ebe	Speckled Killi	103
A03905	Aphyosemion	maculatum	Matora	Speckled Killi	103
A03906	Aphyosemion	maculatum	Lolo I	Speckled Killi	103
A03907	Aphyosemion	maeseni	Beple	Maesen´s Killi	104
A03908	Aphyosemion	maeseni	Gouessesso	Maesen´s Killi	104
A03909	Aphyosemion	maeseni	Lema	Maesen´s Killi	104
A03910	Aphyosemion	maeseni, bred	Liberia	Maesen´s Killi	104
A03911	Aphyosemion	occidentale occidentale	Near Ngabu	Golden Pheasant	108
A03912	Aphyosemion	occidentale occidentale	Moyamba	Golden Pheasant	108
A03913	Aphyosemion	occidentale occidentale	Bahama	Golden Pheasant	108
A03914	Aphyosemion	occidentale occidentale	Magbenta	Golden Pheasant	108
A03915	Aphyosemion	occidentale occidentale	Fallaba	Golden Pheasant	108
A03916	Aphyosemion	occidentale occidentale	Teme Yellah	Golden Pheasant	109
A03917	Aphyosemion	occidentale occidentale	Wanja River	Golden Pheasant	109
A03918	Aphyosemion	occidentale occidentale	Romeni	Golden Pheasant	109
A03919	Aphyosemion	ocellatum	Gabon	Ocellated Killi, "G 80/6"	110
A03920	Aphyosemion	ocellatum	Bolapessa	Ocellated Killi	110
A03921	Aphyosemion	ocellatum	Zenzele	Ocellated Killi	110
A03922	Aphyosemion	ocellatum	Gabon	Ocellated Killi, "PEG 93/9"	110
A03923	Aphyosemion	ocellatum	Gabon	Ocellated Killi, "PEG 96/22"	110
A03924	Aphyosemion	ogoense ottogartneri	30 km. W Malinga	Ogowe Killi	112
A03925	Aphyosemion	ogoense pyrophore, bred	2 km. E Mvengue	Flame-Tailed Killi	112
A03926	Aphyosemion	ogoense pyrophore, bred	Mopia	Flame-Tailed Killi	112
A03927	Aphyosemion	ogoense pyrophore	Mopia	Flame-Tailed Killi	112
A03928	Aphyosemion	ogoense pyrophore	Komono	Flame-Tailed Killi	112
A03929	Aphyosemion	ogoense pyrophore	Mbila	Flamed-Tailed Killi	113
A03930	Aphyosemion	ogoense pyrophore	Road Mossendjo-Komono	Flamed-Tailed Killi	113
A03931	Aphyosemion	passaroi	Gabon	Passaro´s Killi	113
A03932	Aphyosemion	petersi	Bonoua	Peters´Killi	114
A03933	Aphyosemion	petersi	SE Ivory Coast	Peters´Killi	114
A03934	Aphyosemion	petersi	Toupa Falls	Peters´Killi	114
A03935	Aphyosemion	petersi	Awaso	Peters´Killi	114
A03936	Aphyosemion	puerzli	Ndokama	Puerzl´s Killi	115
A03937	Aphyosemion	punctatum	Zoolende	Dotted Killi	116
A03938	Aphyosemion	punctatum	49 km. W Makokou on RN 4	Dotted Killi	116
A03939	Aphyosemion	punctatum	Mekambo	Dotted Killi	116
A03940	Aphyosemion	roloffi, cf.	Matanga	Roloff´s Killi	118
A03941	Aphyosemion	roloffi, cf.	Kasawe	Roloff´s Killi	118
A03942	Aphyosemion	schioetzi	Mindouli	Schioetz´s Killi	120
A03942	Aphyosemion	splendopleure	Bolifamba	Splendid Killi	122
A03943	Aphyosemion	schioetzi	Aquarian strain	Schioetz´s Killi	120
A03943	Aphyosemion	splendopleure	Dizangue	Splendid Killi	122
A03944	Aphyosemion	schioetzi	Taba	Schioetz´s Killi	120
A03944	Aphyosemion	splendopleure	Douala	Splendid Killi	122
A03945	Aphyosemion	splendopleure	Ekondo Titi	Splendid Killi	122
A03946	Aphyosemion	splendopleure	Kumba	Splendid Killi	122,135
A03947	Aphyosemion	splendopleure	Mambanda	Splendid Killi	122
A03948	Aphyosemion	splendopleure	Meme River	Splendid Killi	123
A03949	Aphyosemion	splendopleure	Tiko	Splendid Killi	123
A03950	Aphyosemion	splendopleure	Yoko	Splendid Killi	123
A03951	Aphyosemion	splendopleure	Bibabivotou	Splendid Killi	123

A03952	Aphyosemion	splendopleure	Cap Esterias	Splendid Killi	123
A03953	Aphyosemion	striatum	Cap Esterias	Red Striped Killi	124
A03954	Aphyosemion	striatum	Lambarene	Red Striped Killi	124
A03955	Aphyosemion	striatum	Crystal Mountains, NW Gabon	Red Striped Killi	124
A03956	Aphyosemion	striatum	Macoura	Red Striped Killi	124
A03957	Aphyosemion	viride	Northwestern Liberia	Green Killi	125
A03958	Aphyosemion	wachtersi mikeae	Mpoutoulou River, S Congo	Mike´s Killi	125
A03959	Aphyosemion	walkeri	Agboville	Walker´s Killi	126
A03961	Aphyosemion	walkeri	Ivory coast	Walker´s Killi	127
A03962	Aphyosemion	amieti X A. scheeli		Cross breeding	129
A03963	Aphyosemion	gardneri nigerianum X A. walkeri		Cross breeding	129
A03964	Aphyosemion	gardneri nigerianum X 'A. amieti		Cross breeding	129
A03965	Aphyosemion	gardneri nigerianum X A.walkeri		Cross breeding	129
A03966	Aphyosemion	walkeri "Abidjan" X A. walkeri "Kutunse"		Cross breeding	129
A03967	Aphyosemion	pascheni X A. gardneri nigerianum		Cross breeding	129
A03968	Aphyosemion	fallax X A. sjoestedti		Cross breeding	129
A03969	Aphyosemion	ogoense "GHR 1/88" X A. exigoideum		Cross breeding	129
A03970	Aphyosemion	bivittatum	Funge	Two-banded Killi	61
A03981	Aphyosemion	amoenum, sp. aff.	Cameroon	Red-Finned Killi	52
A03982	Aphyosemion	bamilekorum, sp. aff.	Mapan	Brown Killi	55
A03983	Aphyosemion	heinemanni	Song Mahi	Heinemann´s Killi	94
A04540	Aplocheilichthys	pumilus	Ujiji	"TZ 92/21"	35
A04541	Aplocheilichthys	vitschumbaensis, cf.	Kenyoro	Bitschumbi Lampeye	38
A04546	Aplocheilichthys	normani	Tabili River	Norman´s Lampeye	34
A04550	Aplocheilichthys	bukobanus	Kaloleni SO Kisumu	Bukoba Lampeye	24
A04551	Aplocheilichthys	bukobanus	Entebbe	Bukoba Lampeye	24
A04552	Aplocheilichthys	centralis, cf.	13 km O Masindi	Central African Lampeye	26
A04553	Aplocheilichthys	fuelleborni	Iwanga	Fuelleborn´s Lampeye	27
A04554	Aplocheilichthys	fuelleborni	Nkululu River	Fuelleborn´s Lampeye	27
A04555	Aplocheilichthys	fuelleborni	Rungwa drainage	Fuelleborn´s Lampeye	27
A04556	Aplocheilichthys	fuelleborni	Kigwa	Fuelleborn´s Lampeye	27
A04558	Aplocheilichthys	bukobanus	Bukoba reddish	Bukoba Lampeye	24
A04559	Aplocheilichthys	bukobanus	Bukoba blackish	Bukoba Lampeye	24
A04565	Aplocheilichthys	antinorii		Black Lampeye	24
A04566	Aplocheilichthys	brichardi		Brichard´s Lampeye	24
A04567	Aplocheilichthys	camerunensis	8 km S Sangmelima	Cameroon Lampeye	25
A04568	Aplocheilichthys	centralis	Wogo-River	Central African Lampeye	26
A04569	Aplocheilichthys	centralis	Iwanga	Central African Lampeye	26
A04570	Aplocheilichthys	centralis	Kasama	Central African Lampeye	26
A04571	Aplocheilichthys	centralis	27 km W Mbarara	Central African Lampeye	26
A04572	Aplocheilichthys	bukobanus	Mpugwe NO Masada	Bukoba Lampeye	25
A04573	Aplocheilichthys	bukobanus	13 km SO Masindi	Bukoba Lampeye	25
A04574	Aplocheilichthys	bukobanus	UG 14	Bukoba Lampeye	25
A04575	Aplocheilichthys	bukobanus	Butiaba	Bukoba Lampeye	25
A04576	Aplocheilichthys	camerunensis		Cameroon Lampeye	25
A04578	Aplocheilichthys	fuelleborni, cf.	Lower Wembere River	Fuelleborn´s Lampeye	27
A04579	Aplocheilichthys	fuelleborni, cf.	Lake Chaya	Fuelleborn´s Lampeye	27
A04580	Aplocheilichthys	hutereaui, sp. aff.	Chisimba Falls	Chambeshi Dwarf Lampeye	28
A04581	Aplocheilichthys	jeanneli		Omo Lampeye	28
A04582	Aplocheilichthys	johnstoni, sp. aff.		Johnston´s Lampeye	29
A04583	Aplocheilichthys	kongoranensis	Rufiji Drainage	Kongoro Lampeye	30
A04584	Aplocheilichthys	kongoranensis	Mbezi River	Kongoro Lampeye	30
A04586	Aplocheilichthys	kongoranensis	14 km S Dar es Salaam	Kongoro Lampeye	30
A04588	Aplocheilichthys	hutereaui	Shaba	Hutereau´s Lampeye	27
A04589	Aplocheilichthys	hutereaui, sp. aff.	Kalunga River	Hutereau´s Lampeye	28
A04590	Aplocheilichthys	johnstoni	59 km E Kasama	Johnston´s Lampeye	28
A04591	Aplocheilichthys	johnstoni	Dikuluwe River	Johnston´s Lampeye	28
A04592	Aplocheilichthys	johnstoni	Harare	Johnston´s Lampeye	28
A04593	Aplocheilichthys	johnstoni, cf.	Kyela	Johnston´s Lampeye	29
A04594	Aplocheilichthys	kassenjiensis		Lake Albert Lampeye	29
A04595	Aplocheilichthys	katangae		Blackstripe Lampeye	29
A04596	Aplocheilichthys	kongoranensis	Kibiti	Kongoro Lampeye	29
A04598	Aplocheilichthys	m. lacustris	Kibiti	Kibiti Lampeye	32
A04599	Aplocheilichthys	m. lacustris	40 km S Dar es Salaam	Kibiti Lampeye	32
A04600	Aplocheilichthys	lamberti		Lambert´s Lampeye	30
A04601	Aplocheilichthys	lamberti, cf.		Lambert´s Lampeye	30
A04602	Aplocheilichthys	l. luxophthalmus		Big Eye Lampeye	30
A04603	Aplocheilichthys	l. luxophthalmus	Kribi	Big Eye Lampeye	31
A04604	Aplocheilichthys	l. luxophthalmus	Nigerdelta	Big Eye Lampeye	31
A04605	Aplocheilichthys	l. luxophthalmus	Southern Togo	Big Eye Lampeye	31
A04606	Aplocheilichthys	l. hannerzi		Hannerz´Lampeye	31
A04607	Aplocheilichthys	m. maculatus	Bagamoyo	Spotted Lampeye	31
A04608	Aplocheilichthys	m. maculatus	10 km S Bagamoyo	Spotted Lampeye	31
A04610	Aplocheilichthys	myersi		Hummingbird Lampeye	33
A04611	Aplocheilichthys	nimbaensis		Mt. Nimba Lampeye	33
A04612	Aplocheilichthys	moeruensis		Mweru Lampeye	32
A04613	Aplocheilichthys	myaposae		Natal Lampeye	33
A04614	Aplocheilichthys	moeruensis, sp. aff.		Mweru Lampeye	32
A04615	Aplocheilichthys	normanni	Gambia	Norman´s Lampeye	34
A04616	Aplocheilichthys	normanni	Robertsfield	Norman´s Lampeye	34
A04617	Aplocheilichthys	omoculatus		Ruaha Lampeye	34
A04618	Aplocheilichthys	pfaffi		Pfaff´s Lampeye	35
A04620	Aplocheilichthys	pumilus		Tanganyika Lampeye	35
A04621	Aplocheilichthys	matthesi		Matthes´Lampeye	32
A04622	Aplocheilichthys	omoculatus	Brook W Ifunda	Ruaha Lampeye	34
A04623	Aplocheilichthys	omoculatus	Kinaha	Ruaha Lampeye	34
A04625	Aplocheilichthys	rancureli		Rancurel´s Lampeye	35
A04626	Aplocheilichthys	rancureli	Tweakpoloe River	Rancurel´s Lampeye	35
A04627	Aplocheilichthys	rudolfianus		Lake Rudolf Lampeye	35
A04630	Aplocheilichthys	scheeli		Scheel´s Lampeye	36
A04631	Aplocheilichthys	scheeli	Dizangue	Scheel´s Lampeye	36
A04632	Aplocheilichthys	scheeli	Kribi	Scheel´s Lampeye	36

A04635	Aplocheilichthys	schioetzi	SE Guinea	Schiötz´Lampeye	36
A04636	Aplocheilichthys	schioetzi, cf.	Guinea-Senegal border	Schiötz´Lampeye	36
A04638	Aplocheilichthys	schioetzi	E Liberia	Schiötz´Lampeye	36
A04640	Aplocheilichthys	spilauchen	Gambia	Banded Lampeye	37
A04641	Aplocheilichthys	spilauchen	Westafrica	Banded Lampeye	37
A04642	Aplocheilichthys	spilauchen	Robertsfield	Banded Lampeye	37
A04643	Aplocheilichthys	spilauchen	Aquarium strain	Banded Lampeye	37
A04644	Aplocheilichthys	spilauchen	N Rio Lifune	Banded Lampeye	37
A04650	Aplocheilichthys	usanguensis		Usangu Lampeye	38
A04660	Aplocheilichthys	vitschumbaensis	Kazinga Channel	Bitschumbi Lampeye	38
A04661	Aplocheilichthys	vitschumbaensis, cf.	Bitschumbi	Bitschumbi Lampeye	38
A04701	Aplocheilichthys	sp. "TZ 91/126"	Makere River		38
A04702	Aplocheilichthys	sp. "TZ 91/128"	6 km N Malagarasi River		38
A04703	Aplocheilichthys	sp. "TZ 92/144"	60 km E Kasama		39
A04704	Aplocheilichthys	sp. "TZ 92/131"	Gumba River		39
A04705	Aplocheilichthys	sp. "Kasundu"	Kasundu		39
A04706	Aplocheilichthys	sp. "TZ 89/14"	Malagarasi drainage	Malagarasi-Lampeye	39
A04707	Aplocheilichthys	maculatus, sp. aff.	Molo River	Baringo Lampeye	39
A37775	Hylopanchax	stictopleuron	Makokou	Blue Lampeye	40
A37776	Hylopanchax	stictopleuron	Equateur	Blue Lampeye	40
A38000	Hypsopanchax	catenatus		Chain Lampeye	40
A38005	Hypsopanchax	modestus	Rwimi River	Ruwenzori Lampeye	40
A38006	Hypsopanchax	modestus	12 km W Fort Portal	Ruwenzori Lampeye	40
A38010	Hypsopanchax	platysternus		Zaire Lampeye	41
A38011	Hypsopanchax	platysternus	Kindu	Zaire Lampeye	41
A38015	Hypsopanchax	zebra		Zebra Lampeye	41
A40400	Lamprichthys	tanganicanus		Tanganyikan Pearl Killifish	41
A51956	Pantanodon	stuhlmanni	Dar es Salaam	Eastcoast Lampeye	42
A51957	Pantanodon	stuhlmanni	16 km N Tanga	Eastcoast Lampeye	42
A61203	Plataplochilus	cabindae, cf.	Lebamba	Cabinda Lampeye	42
A61204	Plataplochilus	cabindae, cf.	Mayombe	Cabinda Lampeye	42
A61206	Plataplochilus	cabindae, cf.	Moabi	Cabinda Lampeye	42
A61207	Plataplochilus	cabindae, cf.	Ndende	Cabinda Lampeye	42
A61210	Plataplochilus	loemensis		Loeme Lampeye	43
A61215	Plataplochilus	miltotaenia		Red Striped Lampeye	43
A61216	Plataplochilus	miltotaenia	Aquarium strain	Red Striped Lampeye	43
A61218	Plataplochilus	mimus		Yellow Finned Lampeye	43
A61219	Plataplochilus	mimus, cf.	Kinguele	Yellow Finned Lampeye	44
A61220	Plataplochilus	ngaensis	Crystal mountains	Nga Lampeye	44
A61225	Plataplochilus	ngaensis, sp. aff.		Nga Lampeye	44
A61226	Plataplochilus	ngaensis, sp. aff.	Cap Esterias	Nga Lampeye	44
A61227	Plataplochilus	terveri		Terver´s Lampeye	44
A61228	Plataplochilus	sp.	Mouila	Mouila Lampeye	44
A74020	Procatopus	aberrans	Aquarium strain	Bluegreen Lampeye	45
A74021	Procatopus	aberrans, cf.		Bluegreen Lampeye	45
A74060	Procatopus	nototaenia	Kribi	Large Finned Lampeye	45
A74061	Procatopus	nototaenia		Large Finned Lampeye	45
A74062	Procatopus	nototaenia	Yabassi	Large Finned Lampeye	45
A74100	Procatopus	similis	W Cameroon	Variable Lampeye	46
A74101	Procatopus	similis	Commercial Import	Variable Lampeye	46
A74102	Procatopus	similis	Cameroon	Variable Lampeye	46
A74103	Procatopus	similis	Kumba	Variable Lampeye	46
A74104	Procatopus	similis	Muyuka	Variable Lampeye	46
A74105	Procatopus	similis	Edea	Variable Lampeye	46
X02855	Adrianichthys	kruyti		Duck-bill Poso Minnow	18
X52935	Horaichthys	setnai		Indian Glasskilli	18
X68978	Oryzias	celebensis		Celebes Medaka	19
X69005	Oryzias	javanicus	Java	Javanese Medaka	19
X69015	Oryzias	javanicus	Kuta	Javanese Medaka	19
X69055	Oryzias	latipes		Japanese Medaka	19
X69065	Oryzias	latipes	Gold	Japanese Medaka	20
X69075	Oryzias	marmoratus		Marmorated Medaka	20
X69085	Oryzias	matanensis		Matano Medaka	20
X69105	Oryzias	melastigma	Aquarium strain	Spotted Medaka	20
X69115	Oryzias	melastigma, sp. aff.		Spotted Medaka	20
X69120	Oryzias	melastigma	Calcutta	Spotted Medaka	21
X69135	Oryzias	minutillus	Bangkok	Dwarf Medaka	21
X69136	Oryzias	minutillus	Satul	Dwarf Medaka	21
X69155	Oryzias	nigrimas		Black Medaka	21
X69156	Oryzias	nigrimas	Tentena	Black Medaka	22
X69160	Oryzias	orthognathus		Pointed Head Medaka	22
X69161	Oryzias	profundicola		Yellow Finned Medaka	22
X69165	Oryzias	sp.	Bentota	Bentota Medaka	22
X69168	Oryzias	sp.	China	Chinese Medaka	22
X97230	Xenopoecilus	oophorus		Egg Carrying Poso Minnow	18
X97233	Xenopoecilus	poptae		Elongate Poso Minnow	18
X97235	Xenopoecilus	sarasinorum		Sarasins Minnow	18

INDEX
alphabetisch / alphabetic

aberrans, Procatopus 45
Adamas formosus 12, 49
Adrianichthys kruyti 10, 18
ahli, Aphyosemion 50
Ahl's Lyretail 50
Ahls Prachtkärpfling 50
amieti, Aphyosemion 51
Amiet's Lyretail 51
Amiets Prachtkärpfling 51
amoenum, Aphyosemion 51, 52
antinorii, Aplocheilichthys 24
Aphyoplatys duboisi 12, 49
Aphyosemion ahli 50
Aphyosemion (F?) amieti 51
Aphyosemion amoenum 51, 52
Aphyosemion (F.) arnoldi 53
Aphyosemion aureum 54
Aphyosemion australe 54, 55
Aphyosemion bamilekorum 55
Aphyosemion (F.) batesii 56, 57, 58
Aphyosemion bertholdi 59
Aphyosemion bitaeniatum 59, 60, 61
Aphyosemion bivittatum 61
Aphyosemion brueningi 62
Aphyosemion buytaerti 62
Aphyosemion calliurum 62
Aphyosemion cameronense cameronense 63, 64, 65
Aphyosemion cameronense haasi 67
Aphyosemion cameronense halleri 68
Aphyosemion cameronense obscurum 68
Aphyosemion caudofasciatum 69
Aphyosemion cauveti 69
Aphyosemion celiae celiae 69
Aphyosemion celiae winifredae 69
Aphyosemion chauchei 70
Aphyosemion chaytori 70
Aphyosemion christyi 13, 70, 71
Aphyosemion (F.) cinnamomeum 72
Aphyosemion citrineipinnis 72
Aphyosemion coeleste 73
Aphyosemion cognatum 74, 75
Aphyosemion congicum 76
Aphyosemion, cross-breedings 128
Aphyosemion dargei 76, 77
Aphyosemion decorsei 77
Aphyosemion (F.) deltaense 77
Aphyosemion edeanum 78
Aphyosemion elberti 78, 79
Aphyosemion elegans 80
Aphyosemion escherichi 80
Aphyosemion exigoideum 81
Aphyosemion exiguum 81, 82
Aphyosemion (F.) fallax 83
Aphyosemion (F.) filamentosum 84
Aphyosemion franzwerneri 85
Aphyosemion gabunense boehmi 85
Aphyosemion gabunense gabunense 85
Aphyosemion gabunense marginatum 87
Aphyosemion (F.) gardneri gardneri 87
Aphyosemion (F.) gardneri lacustre 87
Aphyosemion (F.) gardneri mamfense 88
Aphyosemion (F.) gardneri nigerianum 89, 90, 131
Aphyosemion geryi 91, 132
Aphyosemion guignardi 92
Aphyosemion guineense 93
Aphyosemion (F.) gulare 93
Aphyosemion hanneloreae hanneloreae 93
Aphyosemion hanneloreae wuendschi 93
Aphyosemion heinemanni 94
Aphyosemion herzogi 94, 95
Aphyosemion hofmanni 96
Aphyosemion jeanpoli 96
Aphyosemion joergenscheeli 97
Aphyosemion-Kreuzungen 128
Aphyosemion labarrei 97, 98
Aphyosemion lamberti 98
Aphyosemion lefiniense 98
Aphyosemion liberiense liberiense 99, 100
Aphyosemion liberiense schmitti 100

Aphyosemion loennbergii 101
Aphyosemion louessense 102
Aphyosemion lugens 102
Aphyosemion lujae 102
Aphyosemion maculatum 103
Aphyosemion maeseni 104
Aphyosemion marmoratum 104
Aphyosemion mimbon 105
Aphyosemion (F.) mirabile intermittens 105
Aphyosemion (F.) mirabile mirabile 105
Aphyosemion (F.) mirabile moense 106
Aphyosemion (F.) mirabile traudeae 106
Aphyosemion monroviae 107
Aphyosemion (F.) ndianum 107
Aphyosemion occidentale occidentale 108, 109
Aphyosemion occidentale toddi 109
Aphyosemion ocellatum 109, 110
Aphyosemion oeseri 86, 110
Aphyosemion ogoense ogoense 111
Aphyosemion ogoense ottogartneri 86, 111, 112
Aphyosemion ogoense pyrophore 112, 113
Aphyosemion pascheni 113
Aphyosemion passaroi 113
Aphyosemion petersi 114
Aphyosemion poliaki 114
Aphyosemion primigenium 115
Aphyosemion (F.) puerzli 115
Aphyosemion punctatum 116
Aphyosemion raddai 116
Aphyosemion rectogoense 116, 117, 133
Aphyosemion riggenbachi 117
Aphyosemion (F.) robertsoni 117
Aphyosemion roloffi 118
Aphyosemion (F.) rubrolabiale 119
Aphyosemion scheeli 119, 120, 134
Aphyosemion schioetzi 120
Aphyosemion schluppi 120
Aphyosemion (F.) sjoestedti 13, 121
Aphyosemion sp. aff. bamilekorum 55
Aphyosemion sp. aff. cameronense 66, 67
Aphyosemion sp. aff. mirabile 106, 130
Aphyosemion spec. 127
Aphyosemion spec. "GS 2" 128
Aphyosemion spec. "Oyo" 70, 128
Aphyosemion splendopleure 122, 123, 135
Aphyosemion (F.) spoorenbergi 123
Aphyosemion striatum 124
Aphyosemion thysi 124, 125
Aphyosemion viride 125
Aphyosemion wachtersi mikeae 125
Aphyosemion wachtersi wachtersi 125
Aphyosemion (F.) walkeri 126, 127, 136
Aphyosemion wildekampi 127
Aphyosemion zygaima 127
Aplocheilichthys antinorii 24
Aplocheilichthys (Congopanchax) brichardi 24
Aplocheilichthys bukobanus 24, 25
Aplocheilichthys camerunensis 25
Aplocheilichthys centralis 26
Aplocheilichthys fuelleborni 27
Aplocheilichthys hutereaui 27
Aplocheilichthys jeanneli 28
Aplocheilichthys johnstoni 28, 29
Aplocheilichthys katangae 29
Aplocheilichthys kongoranensis 29, 30
Aplocheilichthys lamberti 30
Aplocheilichthys luxophthalmus hannerzi 31
Aplocheilichthys luxophthalmus luxophthalmus 30, 31
Aplocheilichthys maculatus maculatus 31
Aplocheilichthys maculatus lacustris 32
Aplocheilichthys matthesi 32
Aplocheilichthys moeruensis 32
Aplocheilichthys myaposae 33
Aplocheilichthys (Congopanchax) myersi 33
Aplocheilichthys nimbaensis 33
Aplocheilichthys normani 34
Aplocheilichthys omoculatus 34
Aplocheilichthys pfaffi 35
Aplocheilichthys pumilus 35

Aplocheilichthys rancureli .... .35
Aplocheilichthys rudolfianus .... .35
Aplocheilichthys scheeli .... .36
Aplocheilichthys schioetzi .... .36
Aplocheilichthys sp. aff. hutereaui .... .28
Aplocheilichthys sp. aff. johnstoni .... .29
Aplocheilichthys sp. aff. maculatus .... .39
Aplocheilichthys spec. "Kasundu" .... .39
Aplocheilichthys spec. "TZ 89/14" .... .39
Aplocheilichthys spec. "TZ 91/126" .... .38
Aplocheilichthys spec. "TZ 91/128" .... .38
Aplocheilichthys spec. "TZ 92/131" .... .39
Aplocheilichthys spec. "TZ 92/144" .... .39
Aplocheilichthys spilauchen .... .11, 37
Aplocheilichthys usanguensis .... .38
Aplocheilichthys vitschumbaensis .... .38
arnoldi, Aphyosemion .... .53
Arnold's Killi .... .53
Arnolds Prachtkärpfling .... .53
aureum, Aphyosemion .... .54
australe, Aphyosemion .... .54, 55
Bamileke Killi .... .55
Bamileke-Prachtkärpfling .... .55
bamilekorum, Aphyosemion .... .55
Banded Lampeye .... .37
Bangui-Prachtkärpfling .... .77
Banner Lyretail .... .62
Baringo Lampeye .... .30
Baringo-Leuchtauge .... .30
batesii, Aphyosemion .... .56, 57, 58
Bates' Killi .... .56, 57, 58
Bates Prachtkärpfling .... .56, 57, 58
Bentota Medaka .... .22
Bentota-Reiskärpfling .... .22
bertholdi, Aphyosemion .... .59
Berthold's Killi .... .59
Bertholds Prachtkärpfling .... .59
Big Eye Lampeye .... .30, 31
bitaeniatum, Aphyosemion .... .59, 60, 61
Bitschumbi Lampeye .... .38
Bitschumbi-Leuchtaugenfisch .... .38
bivittatum, Aphyosemion .... .61
Black Lampeye .... .24
Black Medaka .... .21, 22
Blackstripe Lampeye .... .29
Blauauge .... .34
Blauer Goldfasan-Prachtkärpfling .... .109
Blauer Leuchtaugenfisch .... .40
Blaugrüner Leuchtaugenfisch .... .45
Blue Calliurum .... .50
Blue-eye .... .34
Blue Golden Pheasant .... .109
Bluegreen Lampeye .... .45
Blue Gularis .... .121
Blue Killi .... .84
Blue Lampeye .... .40
boehmi, Aphyosemion gabunense .... .85
Boehm's Gabon Killi .... .85
Böhms Gabun-Prachtkärpfling .... .85
Brauner Prachtkärpfling .... .55
Breitflossiger Leuchtaugenfisch .... .45
brichardi, Aplocheilichthys (Congopanchax) .... .24
Brichard's Lampeye .... .24
Brichards Leuchtaugenfisch .... .24
Brown Killi .... .55
brueningi, Aphyosemion .... .62
Bruening's Killi .... .62
Brünings Prachtkärpfling .... .62
Bukoba Lampeye .... .24, 25
Bukoba-Leuchtaugenfisch .... .24, 25
bukobanus, Aplocheilichthys .... .24, 25
buytaerti, Aphyosemion .... .62
Buytaert's Killi .... .62
Buytaerts Prachtkärpfling .... .62
cabindae, Plataplochilus .... .42
Cabinda Lampeye .... .42
Cabinda-Leuchtaugenfisch .... .42
calliurum, Aphyosemion .... .62
cameronense cameronense, Aphyosemion .... .63, 64, 65

cameronense haasi, Aphyosemion .... .67
cameronense halleri, Aphyosemion .... .68
cameronense obscurum, Aphyosemion .... .68
Cameroon Killi .... .63, 64, 65,
                                                      66, 67
Cameroon Lampeye .... .25
camerunensis, Aplocheilichthys .... .25
catenatus, Hypsopanchax .... .40
Caudal-stripe Killi .... .69
caudofasciatum, Aphyosemion .... .69
cauveti, Aphyosemion .... .69
celebensis, Oryzias .... .19
Celebes Medaka .... .19
Celebes-Reiskärpfling .... .19
celiae celiae, Aphyosemion .... .69
celiae winifredae, Aphyosemion .... .69
Celia's Aphyosemion .... .69
Celias Prachtkärpfling .... .69
Central African Lampeye .... .26
centralis, Aplocheilichthys .... .26
Chain Lampeye .... .40
Chambeshi Dwarf Lampeye .... .28
Chambeshi-Zwergleuchtaugenfisch .... .28
chauchei, Aphyosemion .... .70
Chauche's Aphyosemion .... .70
Chauches Prachtkärpfling .... .70
chaytori, Aphyosemion .... .70
China-Reiskärpfling .... .22
Chinese Medaka .... .22
Chocolate Lyretail .... .54, 55
christyi, Aphyosemion .... .13, 70, 71
Christy's Lyretail .... .70, 71
Christys Prachtkärpfling .... .70, 71
cinnamomeum, Aphyosemion .... .72
Cinnamon Killi .... .72
citrineipinnis, Aphyosemion .... .72
coeleste, Aphyosemion .... .73
cognatum, Aphyosemion .... .74, 75
congicum, Aphyosemion .... .76
Congo Killi .... .76
Congopanchax = Aplocheilichthys .... .24, 33
cross-breedings, Aphyosemion .... .129
dargei, Aphyosemion .... .76, 77
Darges Prachtkärpfling .... .76, 77
decorsei, Aphyosemion .... .77
Decorse's Killi .... .77
deltaense, Aphyosemion .... .77
Delta Killi .... .77
Delta-Prachtkärpfling .... .77
Dotted Killi .... .116
Douano Killi .... .115
Douano-Prachtkärpfling .... .115
duboisi, Aphyoplatys .... .12, 49
Dubois' Panchax .... .49
Duck-bill Poso Minnow .... .18
Dwarf Medaka .... .21
Eastcoast Lampeye .... .42
Edea Killi .... .78
edeanum, Aphyosemion .... .78
Edea-Prachtkärpfling .... .78
Egg Carrying Poso Minnow .... .18
Eitragender Posokärpfling .... .18
Ejagham Killi .... .87
Ejagham-Prachtkärpfling .... .87
elberti, Aphyosemion .... .78, 79
elegans, Aphyosemion .... .80
Eleganter Prachtkärpfling .... .80
Elegant Killi .... .80
Elongate Poso Minnow .... .18
Entenschnabelkärpfling .... .18
escherichi, Aphyosemion .... .80
Escherich's Killi .... .80
Escherichs Prachtkärpfling .... .80
exigoideum, Aphyosemion .... .81
exiguum, Aphyosemion .... .81, 82
Faden-Prachtkärpfling .... .84
fallax, Aphyosemion .... .83
False Jewel Kill .... .81
Fernando Poo-Prachtkärpfling .... .86, 110

filamentosum, Aphyosemion 84
Flame-tailed Killi 112, 113
Flammenschwanz-Prachtkärpfling 112, 113
formosus, Adamas 12, 49
franzwerneri, Aphyosemion 85
fuelleborni, Aplocheilichthys 27
Fuelleborn's Lampeye 27
Fülleborns Leuchtaugenfisch 27
Gabon Killi 85
gabunense boehmi, Aphyosemion 85
gabunense gabunense, Aphyosemion 85
gabunense marginatum, Aphyosemion 87
Gabun-Prachtkärpfling 85
gardneri gardneri, Aphyosemion 87
gardneri lacustre, Aphyosemion 87
gardneri mamfense, Aphyosemion 88
gardneri nigerianum, Aphyosemion 89, 90, 131
Gardner's Killi 87
Gardners Prachtkärpfling 87
Gebänderter Prachtkärpfling 61
Gefleckter Prachtkärpfling 103
Gefleckter Reiskärpfling 20, 21
Gelber Leuchtaugenfisch 31
Gelber Rotstreifen-Prachtkärpfling 81, 82
Gelbflossen-Gabunprachtkärpfling 87
Gelbflossen-Plataplochilus 43, 44
Gelbflossen-Reiskärpfling 22
geryi, Aphyosemion 91, 132
Géry's Killi 91, 132
Gérys Prachtkärpfling 91, 132
Gestreckter Posokärpfling 18
Glanz-Prachtkärpfling 59, 60, 61, 135
Goby Killi 85
Golden Killi 54
Golden Lyretail 55
Golden Medaka 20
Golden Pheasant 108, 109
Goldfasan-Prachtkärpfling 108, 109
Gold-Kap Lopez 55
Goldprachtkärpfling 54
Gold-Reiskärpfling 20
Goldstein's Killi 76
Grauer Prachtkärpfling 113
Green Killi 125
Großer Tanganjika-Leuchtaugenfisch 41
Grundel-Prachtkärpfling 85
Grüner Glanzprachtkärpfling 122, 123, 135
Grüner Prachtkärpfling 125
guignardi, Aphyosemion 92
Guignard's Killi 92
Guignards Prachtkärpfling 92
Guinean Killi 93
Guinea-Prachtkärpfling 93
guineense, Aphyosemion 93
Gulare 93
gulare, Aphyosemion 93
Haas' Cameroon Killi 67
haasi, Aphyosemion cameronense 67
Haas' Kamerun-Prachtkärpfling 67
halleri, Aphyosemion cameronense 68
Haller's Cameroon Killi 68
Hallers Kamerun-Prachtkärpfling 68
hanneloreae hanneloreae, Aphyosemion 93
hanneloreae wuendschi, Aphyosemion 93
Hannelore's Killi 93
Hannelores Prachtkärpfling 93
hannerzi, Aplocheilichthys luxophthalmus 31
Hannerz' Lampeye 31
Hannerz' Leuchtaugenfisch 31
heinemanni, Aphyosemion 94
Heinemann's Killi 94
Heinemanns Prachtkärpfling 94
herzogi, Aphyosemion 94, 95
Herzog's Killi 94, 95
Herzogs Prachtkärpfling 94, 95
Himmelblauer Prachtkärpfling 73
hofmanni, Aphyosemion 96
Hofmann's Killi 96
Hofmanns Prachtkärpfling 96

Horaichthys setnai 10, 18
Hummingbird Lampeye 33
hutereaui, Aplocheilichthys 27
Hutereau's Lampeye 27
Hutereaus Leuchtaugenfisch 27
Hylopanchax stictopleuron 11, 40
Hypsopanchax catenatus 40
Hypsopanchax modestus 40
Hypsopanchax platysternus 11, 41
Hypsopanchax zebra 41
Indian Glaskilli 18
Indischer Glaskärpfling 18
intermittens, Aphyosemion mirabile 105
Japanese Medaka 19, 20
Japan-Reiskärpfling 19, 20
javanicus, Oryzias 19
Javanese Medaka 19
Java-Reiskärpfling 19
jeanneli, Aplocheilichthys 28
jeanpoli, Aphyosemion 96
Jeanpol's Killi 96
Jeanpols Prachtkärpfling 96
Jewel Killi 81, 82
joergenscheeli, Aphyosemion 97
Joergen Scheel's Killi 97
Joergen Scheels Prachtkärpfling 97
johnstoni, Aplocheilichthys 28, 29
Johnston's Lampeye 28, 29
Johnstons Leuchtaugenfisch 28, 29
Kamerun-Leuchtaugenfisch 25
Kamerun-Prachtkärpfling 63, 64, 65,
                                        66, 67
Kap Lopez 54, 55
katangae, Aplocheilichthys 29
Katanga-Leuchtaugenfisch 29
Ketten-Leuchtaugenfisch 40
Kibiti Lampeye 32
Kibiti-Leuchtaugenfisch 32
Kindia Killi 69
Kindia-Prachtkärpfling 69
Kleiner Tanganjika-Leuchtaugenfisch 35
Kolibri-Leuchtaugenfisch 33
kongoranensis, Aplocheilichthys 29, 30
Kongoro Lampeye 29, 30
Kongoro-Leuchtaugenfisch 29, 30
Kreuzungen, Aphyosemion 129
Kribi Killi 83
Kribi-Prachtkärpfling 83
kruyti, Adrianichthys 18
labarrei, Aphyosemion 97, 98
Labarre's Killi 97, 98
Labarres Prachtkärpfling 97, 98
Laciris pelagicus 11
lacustre, Aphyosemion gardneri 87
lacustris, Aplocheilichthys maculatus 32
Lake Rudolf Lampeye 35
lamberti, Aphyosemion 98
lamberti, Aplocheilichthys 30
Lambert's Killi 98
Lambert's Lampeye 30
Lamberts Leuchtaugenfisch 30
Lamberts Prachtkärpfling 98
Lamprichthys tanganicanus 11, 41
Large Finned Lampeye 45
latipes, Oryzias 19, 20
Léconi Killi 116, 117, 133
Léconi-Prachtkärpfling 116, 117, 133
lefiniense, Aphyosemion 98
Lefini Killi 98
Lefini-Prachtkärpfling 98
Lemon-finned Killi 72
Liberian Killi 99, 100
Liberia-Prachtkärpfling 99, 100
liberiense liberiense, Aphyosemion 99, 100
liberiense schmitti, Aphyosemion 100
Loeme Lampeye 43
Loeme-Leuchtaugenfisch 43
loemensis, Plataplochilus 43
loennbergii, Aphyosemion 101

Loennberg's Killi 101
Lönnbergs Prachtkärpfling 101
louessense, Aphyosemion 102
Louessé Killi 102
Louessé-Prachtkärpfling 102
lugens, Aphyosemion 102
lujae, Aphyosemion 102
Luja Killi 102
Luja-Prachtkärpfling 102
luxophthalmus hannerzi, Aplocheilichthys 31
luxophthalmus luxophthalmus, Aplocheilichthys 30, 31
maculatum, Aphyosemion 103
maculatus lacustris, Aplocheilichthys 32
maculatus maculatus, Aplocheilichthys 31
maculatus sp. aff., Aplocheilichthys 39
maeseni, Aphyosemion 104
Maesen's Killi 104
Maesens Prachtkärpfling 104
Malagarasi Lampeye 39
Malagarasi-Leuchtauge 39
Mamfe Killi 88
mamfense, Aphyosemion gardneri 88
Mamfe-Prachtkärpfling 88
Marbled Killi 104
marginatum, Aphyosemion gabunense 87
Marmorated Medaka 20
marmoratum, Aphyosemion 104
marmoratus, Oryzias 20
Marmorierter Prachtkärpfling 104
Marmor-Reiskärpfling 20
matanensis, Oryzias 20
Matano Medaka 20
Matano-Reiskärpfling 20
matthesi, Aplocheilichthys 32
Matthes' Lampeye 32
Matthes' Leuchtaugenfisch 32
Mbam Killi 76, 77
Mbam-Prachtkärpfling 76, 77
melastigma, Oryzias 20, 21
mikeae, Aphyosemion wachtersi 125
Mike's Killi 125
Mikes Prachtkärpfling 125
miltotaenia, Plataplochilus 43
mimbon, Aphyosemion 105
Mimbon Killi 105
Mimbon-Prachtkärpfling 105
mimus, Plataplochilus 43, 44
Mindouli Killi 127
Mindouli-Prachtkärpfling 127
minutillus, Oryzias 21
mirabile intermittens, Aphyosemion 105
mirabile mirabile, Aphyosemion 105
mirabile moense, Aphyosemion 106
mirabile traudeae, Aphyosemion 106
Miracle Killi 105, 130
modestus, Hypsopanchax 40
moense, Aphyosemion mirabile 106
moeruensis, Aplocheilichthys 32
Moeru-Leuchtaugenfisch 32
monroviae, Aphyosemion 107
Monrovia Killi 107
Monrovia-Prachtkärpfling 107
Mouila Lampeye 44
Mouila-Leuchtaugenfisch 44
Mourning Killi 102
Mt. Kamerun-Killi 114
Mt. Kamerun-Prachtkärpfling 114
Mt. Nimba Lampeye 33
Mweru Lampeye 32
myaposae, Aplocheilichthys 33
myersi, Aplocheilichthys (Congopanchax) 33
Nackenfleck-Leuchtaugenfisch 37
Natal Lampeye 33
Natal-Leuchtaugenfisch 33
Ndian Killi 107
Ndian-Prachtkärpfling 107
ndianum, Aphyosemion 107
ngaensis, Plataplochilus 12, 44
Nga Lampeye 44

Nga-Leuchtaugenfisch 44
Nigerian Killi 89, 90, 131
nigerianum, Aphyosemion gardneri 89, 90, 131
Nigeria-Prachtkärpfling 89, 90, 131
nigrimas, Oryzias 21, 22
nimbaensis, Aplocheilichthys 33
Nimba-Leuchtaugenfisch 33
normani, Aplocheilichthys 34
Norman's Lampeye 34
Normans Leuchtaugenfisch 34
nototaenia, Procatopus 12, 45
obscurum, Aphyosemion cameronense 68
occidentale occidentale, Aphyosemion 108, 109
occidentale toddi, Aphyosemion 109
Ocellated Killi 109, 110
ocellatum, Aphyosemion 109, 110
oeseri, Aphyosemion 86, 110
Oeser's Killi 86, 110
ogoense ogoense, Aphyosemion 111
ogoense ottogartneri, Aphyosemion 86, 111, 112
ogoense pyrophore, Aphyosemion 112, 113
Ogowe Killi 111
Ogowe-Prachtkärpfling 111
omoculatus, Aplocheilichthys 34
Omo Lampeye 28
Omo-Leuchtaugenfisch 28
oophorus, Xenopoecilus 18
orthognathus, Oryzias 22
Oryzias celebensis 19
Oryzias javanicus 19
Oryzias latipes 10, 19, 20
Oryzias marmoratus 20
Oryzias matanensis 20
Oryzias melastigma 20, 21
Oryzias minutillus 21
Oryzias nigrimas 21, 22
Oryzias orthognathus 22
Oryzias profundicola 22
Oryzias sp. aff. melastigma 20
Oryzias spec. "Bentota" 22
Oryzias spec. "China" 22
Ösers Prachtkärpfling 86, 110
Ostküsten-Leuchtaugenfisch 42
ottogartneri, Aphyosemion ogoense 86, 111, 112
Pantanodon stuhlmanni 12, 42
pascheni, Aphyosemion 113
Paschen's Killi 113
passaroi, Aphyosemion 113
Passaro's Killi 113
Passaros Prachtkärpfling 113
pelagicus, Laciris 11
petersi, Aphyosemion 114
Peters' Killi 114
Peters' Prachtkärpfling 114
pfaffi, Aplocheilichthys 35
Pfaff's Lampeye 35
Pfaffs Leuchtaugenfisch 35
Plataplochilus cf. cabindae 42
Plataplochilus loemensis 43
Plataplochilus miltotaenia 43
Plataplochilus mimus 43, 44
Plataplochilus ngaensis 12, 44
Plataplochilus sp. aff. ngaensis 44
Plataplochilus spec. 44
Plataplochilus terveri 44
platysternus, Hypsopanchax 11, 41
Pointed Head Medaka 22
poliaki, Aphyosemion 114
poptae, Xenopoecilus 18
primigenium, Aphyosemion 115
Procatopus aberrans 45
Procatopus nototaenia 12, 45
Procatopus similis 46
profundicola, Oryzias 22
puerzli, Aphyosemion 115
Puerzl's Killi 115
pumilus, Aplocheilichthys 35
punctatum, Aphyosemion 116
Punktierter Kamerun-Prachtkärpfling 68

Punktierter Prachtkärpfling 116
Pürzls Prachtkärpfling 115
pyrophore, Aphyosemion ogoense 112, 113
raddai, Aphyosemion 116
Radda's Killi 116
Raddas Prachtkärpfling 116
rancureli, Aplocheilichthys 35
Rancurel's Lampeye 35
Rancurels Leuchtaugenfisch 35
rectogoense, Aphyosemion 116, 117, 133
Red barred Killi 78, 79
Red-Finned Killi 51, 52
Redlipped Killi 119
Red-spotted Killi 74, 75
Red Striped Killi 124
Red Striped Lampeye 43
riggenbachi, Aphyosemion 117
Riggenbach's Killi 117
Riggenbachs Prachtkärpfling 117
robertsoni, Aphyosemion 117
Robertson's Killi 117
Robertsons Prachtkärpfling 117
roloffi, Aphyosemion 118
Roloff's Killi 118
Roloffs Prachtkärpfling 118
Roter Leuchtaugenfisch 30, 21
Roter Prachtkärpfling 74, 75
Rotflossen-Prachtkärpfling 51, 52
Rotlippen-Prachtkärpfling 119
Rotpunkt-Prachtkärpfling 81i
Rotsaumprachtkärpfling 62
Rotstreifen-Leuchtaugenfisch 43
Rotstreifen-Prachtkärpfling 78, 79
Ruaha Lampeye 34
rubrolabiale, Aphyosemion 119
rudolfianus, Aplocheilichthys 35
Rudolfsee-Leuchtaugenfisch 35
Ruwenzori Lampeye 40
Ruwenzori-Leuchtaugenfisch 40
sarasinorum, Xenopoecilus 18
scheeli, Aphyosemion 119, 120, 134
scheeli, Aplocheilichthys 36
Scheel's Killi 119, 120, 134
Scheel's Lampeye 36
Scheels Leuchtaugenfisch 36
Scheels Prachtkärpfling 119, 120, 134
schioetzi, Aphyosemion 120
schioetzi, Aplocheilichthys 36
Schioetz's Killi 120
Schiötz' Lampeye 36
Schiötz' Leuchtaugenfisch 36
Schioetz' Prachtkärpfling 120
schluppi, Aphyosemion 120
Schlupp's Killi 120
Schlupps Prachtkärpfling 120
schmitti, Aphyosemion liberiense 100
Schmitt's Liberian Killi 100
Schmitts Liberia-Prachtkärpfling 100
Schulterfleck-Leuchtaugenfisch 34
Schulterfleck-Prachtkärpfling 109, 110
Schwanzstreifen-Prachtkärpfling 69
Schwarzer Leuchtaugenfisch 24
Schwarzer Reiskärpfling 21, 22
Schwarzflossen-Prachtkärpfling 76
setnai, Horaichthys 18
similis, Procatopus 46
sjoestedti, Aphyosemion 13, 121
Sjöstedts Prachtkärpfling 121
Sky-blue Killi 73
sp. aff. *bamilekorum, Aphyosemion* 55
sp. aff. *cameronense, Aphyosemion* 66, 67
sp. aff. *hutereaui, Aplocheilichthys* 28
sp. aff. *johnstoni, Aplocheilichthys* 29
sp. aff. *melastigma, Oryzias* 20
sp. aff. *mirabile, Aphyosemion* 106, 130
Speckled Killi 103
spilauchen, Aplocheilichthys 11, 37
Spitzkopf-Reiskärpfling 22

Splendid Killi 122, 123, 135
splendopleure, Aphyosemion 122, 123, 135
Spotted Cameroon Killi 68
spoorenbergi, Aphyosemion 123
Spoorenberg's Killi 123
Spoorenbergs Prachtkärpfling 123
Spotted Lampeye 31
Spotted Medaka 20, 21
Starhead Killi 49
stictopleuron, Hylopanchax 11, 40
Streifen-Prachtkärpfling 124
striatum, Aphyosemion 124
stuhlmanni, Pantanodon 12, 42
tanganicanus, Lamprichthys 11, 41
Tanganjika-Leuchtaugenfisch, Großer 41
Tanganjika-Leuchtaugenfisch, Kleiner 35
Tanganyika Lampeye 35
Tanganyikan Pearl Killifish 41
terveri, Plataplochilus 44
Terver's Lampeye 44
Tervers Leuchtaugenfisch 44
Thys' Killi 124, 125
Thys' Prachtkärpfling 124, 125
toddi, Aphyosemion occidentale 109
traudeae, Aphyosemion mirabile 106
Trauer-Prachtkärpfling 102
Turkana-Leuchtaugenfisch 35
Two-banded Killi 61
Two-striped Aphyosemion 59, 60, 61
usanguensis, Aplocheilichthys 38
Usangu Lampeye 38
Usangu-Leuchtaugenfisch 38
Variable Lampeye 46
Variabler Leuchtaugenfisch 46
viride, Aphyosemion 125
vitschumbaensis, Aplocheilichthys 38
wachtersi mikeae, Aphyosemion 125
wachtersi wachtersi, Aphyosemion 125
Wachters' Killi 125
Wachters' Prachtkärpfling 125
walkeri, Aphyosemion 126, 127, 136
Walker's Killi 126, 127, 136
Walkers Prachtkärpfling 126, 127, 136
Weißkehl-Prachtkärpfling 93
wildekampi, Aphyosemion 127
Wildekamp's Killi 127
Wildekamps Prachtkärpfling 127
winifredae, Aphyosemion celiae 69
wuendschi, Aphyosemion hanneloreae 93
Wuendschs' Killi 93
Wunderkärpfling 105, 130
Wündschs Prachtkärpfling 93
Xenopoecilus oophorus 18
Xenopoecilus poptae 18
Xenopoecilus sarasinorum 10, 18
Yellow Finned Lampeye 43, 44
Yellow Finned Medaka 22
Yellow Gabon Killi 87
Zaïre Lampeye 41
Zaïre-Leuchtaugenfisch 41
zebra, Hypsopanchax 41
Zebra Lampeye 41
Zebra-Leuchtaugenfisch 41
Zentralafrikanischer Leuchtaugenfisch 26
Zickzack-Prachtkärpfling 91, 132
Zimt-Prachtkärpfling 72
Zitronenflossen-Prachtkärpfling 72
Zweistreifen-Prachtkärpfling 59, 60, 61
Zwerg-Kongohechtling 49
Zwerg-Prachtkärpfling 49
Zwerg-Reiskärpfling 21
zygaima, Aphyosemion 127

Literaturhinweise
Bibliography

AHL, E. (1924a): Zur Systematik der Altweltlichen Zahnkarpfen der Unterfamilie Fundulinae. – Zool. Anz., **60** (1-2): 49-55.
– (1924b): Über neue afrikanische Zahnkarpfen der Gattung *Panchax*. – Zool. Anz., **60** (3-4): 303-312.
AMIET, J.L. (1987): Le genre *Aphyosemion* Myers (Pisces, Teleostei, Cyprinodontiformes). Faune du Cameroun, Vol. 2. – Sciences Nat, Compiègne, France: 1-262, Pl. 1-68.
ARNOLD, J.P. (1908): Westafrikanische *Fundulus*-Arten. – Blätter Aquar. Terrar. Kde., **19** (35): 469-470; (38): 517-520; 536-540; 568-570; 489-491; 585-586; (46): 653-655, Taf..
ARNOLD, J.P. & E. AHL (1936): Fremdländische Süßwasserfische. – Gustav Wenzel & Sohn, Braunschweig. 529 pp.
BAENSCH, H.A., & R. RIEHL (1993): Aquarien-Atlas, Band 2 (6. Aufl.). – Mergus Verlag, Melle.
– (1995): Aquarien-Atlas, Band 4. – Mergus Verlag, Melle.
– (1997): Aquarien-Atlas, Band 5. – Mergus Verlag, Melle.
BOULENGER, G.A. (1903): On the fishes collected by Mr. G.L. Bates in southern Cameroon. – Proc. Zool. Soc. London, 1903 (1): 21-29, plates.
– (1908): Description of two new Cyprinodontid fishes from west Africa. – Ann. Mag. Nat. Hist., ser. 8, **2** (7): 29-30.
– (1915): Catalogue of the fresh-water fishes of Africa in the British Museum (Natural History). – The British Museum (Natural History), London, Vol. **3**: i-xii+1-526, figures.
BRÜNING, C. (1929): Der grüne Leuchtaugenfisch und der afrikanische Glanzkärpfling. – Wochenschr. Aquar. Terrarienk., **26** (23): 356, figures.
CLAUSEN, H.S. (1959): Description of two subgenera and six new species of *Procatopus* Boul., a little-known West African genus of cyprinodont fishes. – Vidensk. Meddel. Dansk naturh. For., **121**: 261-291.
– (1966): Definition of a new cyprinodontid genus and description of a "new" but well-known West African cyprinodont, with clarification of the terms "sjoestedti", *Aphyosemion sjoestedti* (Lönnberg) and *Aphyosemion coeruleum* (Boulenger). – Rev. Zool. Bot. afr., **74** (3-4): 331-341.
– (1967): Tropical Old World cyprinodonts. – Akademisk Forlag, Kopenhagen. 64 pp.
DADANIAK, N., R. LÜTJE & W. EBERL (1995): Faszination Killifische: Die "*Aphyosemion cameronense*"-Gruppe. – Eigenverlag ohne Ortsangabe. 480 pp., 203 Farbfotos, 37 Zeichnungen, 49 Karten.
DAGET, J. (1962): Les poissons du Fouta Dialon et de la Basse Guinée. – Mém. Inst. fr. Afr. Noire (I.F.A.N.), **65**: 210 pp., figs, pls.
EBERL, W. (1996): Die Untergattung *Chromaphyosemion*. – Deutsche Killifisch Gemeinschaft, Journal, Suppl. **4**: 1-88.
EWING, A.W. (1975): Studies on the behaviour of Cyprinodont fish, II. – Behaviour, **52** (3-4): 172-195.
EWING, A.W., & V. EVANS (1973): Studies on the behaviour of Cyprinodont fish, I. – Behaviour, **46**: 264-278.
GARMAN, S. (1895): The Cyprinodonts. – Mem. Mus. Comp. Zoöl. Harvard Coll., **19** (1): 1-179, Pl. I-XII.
GRIMM, H. (1972): Cytologische Untersuchungen an westafrikanischen Zahnkarpfen der Gattungen *Aphyosemion* Myers, 1924 und *Roloffia* Stenholt Clausen, 1966. – Mitt. Hamburg. Zool. Mus. Inst., **68**: 195-205.
– (1974): Zum Problem der Unterscheidung der Gattungen *Roloffia* und *Aphyosemion*. – DATZ, **27** (2): 50-53.
HESDÖRFFER, M. (1904): Der zierliche Rivulus *(Rivulus elegans Steind.)*, ein neuer Aquariumfisch. – Natur und Haus, **12** (14): 209-210, Fig.
HOLLY, M. (1930): Synopsis der Süßwasserfische Kameruns. – Sitzber. Akad. Wiss. Wien, I. Abt., Math.-nat. Kl., **139** (3-4): 195-281, figs., pls.
HUBER, J.H. (1978): Contribution à la connaissance des Cyprinodontidés de l'Afrique occidentale. Caractères taxinomiques et tentative de groupement des espèces du genre *Aphyosemion* (Cyprinodontidés, Athériniformes). – Rev. fr. Aquariol., **5** (1): 1-28, 46 figs., map.
– (1979): Cyprinodontidés de la cuvette congolaise. – Rev. fr. Aquariol., **6** (1): 5-10.
– (1980): Rapport sur la deuxième expédition au Gabon (Août '79). Étude des Cyprinodontidés récoltes. – Rev. fr. Aquariol., **7** (2): 37-42, 10 figs.
– (1981): A Review of the Cyprinodont Fauna of the Coastal Plain in Rio Muni, Gabon, Congo, Cabinda and Zaïre. With taxonomic Shifts in *Aphyosemion*, *Epiplatys* and West African Procatopodins. – British Killifish Association, Publication: 1-46.
– (1982a): Cyprinodontidés récoltés en Côte d'Ivoire (1974-1978). – Cybium, 3e sér., **6** (2): 49-74.
– (1982b): Rapport de synthèse sur l'expédition au Congo (1978). Cyprinodontidés récoltés et *Micropanchax sylvestris* synonyme de *stictopleuron*. – Rev. fr. Aquariol., **9** (1): 1-12, figs.
HUBER, J.H. & A.C. RADDA (1977): Cyprinodontiden-Studien in Gabun. 4. Das Du Chaillu Massiv. – Aquaria, **24**: 99-110, 10 figs., map.
– (1979): Die Rivulinen des südlichen Kongo (Brazzaville). 2. Der *Aphyosemion lujae*-Komplex. – Aquaria, **26** (11): 175-185, 12 figs., map.
KNAACK, K. (1970): Killifische im Aquarium. – Franckh'sche Verlagshandlung, Stuttgart.
KOTTELAT, M. (1990a): Synopsis of the endangered Buntingi (Osteichthyes: Adrianichthyidae and Oryziidae) of Lake Poso, Central Sulawesi, Indonesia, with a new reproductive guild and description of three new species. – Ichthyol. Explor. Freshwaters, **1** (1): 49-67, 7 figs., 5 tabs.
– (1990b): The ricefishes (Oryziidae) of the Malili Lakes, Sulawesi, Indonesia, with description of a new species. – Ichthyol. Explor. Freshwaters, **1** (2): 151-166, 11 figs., 6 tabs.
KULKARNI, C.V. (1940): On the systematic position, structural modifications, bionomics and development of a remarkable new family of cyprinodont fishes from the province of Bombay. – Rec. Indian Mus., **42** (2): 379-423.
LAMBERT, J.G., & H.S. CLAUSEN (1967): The Genus *Plataplochilus* Ahl, 1928 redefined (Pisces, Cyprinodontidae). – Rev. Zool. Bot. Afr., **76** (3-4): 392-396.
LAMBERT, J.G., & J. GÉRY (1967a): Poissons du bassin de l'Ivindo. III. Le genre *Aphyosemion*. – Biol. Gabonica, **3** (4): 291-315.

LAMBERT, J.G., & J. GÉRY (1967b): Poissons du bassin de l'Ivindo. V. Rivulinae (suite) et Procatopodinae. – Biol. Gabonica, **5** (3): 223-231.

LANGTON, R.W. (1996): Wild Collections of Killifish 1950-1995. – American Killifish Association. Second Edition, pp. 1-70.

LAZARA, K.J. (1984): Killifish Master Index (3rd ed.). – American Killifish Association, Cincinnati. 295 pp.

MYERS, G.S. (1924a): A new poeciliid fish from the Congo, with remarks on Funduline genera. – Amer. Mus. Novitates, **116**: 1-9.

–   (1924b): A new poeciliid fish of the genus *Micropanchax* from Ubangi. – Amer. Mus. Novitates, **122**: 1-3.

–   (1931): The primary groups of oviparous cyprinodont fishes. – Stanf. Univ. Ser., Biol. Sci., **6** (3): 243-254.

–   (1933a): The classification of the African cyprinodont fishes with a discussion of the geographical distribution of the Cyprinodontidae of the world. – Stanf. Univ. Bull., **8** (5): 10-12.

–   (1933b): The genera of Indo-Malayan and African Cyprinodont fishes related to *Panchax* and *Nothobranchius*. – Copeia, 1933 (4): 180-185.

–   (1955): Notes on the classification and names of cyprinodont fishes. – Tropical Fish Magazine, March 1955: 7-7.

–   (1971): *Callopanchax* Myers 1933 (Pisces): Request for a ruling as to the type-species. Z.N.(S.) 1910. – Bull. Zool. Nomencl., **27** (5/6): 246-249.

NELSON, J.S. (1994): Fishes of the World (3rd ed.). – John Wiley & Sons, New York etc. 600 pp.

PAEPKE, H.-J., & L. SEEGERS (1986): Kritischer Katalog der Typen und Typoide der Fischsammlung des Zoologischen Museums Berlin. Teil 1: Atheriniformes. – Mitt. Zool. Mus. Berlin, **62** (1): 135-186.

PARENTI, L.R. (1981): A phylogenetic and biogeographic analysis of cyprinodontiform fishes (Teleostei, Atherinimorpha). – Bull. Amer. Mus. Nat. Hist., **168** (4): 335-557, figs. 1-99, tab. 1-3.

POLL, M. (1951): Notes sur les Cyprinodontidae du Musée du Congo belge. Première partie: les Rivulini. – Rev. Zool. Bot. Afr., **45** (1-2): 157-171, map.

RADDA, A.C. (1971a): Cyprinodontiden-Studien im südlichen Kamerun. 1. Das Gebiet um Kribi. – Aquaria, **18**: 77-88, 9 figs., 2 maps.

–   (1971b): Cyprinodontiden-Studien im südlichen Kamerun. 2. Das Tiefland der Küste. – Aquaria, **18**: 109-121.

–   (1971c): Cyprinodontiden-Studien im südlichen Kamerun. 3. Das Gebiet um Kumba. – Aquaria, **18**: 125-134.

–   (1971d): Cyprinodontiden-Studien im südlichen Kamerun. 4. Das Inlandplateau im südwestlichen Ostkamerun. – Aquaria, **18**: 157-167.

–   (1971e): Cyprinodontiden-Studien im südlichen Kamerun. 5. Das Wald- und Grasland im westlichen Kamerun. – Aquaria, **18**: 173-182.

–   (1972): Cyprinodontiden-Studien im südlichen Kamerun. 6. *Aphyosemion franzwerneri* und Zusammenfassung. – Aquaria, **19**: 30-32.

–   (1975): Contribution to the knowledge of Cyprinodonts in Gabon. – British Killifish Ass., Separatum: 1-20.

–   (1976): Die Cyprinodontidenfauna von Sierra Leone. – Aquaria, **23**: 137-149.

–   (1977a): Cyprinodontiden-Studien in Gabun. II. Nordgabun. – Aquaria, **24** (2): 21-31, 8 figs.

–   (1977b): Vorläufige Beschreibung von vier neuen Subgenera der Gattung *Aphyosemion*. – Aquaria, **24**: 209-216.

–   (1980): Die Rivulinae des südlichen Kongo (Brazzaville). 3. Revision des *Aphyosemion ogoense*-Komplexes. – Aquaria, **27**: 193-200, 10 figs., 2 maps.

RADDA, A.C. & J.H. HUBER (1976): Cyprinodontiden-Studien in Gabun. I. Allgemeines - Nordwestgabun. – Aquaria, **23**: 179-189.

–   (1977a): Cyprinodontiden-Studien in Gabun. 3. Zentral- und Südostgabun. – Aquaria, **24** (4): 59-69, 9 figs, 3 tabs.

–   (1977b): Cyprinodontiden-Studien in Gabun. 5. Das Tiefland Westgabuns und die Mayumbe-Berge. – Aquaria, **24** (8): 145-150, 8 figs, 4 tabs.

–   (1978): Die Rivulinae des südlichen Kongo (Brazzaville). I. Beschreibung von vier neuen Arten der Gattung *Aphyosemion* Myers. – Aquaria, **24** (12): 173-187.

RADDA, A.C., & E. PÜRZL (1976): Der *Aphyosemion cameronense*-Komplex. – Deutsche Killifisch-Gemeinschaft, Journal, **8**: 131-144.

–   (1977): Cyprinodontiden-Studien in Gabun. 2. Nordgabun. – Aquaria, **24**: 21-31, 8 figs, 2 maps.

–   (1981): Killifische aus aller Welt. Band 1. Feldführer der Cyprinodontiformes der Länder der Regenwaldlücke Westafrikas (Togo, Benin, SW-Nigeria). – Verlag Otto Hofmann, Wien. 48 pp.

–   (1982): Killifische aus aller Welt. Band 2. Feldführer der Cyprinodontiformes der Länder der Bucht von Biafra (SO-Nigeria, West-Kamerun). – Verlag Otto Hofmann, Wien. 72 pp.

–   (1983): Killifische aus aller Welt. Band 3. Feldführer der Cyprinodontiformes der Küstenländer Zentralafrikas. I. Ostkamerun. – Verlag Otto Hofmann, Wien. 80 pp.

–   (1985): Killifische aus aller Welt. Band 4. Feldführer der Cyprinodontiformes der Küstenländer Zentralafrikas. II. Gabun. – Verlag Otto Hofmann, Wien. 96 pp.

–   (1987): Colour Atlas of Cyprinodonts of the Rain Forests of Tropical Africa. – Verlag Otto Hofmann, Wien. 160 pp.

RADDA, A.C., & J.J. SCHEEL (1974): *Aphyosemion puerzli* und *A. robertsoni*, zwei neue Rivulinen aus Kamerun. – Aquarium Journal, **4** (3): 33-41.

–   (1975): Neue Formen der Gattung *Aphyosemion* Myers aus dem südwestlichen Kamerun. – Das Aquarium, **9**: 98-103.

REGAN, C.T. (1911): The osteology and classification of the teleostean fishes of the order Microcyprini. – Ann. Mag. Nat. Hist., ser. 8, **7** (40): 320-327.

RIEHL, R., & H.A. BAENSCH (1992): Aquarien-Atlas, Band 1 (9. Aufl.). – Mergus Verlag, Melle.

–   (1995): Aquarien-Atlas, Band 3 (3. Aufl.). – Mergus Verlag, Melle.

ROMAN, B. (1971): Peces de Rio Muni, Guinea Ecuatorial. – Fundacion La Salle de Ciencias naturales, Barcelona, 296 pp.

ROSEN, D.E. (1964): The relationships and taxonomic position of the halfbeaks, killifishes, silversides, and their relatives. – Bull. Amer. Mus. Nat. Hist., **127** (5): 217-268, pls. 14-15.

ROSEN, D.E.,& L.R. PARENTI (1982): Relationships of *Oryzias* and the groups of atherinomorph fishes. – Amer. Mus. Novitates, **2719**: 1-25.

SCHEEL, J.J.   (1966): Notes on the phenotypy, distribution and systematics of *Aphyosemion bivittatum* (Lönnberg), with remarks on the chromosome number in the Rivulinae. – Ichthyologica, Jersey City, **38** (3): 261-278.

–   (1968): Rivulins of the Old World. – T.F.H. Publications, Jersey City, N.J., USA.

–   (1972): Rivuline karyotypes and their evolution. – Z. Zool. Syst. Evolutionsforsch., **10**: 180-209.

–   (1974): Rivuline studies. Taxonomic studies of rivuline cyprinodonts from tropical Atlantic Africa (Rivulinae, Cyprinodontidae, Atheriniformes, Pisces). – Annls Mus. r. Afr. cent., Tervuren, **211**: 1-150.

–   (1990): Atlas of Killifishes of the Old World. – T.F.H. Publications, Neptune City, NJ., USA.

SEEGERS, L. (1980): Killifische. Eierlegende Zahnkarpfen im Aquarium. – Verlag Eugen Ulmer, Stuttgart: 1-174, figs.

–   (1981): *Chromaphyosemion* - kleine Farbwunder aus Westafrika. – Die Aquar. Terrar. Zeitschr., **34** (5): 155-163.

–   (1986): Bemerkungen über die Sammlung der Cyprinodontiformes (Pisces: Teleostei) des Zoologischen Museums Berlin. I. Die Gattungen *Aphyosemion* Myers, 1924 und *Fundulosoma* Ahl, 1924. Teil 1. – Mitt. Zool. Mus. Berlin, **62** (2): 303-321.

–   (1986): Bemerkungen über die Sammlung der Cyprinodontiformes (Pisces: Teleostei) des Zoologischen Museums Berlin. I. Die Gattungen *Aphyosemion* Myers, 1924 und *Fundulosoma* Ahl, 1924. Teil 2. – Mitt. Zool. Mus. Berlin, **64** (1): 3-70.

–   (1996): The Fishes of the Lake Rukwa Drainage. – Ann. Mus. r. Afr. centr. Tervuren, Sci. Zool., **278**: 407 pp., 281 figs., drawings.

SETHI, R.P. (1960): Osteology and phylogeny of oviparous cyprinodont fishes (order Cyprinodontiformes). – Ph.D. dissertation, Univ. Florida, Univ. Microfilms, Ann Arbor: 1-275.

SMITH, H.M. (1938): On the genera *Aplocheilus* and *Panchax*. – Proc. Biol. Soc. Washington, **51**: 165-166.

TERCEIRA, A.C. (1974): Killifish. Their care and breeding. – Pisces Publishing Corp., Belden Station Norwalk, CT, USA. 140 pp.

THYS VAN DEN AUDENAERDE, D.F.E. (1967): The freshwater fishes of Fernando Poo. – Verh. Koninkl. Acad. Wet., **29** (100): 167 pp., figs., maps.

TREWAVAS, E. (1974): The Freshwater fishes of rivers Mungo and Meme and Lakes Kotto, Mboandong and Soden, West Cameroon. – Bull. Br. Mus. (Nat. Hist.), Zool., **26** (5): 229-419, 17 figs., 5 pls.

WEBER, M. (1913): Neue Beiträge zur Kenntnis der Süsswasserfische von Celebes. – Bijdr. Dierk., Amsterdam, **19**: 197-213.

WILDEKAMP, R. (1982): Prachtkärpflinge. – Alfred Kernen Verlag/Reimar Hobbing Verlag, Essen.

–   (1993): A World of Killies. Atlas of the Oviparous Cyprinodontiform Fishes of the World. – The American Killifish Assoc., Vol. **1**: 1-311, figs.

–   (1995): A World of Killies. Atlas of the Oviparous Cyprinodontiform Fishes of the World. – The American Killifish Assoc., Vol. **2**: 1-384, figs.

Die wichtigsten Killifischgemeinschaften:
The most important Killifish associations:

Austria
DKG-Regionalgruppe Wien
Hans Gamperl
Marchfeldstraße 14/4/7/25
A-1200 Wien

Belgium
Association Killiphile Francophone de
Belgique (A.K.F.B.)
Jean Pol Vandersmissen
rue des Haies 77
B-6001 Marcinelle

Belgium
Belgische Killifish Vereniging
(B.K.V.)
Marcel Wuyts
Massenhovensesteenweg 2a
B-2520 Broechem-Ranst

Danmark
Skandinaviska Killi Sällskapet
(S.K.S.)
Peter Kirchhoff
Holte Stationsvej 16
DK-2840 Holte

France
Killi Club de France
(K.C.F.)
Daniel Poliak
9, rue Lucien Oriol
F- 77570 Chateau Landon

Germany
Deutsche Killifisch Gemeinschaft e.V.
(DKG)
Markus Thun
Sandfuhrstraße 1
D-44797 Bochum

Spain
Sociedad Española de Cyprinodóntidos
(SEC)
Dr. Franzisko Malumbres
El Algabeno 86
E-28043 Madrid

Sweden
Skandinaviska Killi Sällskapet
(S.K.S.)
Gunnar Åsblom
Mejerivägen 55
S 439 36 Onsala

Switzerland
DKG-Regionalgruppe Bodensee
Otto Binkert
St. Galler Straße 219
CH-9320 Stachen/Arbon

The Netherlands
Killi Fish Nederland
(K.F.N.)
F. Kaijser
Bergstraat 13
NL 4641 RD Ossendrecht

United Kingdom
British Killifish Association
(B.K.A.)
Richard Cox
18, Nettleton Close, Poole
Dorset. BH17 8PL

U.S.A.
The American Killifish Association, Inc.
(A.K.A.)
903 Merrifield Place
Mishawaka, Indiana 46544

Anmerkung:
Sämtliche Angaben ohne Gewähr, Irrtum vorbehalten. Die Liste erhebt keinen Anspruch auf Vollständigkeit.

Please note:
All information without guarantee. This list may not be complete.

Halten Sie Ihren AQUALOG über Jahre aktuell
Keep your AQUALOG up-to-date for years

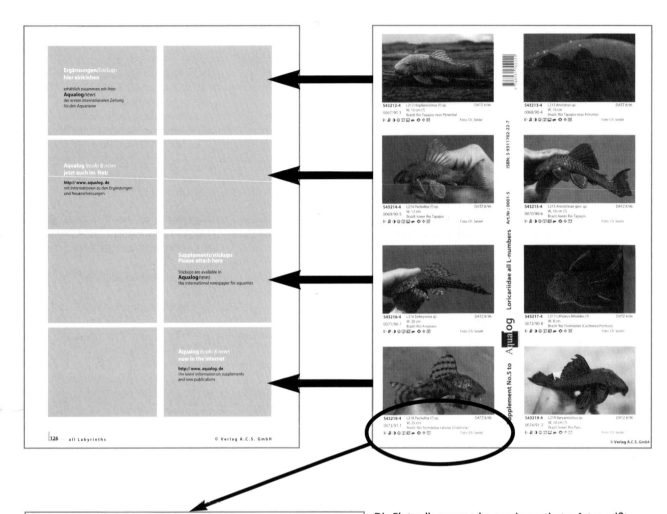

① S43218-4   L218 *Peckoltia* (?) sp.   DATZ 8/96
         W, 25 cm
② 0073/91-1   Brazil: Rio Trombetas (above Oriximina)
③ ▷ ℬ ◐ ☺ ⬜ 🖼 ➠ ◇ ◈ ⬜   Foto: Chr. Seidel
         ④

① Code Nummer

② 1.Zahl: fortlaufende Bildnummer.
2.Zahl: Seitennummer des betr. Buches.
3.Zahl: Bildnummer auf der Seite (durchlaufend numeriert von 1-8 von oben links nach unten rechts)

1.number: continuous picture-number
2.number: page number in the book
3.number: picture- number on the page (continuously numbered from 1-8 from the top left corner to the down right)

③ Symbol Leiste Aqualog-Bücher
Symbol-text (Aqualog-books)

④ Bildautor
Photographer

Die Flutwelle neuer oder neu-importierter Arten reißt nicht ab. Es ist leider unmöglich, sie alle in der Zeitung "AQUALOGnews" als Stickups zu präsentieren. Daher haben wir uns entschlossen, Ergänzungsbögen mit je acht Einklebebildern zu einem Buch herzustellen. Lieferbar über den guten Zoofachhandel und den Buchhandel zum Preis von DM 4.80 pro Stück. Viel Freude damit! Übrigens: die Stickups aus der news befinden sich nicht nochmals auf den Ergänzungsbögen!

The flood of new or new-imported species doesn´t stop. It is impossible to show them all as stickups in our Newspaper AQUALOGnews. So we decided to print supplements with eight stickers each (each supplement contents pictures for only one volume of AQUALOG). They can be ordered at well-equipped pet-shops or in every bookshop. We hope you enjoy them! By the way: the stickups are not reprinted on the supplements!

Bitte beachten Sie nebenstehendes Schema, bevor Sie die Bilder einkleben. Die Ergänzungen erscheinen nicht zwangsläufig in der Reihenfolge, in der sie eingeklebt werden, sondern in der Reihenfolge ihrer Verfügbarkeit. Wenn wir z.B. anfangs nur das Bild eines Weibchens als Ergänzung haben, jedoch sicher sind, früher oder später auch das Bild eines Männchens zu bekommen, sollte das Bildkästchen links vom Weibchenbild frei bleiben.

Please follow the scheme given here, before you stick in the pictures. The supplements are not necessarily in the correct order. For example: if we have only the photo of a female, but we are sure to get the photo of the male sooner or later, too, please keep the space to the left of the female free.

Update Service für Ihre Aqualog Bücher

Update Service for your Aqualog Books

Supplement No.1 to
Loricariidae all I-Numbers
ISBN 3-931702-15-4

Supplement No.2 to
Loricariidae all I-Numbers
ISBN 3-931702-16-2

Supplement No.3 to
Loricariidae all I-Numbers
ISBN 3-931702-17-0

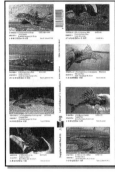

Supplement No.4 to
Loricariidae all I-Numbers
ISBN 3-931702-20-0

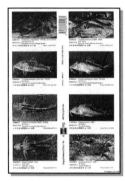

Supplement No.1 to
all Corydoras
ISBN 3-931702-18-9

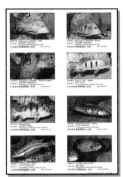

Supplement No.1 to
Southamerican Cichlids 1
ISBN 3-931702-19-2

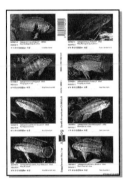

Supplement No.1 to
Southamerican Cichlids 2
ISBN 3-931702-12-X

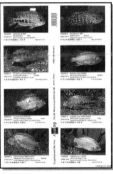

Supplement No.1 to
Southamerican Cichlids 3
ISBN 3-931702-24-3

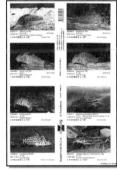

Supplement No.2 to
all Corydoras
ISBN 3-931702-23-5

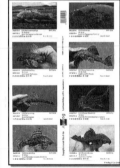

Supplement No.5 to
Loricariidae all I-Numbers
ISBN 3-931702-22-7

Mit den aktuellen Ergänzungen sind Sie immer auf dem neuesten Stand !

With the actual supplements your books stay always up-to-date!

Wo bekomme ich diese schönen Fische ???

Der gute Zoofachhandel hat normalerweise einige dieser Arten vorrätig, oder kann sie besorgen, wenn Sie ihm genügend Zeit geben. Andernfalls wenden Sie sich an den Verlag, wir nennen Ihnen gerne Bezugsquellen in Ihrer Nähe.

Where can I get hold of these beautiful fish ???

Any reputable specialist pet shop should normally stock some of the species or be able to order them for you, if you give them sufficient time. Otherwise contact the publishers and we will gladly provide you with addresses in almost every country and city close to where you live.

Key to the *Symbols*

fold out ➔